The Nervous System

The Nervous System

PETER NATHAN

J. B. LIPPINCOTT COMPANY
Philadelphia and New York

To Ursula, Nicky, Jenny and Brian

The quotations used at the beginning of
many of the sections of the book are from
Christopher Smart's poem *My Cat Jeoffrey*.

Contents

CONTENTS

List of Plates

Acknowledgements

I have much pleasure in thanking the following people for the drawings and photographs used as illustrations:

Sidney Woods for Figures 1, 2, 3, 5, 7, 8, 9, 10, 12, 13, 14, 15, 16, 17, 18, 19, 20a, 20b, 21a, 21b, 22, 23, 24, 25, 26 and 27; Leslie Frampton for Plates 2, 7, 8, 9, 10 and 11; John Armstrong for Plate 5; Dr Sybil Cooper and Professor Peter Daniel for Figure 11; Dr Serge Duckett for Plate 6; Professor H. Hydén for Plate 1; Professor Ida Mann and Dr Antoinette Pirie for Figure 4; Dr Alan Ridley for Plates 3 and 4; Dr Juergen Tonndorf for Figure 6 and Professor E. W. Walls for Plate 2.

I should like to express my thanks to the following scientific workers who have allowed me to quote from their work:

Dr Macdonald Critchley; Dr Dalle Ore; Dr Michael Espir; Professor Robert G. Heath; Professor Wilder Penfield, O.M., C.M.G., F.R.S.; Dr Curt Richter; Professor W. Ritchie Russell; Dr W. B. Scoville; Dr H. Terzian and Dr D. E. Wooldridge.

I should like to take this opportunity of thanking the following editors of scientific journals and publishers of encyclopedias, journals and books:

Dr Russell de Jong, editor of *Neurology*; Dr Bruce Lindsay, editor of the *Journal of the Acoustical Society of America*; Dr Robert Mayor, editor of the *Journal of the American Medical Association*; Professor W. Ritchie Russell, editor of the *Journal of Neurology, Neurosurgery and Psychiatry*; Dr Victor Soriano, editor of the *International Journal of Neurology*; Harper & Row for permission to quote from *The Role of Pleasure in Behaviour*, edited by Robert G. Heath; Major C. W. Hume for permission to quote from material by myself in *The Assessment of Pain in Man and Animals*, published by the University Federation for

ACKNOWLEDGEMENTS

Animal Welfare; Professor Cyril Keele, editor, and Oxford University Press for permission to quote from *Applied Physiology* by Samson Wright; McGraw-Hill for permission to quote from *The Machinery of the Brain* by Dean E. Wooldridge; J. R. Newman, editor, and Thomas Nelson & Sons and Harper & Row for permission to quote from the *International Encyclopaedia of Science*; and Oxford University Press for permission to quote from *Traumatic Aphasia* by W. Ritchie Russell and Michael Espir.

I take this opportunity of thanking Sheridan Russell, who criticized the book from the point of view of the interested non-medical reader. I am also grateful to Dr Catherine Storr, who went through the book with a tooth comb. Above all, I am grateful to Dr Marion Smith and Martin Starkie, who read each chapter and criticized it in detail and whose advice in ways of improving the earlier versions was of great value.

P.N.

Introduction

People often say when they are feeling irritable that their nerves are on edge and when they are apprehensive they say they are feeling nervous. What this has to do with the structures in their bodies called nerves, they have no idea. Probably they forget that their nerves are actual things one can touch and see; perhaps they do not know that if they have a nervous breakdown there is nothing wrong with their nerves.

These words are misused because a hundred years ago the sort of physician to whom someone in an upset psychological state would have gone would have been a neurologist – a physician specializing in disorders of the nervous system. He was popularly called a nerve specialist. Nowadays we would go to a psychiatrist or psychotherapist. As even well-educated people are not clear about the differences between these related subjects, it may be best to start by considering them.

Neurology is the study of the nervous system. Its field of interest is the actual structure and the functioning of the brain, the spinal cord and the nerves. Neurologists are physicians who specialize in such disorders as epilepsy, paralysis, shingles and disseminated sclerosis.

Psychology is theoretically a part of neurology, as it is concerned with behaviour; and behaviour is the result of what goes on within the brain. But it is practical and convenient to keep it as a different subject. Psychologists are not medically trained. They do mental and intellectual testing, vocational guidance, and some of them do research on movement, sensation, perception and deduction.

Psychiatry is the study and treatment of diseases of the

personality and character. Psychiatrists are medically trained. They help people who are not ill but who wish to discuss their problems with someone who is outside their situation and who does not make ethical judgements. They also look after the mentally ill, those with such disorders as schizophrenia and manic-depressive psychosis.

The boundaries between neurology, psychiatry and psychology are indistinct and changing. This situation is a common one in medicine. At one time the treatment of a disease is by operation, and so that disease comes into surgery. Then a drug is found that cures the disease; and so the disease becomes a part of medicine. It is the same with neurology and psychiatry. By and large, one can say that the neurologist deals with the actual structure of the brain, spinal cord and nerves, whereas the psychiatrist deals with mental and emotional disorders. If someone starts behaving abnormally, he may require investigation and treatment by a psychiatrist, a neurologist or a neurosurgeon. It depends whether the cause of this behaviour is depression, encephalitis or a tumour of the brain.

While on the subject of terms and definitions, we may mention the term 'psychoanalysis', as this is used in two ways. Strictly speaking, psychoanalysis means the theories and treatment of Freud and his disciples. But it is often used to mean any form of psychotherapy which entails treatment continuing for months or years and which uses introspection, free association and the interpretation of dreams.

Owing to the confusion, the word 'nervous' will be avoided here, except where it has passed into current speech, as, for instance, in 'the nervous system'. As is often done nowadays, the word 'neural' will be used as the adjective for nerve or central nervous system.

A book on psychoanalysis, psychotherapy or psychology can be understood by anyone who is educated in non-biological subjects. But a book on neurology demands some knowledge of physics, chemistry and anatomy. I have given a few introductory pages of anatomy, but have depended on the reader's own knowledge of physics and chemistry.

Of course the author of any book imagines his favourite and fictional reader starting on page one and continuing absorbed to the hard-won words – The End. But I have tried to write this book in such a way that any single chapter could be read on its own or left out. Though the earlier chapters may require some familiarity with physics and chemistry, the later chapters do not.

The first chapter describes the essential anatomy of the nervous system, for none of the rest of the book can be understood without this. Other anatomical aspects of the subject come throughout the book, where they are necessary. Chapters 2 to 7 describe the structure and function of the sense organs. How nerve fibres transmit nerve impulses and what nerve impulses are from a physical and chemical standpoint is the subject matter of Chapter 8. Chapter 9 considers how nerve impulses are relayed in the brain and spinal cord. Chapter 10 discusses how the nervous system controls the information coming to it, how it selects and distributes it to the various parts of itself, focusing attention on one part and neglecting another. Everything that comes to the central nervous system finally causes a response, and this response is some sort of movement, or, on rare occasions, the freezing of all movement. What we know about movement and posture is considered in Chapter 11.

In medicine, the study of hormones and their effects on the tissues of the body is called endocrinology. As the most important tissue affected by hormones is neural tissue, and as the control and production of hormones is organized by the brain, this subject comes to a certain extent within the realm of neurology; it forms the subject matter of Chapter 12. How the brain organizes behaviour is discussed in Chapters 13 and 14. Chapter 15 returns to anatomy, as further consideration of the so-called higher neural functions cannot be carried out without first describing the general plan of the brain. Chapter 16 describes the various observations made on conscious patients during electrical stimulation of their brains. This work has helped us to find out a great deal about the brain. The subjects of sensation and perception are discussed in Chapter 17. Speech, thought, writing, reading and other cerebral activities are considered from the point of view of neurology in Chapter 18. Neural aspects of learning are described in Chapter 19 and of memory and remembering in Chapter 20. The final chapter discusses some aspects of personality and the brain, and relates how we have learned to connect behaviour with parts of the brain.

Chapter 1

Structure of the Nervous System

The nervous system is the organ that controls the whole body. It has two parts: the central nervous system and the peripheral nervous system. The peripheral nervous system is made up of nerves, some of which you can easily feel in your own body. There is one behind your elbow which you can roll against the bone; this is the one you knock when you hit your 'funny bone'. The brain and spinal cord make up the central nervous system. Their importance is shown by the fact that they are the most protected part of the body, being enclosed inside the bones of the skull and the vertebral column. If the animal starves to death, the only part of its body that does not lose weight and waste away is the central nervous system.

The nerves running to the central nervous system are called afferent nerves and those running from it are called efferent nerves. The afferent nerves keep the central nervous system in touch with the world around the body and with the body itself. The efferent nerves enable the animal to respond to the world; they run to the muscles and enable the animal to move. The central nervous system receives the messages from the nerves coded in pulses, rather like the morse code; and it sends messages out to the muscles in the same code.

The nervous system consists of cells, like every other tissue of the body. Here, the main cell is the nerve-cell or neuron; and, like all other cells, it is made up of carbohydrate, fat, protein, salts and fluid. In the middle of every live cell is the nucleus, within which are the chromosomes and genes. The cell itself, its nucleus, and various other structures within the cell are surrounded by membranes. The neuron consists of three parts, the cell-body, the dendrites and the axon; these will be described later.

Plate 1 shows something amazing. It is a living neuron dissected out of the brain of a rabbit by Professor Hydén of Göteborg University in Sweden. This neuron is magnified 1,800 times and it was photographed down a phase-contrast microscope. How any human being can dissect out of the brain a cell as small as this is all but incredible. The main mass of this cell is the cell-body; the arm-like structures streaming out of it are the dendrites, prolongations of the cell making the cell bigger with a larger surface. In the centre is the nucleus, and in the centre of the nucleus, the nucleolus. The dark spots on the surface of the cell are nerve-endings of other neurons. Each nerve-ending forms a contact with the neuron, which is called a 'synapse' (from the Greek for grasp). At the synapse one neuron sends a message to another. The wrinkled surface can be seen clearly in this marvellous photograph of the cell.

As soon as we cut across any part of the central nervous system, we find that parts of it are greyish and that the larger part is creamy-white. Anatomical nomenclature is always very simple (it is no less so for being derived from Latin and Greek), and these two parts are called white matter and grey matter. The white matter consists mostly of nerve fibres and the grey matter mostly of the bodies of nerve-cells. The difference between the grey and the white matter is seen most clearly when the spinal cord is cut across or when the cerebral hemispheres are cut open. In the spinal cord the grey matter forms the centre, looking in outline very like a butterfly, and it is surrounded by the white matter. In the cerebral hemispheres it is the other way round; the grey matter forms the rind or cortex and the white matter fills up the centre.

Drawings of the human spinal cord are shown in Figures 1 and 2, Figure 1 showing the spinal cord cut along its long axis, and Figure 2 showing it cut across this axis. The position of the afferent and efferent nerves can be seen, all afferent nerves coming into the spinal cord posteriorly or from the part nearest

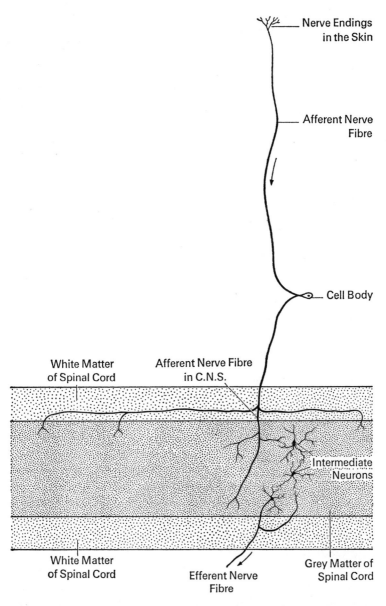

Nerve Endings in the Skin

Afferent Nerve Fibre

Cell Body

White Matter of Spinal Cord

Afferent Nerve Fibre in C.N.S.

Intermediate Neurons

White Matter of Spinal Cord

Efferent Nerve Fibre

Grey Matter of Spinal Cord

1. The spinal cord cut lengthwise, the brain on the left, the tail on the right

the back of the animal, and all efferent nerves leaving the spinal cord anteriorly, nearest the front of the animal.

The nerves are bundles of nerve fibres. The nerve fibre is a long thread of protoplasm, surrounded by its cell membrane; it is a continuation of the cell-body of the neuron. The nerves one can feel in one's body consist of hundreds or thousands of nerve fibres, wrapped up in connective tissue.

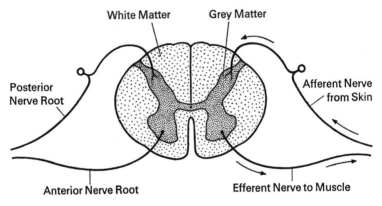

2. The spinal cord cut across its long axis

The thousands of nerve fibres coming to and from the spinal cord are collected together into large bundles, called the posterior (or sensory) and anterior (or motor) nerve roots. All afferent nerve fibres, on reaching the white matter of the spinal cord, divide up into several branches, so as to spread the messages they bring to various regions of the cord. Most of these branches run to neurons near the region of entry of the nerve fibre. These branches make connexions with many intermediate neurons (two of which are indicated in Figure 1); and these intermediate neurons are finally connected to motoneurons, the neurons which control the muscles.

The grey matter of the spinal cord organizes and co-ordinates all those functions of the trunk and limbs that work at a reflex level. The white matter connects up the different regions of the spinal cord and connects the brain and spinal cord together. Since the brain is thought of as being the most important part of the nervous system, the tracts are named in relation to it as ascending or descending. The ascending tracts take all the information the brain receives from the whole body. The descending tracts take messages from the brain to the spinal cord.

The brain is the top of the spinal cord, enormously enlarged. The spinal cord is joined to the brain just where the skull meets the spinal column. This part of the brain that joins on to the spinal cord has no name in English and is called by its name in Latin – the medulla oblongata. It can be seen in Plates 9 and 10. This part of the brain is the lowest and most essential part, for here are situated the neurons organizing the vital functions: breathing, the beating of the heart, the maintenance of blood pressure, sucking and swallowing. The main mass of the brain one sees when one looks at any vertebrate brain consists of the two cerebral hemispheres. They are the latest part to develop during evolution, though they already started to develop in fossil fish. They are most evolved in man, and so in his brain they are of enormous size.

In vertebrates there is another part of the total nervous system, which cannot be classified either as within the peripheral or within the central nervous system, as it has parts within both. This is the autonomic nervous system. It is related to the viscera more than to the muscles and is an important factor in adjusting the animal to its environment, either in preparing it for action, for fleeing or fighting, or for relaxing, digesting, excreting waste matter and for sleeping. It helps to alert the animal when danger threatens or something interesting is likely to happen.

Nerve fibres not only transmit the messages known as nerve impulses; they also secrete chemical substances at their endings. Certain nerve fibres have become specialized to do only one of these functions: some only transmit nerve impulses and others have become long-distance secreting glands. When these neurosecretory nerve fibres are active, they pour out a secretion from their endings, which has effects on the cells among which they end.

The position of the central nervous system in the body of man is shown in Plate 2. The lowest part of the brain, the medulla oblongata, is seen to lie behind the hard palate and the upper part of the cavity of the mouth. The cerebral hemispheres, of which the left one is seen here from the midline, are by far the largest part of the brain and they fill most of the cavity of the skull. The hypothalamus is in the centre of the front part of the brain. Running forward from it, the stalk of the pituitary gland can be seen. The various structures shown in this photograph will often be referred to in the subsequent chapters of the book; and reference to it will show why we speak of the parts as being in front, behind, above and below.

Chapter 2

Receptors

All animals except unicellular organisms have special cells that
have developed to sample the environment; these are the receptors. They are the parts of the nervous system that put the
animal in touch with the world. They developed out of the
nervous system or from the surface layers of the foetus. It is
from these layers that the nervous system itself developed in the
embryo.

Receptors are either specialized cells connected to afferent
nerve fibres, or they are modified nerve fibres, or they are
actual nerve fibres, freely ending in the skin or the deeper
tissues of the body. Receptors convert the stimuli they receive
into the sort of physical event that passes along nerve fibres;
this is called a nerve impulse, the term not attempting to
define what the physical event actually is.

Receptors have been evolving by natural selection for
millions of years, always in relation to the same forces as affect
them today: light, smells, sounds, gravity. Those sense organs
and receptors that were unsuitable failed and their possessors
died out. All animals that survived and are with us today are
well adapted to their environment and their component parts
are efficient. We shall then expect to find that each receptor is
exceedingly sensitive to the particular sort of energy it evolved
to cope with.

The various sorts of physical energy of the world, such as
light, heat and sound, affect nearly all animals. But not all
kinds of animals are sensitive to every physical aspect of the
world. Each species has evolved to be particularly sensitive to
those aspects that are important for it. It has no receptors for
other sorts of energy. The mole is blind; sight is of no use

underground. The tick has neither sight nor hearing, but its sense of smell is very sensitive to the sour smell of the mammals on which it feeds. It is also sensitive to warmth, so that it can tell when it has landed on a warm-blooded creature.

Of the many kinds of animals that are sensitive to the same sort of energy, each class of animal does not have the same sort of receptor, nor does it have the receptors in the same part of the body. Many fish, for instance, have taste receptors not only in their mouths but also scattered over the surface of the body. These are not so much to enjoy food with as to detect it, to find the particles of it suspended in the water. Fish with barbels, such as the sturgeon or the red mullet, have taste receptors on the barbels. The barbels are like the antennae of insects, on which there are olfactory receptors, the sense organs for smelling. Mosquitoes also feel radiant heat with their antennae. The receptors of those spiders which build webs are on their legs; they feel the vibration which is set up by the insect caught in the web with their feet and legs. Many sorts of butterflies and most flies taste with their feet. Flies have their olfactory receptors for smelling on their antennae and palpi. When a fly finds some food, it steps into it so as to taste it. It then makes use of other taste receptors on the hairs surrounding its mouth. If the food tastes good, it sucks it up. When it is replete, it vomits a little and then defaecates. If we behaved in this way, we would find a restaurant by smell and not by sight. We would go in and stand in the food. We would give a preliminary opinion on the food, put our moustaches in it, and then give a definite opinion on it. If the food was good, we would suck it up until we felt full, vomit some back on the plate, defaecate on the floor and go. Clearly, it takes all sorts to make a world.

If one were to design a nervous system, one might have had the receptors signalling all physical events to the central nervous system and leave the brain to sort out the vast mass of incoming messages. Thus the ear might report every sound within range, and the eye everything visible, coloured, still or moving, and so on for all receptors all the time. But that is not how it is done. What is reported to the central nervous system has already been sorted and selected by the receptors of the sense organs; and this sorting, selecting and arranging is continued throughout the central nervous system itself. What the brain finally receives is news specially selected for its value to that animal.

The selection of the visual aspects of the world starts at the retina. Retinae are organized to be particularly sensitive to anything moving. To be aware of movement is essential for all animals. This is obvious even to an animal as specialized and sophisticated as ourselves. Movement means life. If you relax and lie down in the grass, in the first moment you see nothing. Then gradually it all becomes alive; thousands of insects, creeping, hopping, flying and crawling, will spread themselves before your eyes. Preying animals act as if they know this. The lion stalks so slowly that its necessary movements may awaken no response in the retina of its prey.

We all have our limits; and man is able to sample only certain aspects of the world. Mammals on the whole are less limited in their sampling of the environment than insects, for instance. Simpler animals may be able to use only one kind of sensory information. Female crickets recognize the male of their own species only by the chirping sound it makes with its wing-covers. If male crickets are placed beneath a glass from which no sound escapes, the females take no notice of them, even though they can see them. Wasps recognize female wasps entirely by their sense of smell. Blinded wasps can easily find the females. But wasps in which the antennae have been removed do not recognize female wasps; for on the antennae are the chemoreceptors sensitive to the smell of the female abdominal gland secretion. So important is the sense of smell that after the female's scent glands have been dissected out, many male insects attempt to copulate with the glands and not with the female herself.

Certain animals are sensitive to physical and chemical aspects of the world which man cannot experience directly.

One example is a colour in the ultra-violet range to which bees and ants respond. Another example is the direction of polarized light, to which, again, bees and ants are sensitive, in company with many other insects. But man is intelligent enough to make use of the receptors and sensory systems of other animals. He trains pigs and truffle-hounds to smell out truffles beneath the ground; he uses bloodhounds to smell out the trails of men he wants to track down and St Bernards to find men lost on the mountainside. As we have only recently learned about animals being sensitive to sounds of very high frequency and insects being sensitive to polarized light, we may well learn of further sensitivities of living organisms and through them come to appreciate other aspects of the world.

The only way into the central nervous system is through some sense organ. Sense organs are banks of receptors situated between the brain and the world. In general, receptors to examine the world are used in one and the same general manner by all animals. Animals do not wait around to respond to stimuli. They seek the stimulus to which they need to respond. Being active, they use their receptors to explore. Most people would say that the eye is for seeing; it is not, it is for looking. Similarly ears are not for hearing, they are for listening.

All receptors function by generating nerve impulses when energy from the environment acts upon their outer surfaces. The nerve impulses are then conveyed along nerve fibres to the central nervous system. In the lower part of the brain an alerting system is excited and so the animal becomes vigilant and ready to find out what is happening. To do this, it uses many receptors in all its sense organs. One can easily observe an animal doing this. A deer, for instance, which depends mostly on smell, will first sniff what is in the wind and will then turn round and look, using its eyes to confirm what it has smelt or heard. Every kind of confirmatory information is gathered till the animal is satisfied it has obtained an adequate picture of what is going on.

Man behaves in the same way. If you go into a dark room

and your foot touches something unexpected, you bend down and bring the sensitive parts of your fingers and hand into contact with it, to find out what it is by exploring its temperature, its smoothness or roughness, its general shape.

All receptors signal the intensity of stimulation by varying the number of impulses sent along the nerve fibres in a certain time. When stimulation is slight, only a few impulses per second will be sent; when stimulation is intense the receptor and the nerve fibre send in as many impulses per second as they can. Further, only a few nerve fibres and their receptors are used to signal slight stimulation. As the intensity of stimulation is increased, more and more receptors are stimulated and more nerve impulses reach the central nervous system. Thus with a strong stimulus, the central nervous system receives a barrage of impulses; with a weak one, it receives relatively few.

As an example of the use of receptors in all animals, we may consider vision in ourselves. We are concerned only with the act of seeing; to do this, nerve fibres go from the retina to the visual areas of the cerebral cortex of the brain. In addition to this, many other activities to do with the retina and the eye have to be carried out; for these, nerve fibres go from the retina to other regions of the brain. These various parts of the brain and their activities have developed at different periods during evolution. One may exaggerate a little and say that the older parts of the brain are for looking, and the most recently developed part is for seeing. The older part provides a self-regulating mechanism for co-ordinating the movements of the head and neck and body in relation to the eyes, for moving the eyes in the direction of anything heard, for controlling the size of the pupils and the convexity of the lens. This part is particularly sensitive to things moving in the visual field. When something moves, we do not immediately see what it is. This part of the brain provides reflexes which bring both eyes round so as to get the image of something seen to be moving on to the most sensitive part of the retina for detailed seeing. There are also audio-visual reflexes here. And so when we suddenly hear something, our eyes are turned in the direction from which the sound comes. The optical apparatus of the eye, the cornea and the lens, has also to be adjusted, so that parallel rays from the object focus on this part of the retina. If the rays did not fall on the same part of both retinae, we would see double. The size of the pupils has to be adjusted by the muscles of the iris. When you hand someone something and say 'Look at this!', you can see his eyes roll inwards and downwards and you will see his pupils contract. The accompanying change in the lens cannot be seen. The size of the pupil is altered to deal with the extremes of illumination. Where the light is poor, the pupil is dilated to let more light into the eye. If the light is very bright, the pupils are brought down to pinpoint size. This may seem to be as quick as a flash, but it is not. That is why photos taken by synchronized flash show pupils of normal size. The picture is taken before the light stimulating the retina sends nerve impulses to the centre of the brain and other impulses run along other nerve fibres to make the iris contract. But if you shine a light into the eyes of a friend, human, canine or feline, you will have time to see the pupils constricting.

The control of the admission of light into the eye is organized by a stabilizing self-regulating control system. In this typical servo-mechanism, the output is controlled so as to bring it as near as possible to a reference input. The difference at any time between the actual output and the reference input is called the error. The purpose of the system is to correct the error; although the error always oscillates around a mean, stability is achieved when the error is zero. To achieve this, servo-mechanisms use a loop, in which a part of the output is fed back to the input. All servo-mechanisms can be represented by this diagram:

$$\rightarrow \boxed{\begin{array}{c}\text{reference}\\\text{input}\end{array}} \rightarrow \boxed{\begin{array}{c}\text{error}\\\text{measuring}\\\text{device}\end{array}} \rightarrow \boxed{\begin{array}{c}\text{error-}\\\text{corrector}\\\text{or control}\\\text{system}\end{array}} \rightarrow \boxed{\begin{array}{c}\text{controlled}\\\text{output}\end{array}} \rightarrow$$

feedback path of controlled output ←

In the case of the eye, the amount of light falling on the retina is the output that has to be automatically controlled. The error is the difference between the most suitable amount of light and the actual amount. The error measuring device is the retina. The control system is made up of a part of the brain, the nerves to and from the eye, and the muscles within the eye itself. The controlled output is the final and corrected amount of light reaching the retina.

The receptors, the first link in the chain of information to the central nervous system, are usually divided into exteroceptive receptors, sampling the environment, interoceptive receptors, sampling what is going on within the body itself, and proprioceptive receptors, used for controlling the position of the body and its parts. Exteroceptive receptors are receptors of the special senses, taste, smell, vision and hearing. The proprioceptive receptors or proprioceptors are receptors within the inner ear used to report the position of the body in space and those used for sampling the position and the movement of the head, the limbs and parts of the limbs. The interoceptive receptors convey information about the bladder, the gut and the pressure the blood exerts against the walls of the heart, the blood vessels, and within the brain itself; others report on the amount of oxygen, carbon dioxide and glucose in the blood, and others are sensitive to the osmotic pressure of the blood, others to the temperature of the circulating blood. There are receptors sensitive to stimulations that cause pain throughout most structures of the body. There are no receptors sensitive to painful stimulation in the brain itself. Patients carry on conversations unconcernedly while needles are passed through their brains.

Receptors are also classified according to the sorts of stimuli to which they are sensitive. In this classification we have the chemoreceptors, for instance receptors sensitive to carbon dioxide or glucose; mechanoreceptors, those sensitive to stretch, pull, pressure or touch; distance receptors, those sensitive to energies at a distance from the body, such as light or sound; and nociceptors, those sensitive to anything that may damage the body and cause pain.

Receptors are also classified according to whether they report a constant state or a changing state. Constant state receptors continue to send in impulses to the central nervous system as long as a certain state, such as a temperature, remains constant. They record various ranges of stimulation. Changing state receptors signal a change in the stimulus. These are the commonest sort of receptors, for all animals need to know about new events. Whenever a stimulus first affects the body, that is something new and may be important; so this kind of receptor sends in a burst of nerve impulses. It is of equal or almost equal importance to know when the stimulus goes; so that is signalled with equal intensity. The continued presence of the stimulus may be less important, and so this is signalled with fewer and fewer impulses. In some cases there is a constant slow discharge of impulses; in others, they cease altogether.

While a suddenly applied stimulus sends off an immediate rapid discharge of nerve impulses, a slowly applied one may send off none at all. The way in which a receptor alters its discharge in relation to a constant stimulus is called adaptation, because the receptor adapts itself to the stimulus. There are some receptors which never adapt; as long as the same intensity of stimulus is affecting the receptor, they continue to respond and to send off nerve impulses. Others adapt rapidly; they respond immediately to the onset of the stimulus, then respond less and less, and finally not at all. They respond again when the stimulus is suddenly removed. Obviously where constant information is needed, such as the state of the blood pressure or the position of the limbs, a rapidly adapting receptor would be useless. Between these two sorts of receptor, rapidly adapting and never adapting, there are receptors with every grade and rate of adaptation.

This phenomenon of adaptation also occurs with sensation. You can easily observe it with the sensation of touch. Touch the back of your hand with the tip of a hair. This gives you a just palpable sensation; it is near the threshold for tactile sensation, so we can just feel it. If you apply it quickly you will easily feel it. Now apply it very slowly and you probably will not feel it at all. In this experiment, the sensation you experience faithfully copies the mode of discharge of nerve impulses into the spinal cord.

Chapter 3

Light Receptors: Seeing

For he keeps the Lord's watch in the night against the adversary.

For he counteracts the powers of darkness by his electrical skin and glaring eyes.

As everyone who ever learned any science knows, a large bandwidth of electromagnetic radiation permeates the universe. Throughout the millions of years during which everything that lives has been evolving, it has done so in the presence of this radiation. To certain regions of this radiation, protoplasm is sensitive and to others there is no sensitivity and no reaction. Those bandwidths we experience as light affect the protoplasm of even single-celled organisms – in some cases they attract, in others they repel it. As animals developed throughout the course of evolution, it must have been advantageous to collect in one place in the body the tissues sensitive to light. To enable these tissues to absorb light more effectively, a light-sensitive pigment developed in these cells. In higher forms of animals this region becomes the retina.

As has often been said, the mammalian eye is like a camera. The light-sensitive film of the camera is the retina of the eye. The light-sensitive elements in film consist of many small crystals of silver bromide. In the retina there is a similar graining, brought about by a different sort of light receptor. The black backing of the film, which absorbs stray light, has its counterpart in a layer of cells filled with black pigment. In both, there is an iris or diaphragm, which controls the amount of light to be let into the apparatus. Both have a lens, though the two lenses differ in certain ways. The lenses of mammals are elastic; to focus, we alter the curvature. We flatten the lens by the activity of ciliary muscles in the eyeball; we then let it return to its previous more spherical form by relaxing the muscle. Glass lenses of cameras are of course hard and rigid. But now that we have plastics, it might be possible to imitate the mammalian lens. The mammalian lens is also slightly yellow; this is like a yellow filter, and cuts out some of the violet light. As we become older, the lens becomes yellower and blue light is not seen so well. Colours appear more orange. It has been suggested that Turner's later pictures all have this orange tone and are lacking in blues on account of this change in his lens, of which he himself would not have been aware.

The human retina is amazingly sensitive to light; it can register a minute amount, an amount such as 5×10^{-10} ergs. In more homely terms, we can see a single candle at night five miles away. The range of light intensity to which the retina can respond is equally amazing, for between the slightest amount of light just visible in the dark and the brightest sunlight, there is a difference in intensity of about ten thousand million to one (10,000,000,000 to 1).

Birds have far better sight than other animals. They are able to keep objects in focus hundreds of metres away and also within a few centimetres of their eyes. Probably the winner is the great condor, who from a height of 15,000 feet can see small rodents moving on the ground.

Both cameras and eyes work with an optimum amount of light, and modern automatic cameras and age-old eyes automatically adjust the size of the aperture to let in this correct amount. In the eye the difference between the amount of light falling on the retina and the optimum amount of light for seeing is eliminated by automatic and continuous adjustment of the size of the pupil.

With photography, once the light has been taken in, it is fixed; and once it has been fixed, this chemical reaction is irreversible. This is not so for the eye. After receiving light, the retina is ready again almost immediately for the next picture.

33

It is not quite immediate, as we learn if we go out of strong sunlight into a dark room. For the first second, we cannot see properly. During this time the photoreceptors are becoming re-adjusted by means of a chemical reaction so as to be ready to absorb light again.

Both the film and the retina absorb light and the light brings about a chemical reaction. In the retina, the light is absorbed by a pigment present in the photoreceptors; in the film it is absorbed by the emulsion in the gelatin.

There are of course some very obvious differences between cameras and eyes. Cameras work whether they are constantly in use or not; but eyes and the whole visual system have to learn in order to see. Chimpanzees brought up in darkness for sixteen months from birth are blind when they are first brought out into the light. It then takes them a long time to acquire sight and to learn to identify objects. Our vision has gone through a long period of learning when we were too young to remember how we were doing it. But some of our vision is innate and does not require learning or practice. Turning the eyes and the head towards a light or a sound is a reflex and does not need the higher parts of the brain.

The eye selects; it does not record everything there is in front of it in the indiscreet manner of the camera. Animals analyse their environments continuously; and the first step in this selection and analysis occurs in the receptor organ.

Eyes throughout the animal kingdom tend to be similar, though most insects have compound eyes and vertebrates have single eyes. A compound eye is somewhat like several vertebrate eyes tightly packed together to form a membrane. Each receptor, known as an ommatidium, has its own lens. Some insects have one lens for every two or three light-sensitive receptors. There is one insect which has one large lens but only one light-sensitive receptor cell; this receptor is moved so as to scan the total image formed by the lens. There are also eyes without lenses. The eyes of certain molluscs work like pin-hole cameras. Being always in focus they do not need a lens to bring the rays of light into focus on the retina; but they have the disadvantage of admitting only a very small amount of light.

How the retina works is more easily investigated in animals less complicated than man. A very ancient arthropod, the horseshoe crab, has provided more information on the mechanisms of vision than any other animal. This crab has a compound eye made up of ommatidia, like the eyes of spiders and many insects. Every ommatidium discharges impulses along its afferent nerve fibre at a rate related to the intensity of light. Thus the animal's brain will be informed not only when the crab is in the shadow or in the light, but it will also receive information about patterns of light and dark in the environment of the crab's eyes; this provides it with some information about the objects around it. The research workers studying vision made a very narrow beam of light so that they could use it to shine on only one ommatidium at a time. With this technique, they discovered in this eye a general mechanism of the nervous system, called surround inhibition. When one receptor is excited, those surrounding it are inhibited. The central nervous system will receive a large number of nerve impulses from the central receptor and few from surrounding ones; the more intense the stimulation of the central receptors, the less activity there will be in the neighbouring receptors. The amount of inhibition is linearly related to the distance between any two ommatidia; and so each ommatidium reduces the nearest ommatidium to silence, the nearby ones to relative quiet and those a little farther off suffer only a slight damping down of their activity. Surround inhibition is done by each nerve fibre from every ommatidium having inhibitory connexions with its neighbours; this anatomical arrangement is within the eye itself. The effect of the mechanism is to highlight contrasts and show up features against the background.

A more complex retina than that of the horseshoe crab is that of the frog. In this retina there are three sorts of photoreceptors. One kind is excited when the light falls on them and ceases to discharge impulses when the light leaves them; as they are excited by the light, they are called 'on-receptors'.

Another kind discharges nerve impulses both when the light reaches them and also when it leaves them, and so they are called 'on–off receptors'. The third kind is excited only when the light leaves them; and so they are called 'off-receptors'. When a large object moves across the frog's field of vision, it will excite all these receptors; and something small and dark, moving jerkily, will maximally stimulate the retina. A still environment does not excite the off-receptors, it excites the on–off receptors only when it first affects them, and it excites the on-receptors as a moving object does. Thus the retina gives the frog a picture of the world particularly suitable for frogs. It is prejudiced in favour of things which move; for these are the kinds of things a frog wishes to see.

Although the retina is paper thin, it consists of several layers of cells. It is drawn rather diagrammatically in Figure 3.

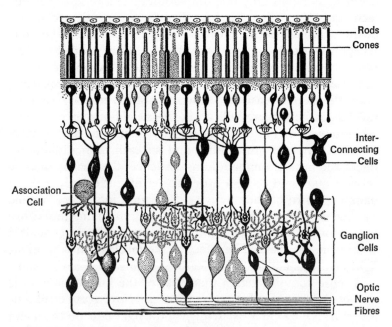

3. The retina. The light comes from the bottom of the picture and runs through the paper-thin retina to the rods and cones at the top

The photoreceptors are named in accordance with their shape – rods and cones. In man, there are about 123 million rods and 7 million cones in each eye.

The rods and cones are connected together by interconnecting neurons; and these neurons are connected to some large neurons, called ganglion cells. The ganglion cells are also interconnected by other neurons, association neurons. Thus the cells of the retina are interconnected in two ways, from side to side and from front to back. From the ganglion cells arise the nerve fibres that constitute the optic nerve.

Each ganglion cell collects nerve impulses from a little circle of retina. They can also be classified as 'on' and 'off' cells. They show surround inhibition like the cells of the retina of the horseshoe crab. The retina is specialized to be sensitive to anything moving, to report borders, edges and contrasts, and any objects showing out against the background.

Rods and cones work by containing pigments which are affected by light. In man, there are three sorts of cones, each containing a different pigment; these are for seeing the three primary colours. The rods contain a pigment called visual purple or rhodopsin. This substance is a protein containing a chemical substance called retinene, which is a form of Vitamin A. If Vitamin A is lacking in the diet, vision is upset; and the first manifestation of this is night-blindness. When the light is absorbed by retinene, the shape of the molecule of the substance is altered; and this change in the molecule sends off a nerve impulse.

The rods absorb blue-green light; they are unaffected by light of other wave-lengths, and so they cannot be used for seeing colour. They are used when the light is poor. And so at twilight we cannot see colours and everything looks more or less grey. When there is less light, as at night-time, only rods are used.

Man is not particularly good at seeing in poor light. The cat is far better; hence man's saying that cats see in the dark. Animals which are good at seeing in poor light are most active at twilight. For example, the Australian opossum is shy during the bright light of the day, preferring to relax, protected by law, in the attics of houses; at twilight it saunters bravely out. The South American night monkey has only rods in its retina, being especially adapted for night vision. Deep-sea fish also have only rods in their retinae. They have enormous lenses, so as to catch all the light there is in the depths of the ocean.

Cones need more light than rods to be excited; in fact a thousand times more light is needed to affect the cones than the rods. Cones are used for seeing detail when the light is good and they are sensitive to colour. They are scattered throughout the whole extent of the retina; there is also a concentration of them at one small area, called the fovea. This is a region of the retina a little smaller than the head of a pin and it is used when careful, detailed vision is necessary, and for colour vision. The rods are also scattered throughout the retina, but they are absent from the fovea. They are used particularly for seeing movement. This is achieved by making them sensitive to on and off changes. A moving object stimulates rows of these receptors as it passes across the visual field, stimulating them in turn, first on, then off, as the light strikes each receptor. Man's eyes are less sensitive to rapid movements than are those of many insects; and so the rapid movement we make when we swat a fly appears quite leisurely to the intended victim.

Man is better at seeing colours than most other mammals. Cows, cats, dogs, pigs and sheep do not see colours; red rags are of no interest to bulls. Of the mammals, only man and most monkeys can see colour. Birds, certain reptiles, most fish, butterflies and bees can see colour. Bees cannot tell red from black, but they can see a colour in the ultra-violet which we cannot appreciate.

Von Frisch points out that scarlet flowers are very rare among the indigenous flowers of Europe, because the insects that pollinate flowers cannot see red. But in Africa and America scarlet flowers are common; this is because flowers there are pollinated by birds which can see red very well. In America this is done by humming birds and in Africa by the sunbirds. Interestingly enough the strelitzia is pollinated by the sun-bird's feet, as it lands on the horizontal petals. Red European flowers, such as dianthus, daphne and erigeron, are all pollinated by butterflies which are the only insects able to see the colour red. Poppies which are bright red to us reflect ultraviolet light, and so bees can see them. Thus flowers and insects form good examples of symbiosis in evolution, the two developing together, each making use of the other.

On the whole, animals which are themselves brightly coloured are able to see colour, for usually colour is there for other members of the species to see. There would be no point in having colours to display if no one else could see them. Peacocks display for peahens, butterflies for butterflies. But certain animals are coloured especially for other species. Presumably the wasp is indifferent to its own colours; they are there to warn birds to keep off.

Vertebrates that can see colour have three sorts of cones, each containing different pigments. One of the pigments is most sensitive to yellow-red light, another to green and the third to violet-blue. All the other colours we can see are combinations which affect these three sorts of receptors in various degrees. There are no receptors for yellow, the sensation of yellow resulting from excitation of the receptors most sensitive to red and to green.

The photo-sensitive pigment of the rods is not used for colour vision. This pigment has been prepared in solution, mixed with gelatin and then spread on celluloid, just like a silver bromide film. It has then been used for photography, being developed in the dark by hydroxylamine.

The inability to appreciate colours is surprisingly common. Among Europeans, colour-blindness is present in 7 to 8 per cent of men and in 0·45 per cent of women, a distribution showing that it is sex-linked. Most colour-blind people cannot tell red from green; the red end of the spectrum is not seen as a colour; deep red looks black to them. Others see both red and green as yellow. In a much rarer form, there is yellow-blue colour blindness. Most colour-blind people lack one of the three colour sensitive pigments and have to make out colours with a combination of the remaining two. There are some very rare people who have total colour blindness; they can see no colours. Everything appears grey to them, like pictures in the newspaper.

Eyes, we have all noticed, face different directions in different animals. The total field of the environment that is seen by the eyes, called the field of vision or visual field, is shown in Figure 4, for man, bird and fish. Not all fish have this visual field; the flounder who dwells on the bottom of the sea has a panoramic field of vision, taking in about 180° around his head. The dragon-fly also has the same large visual field, but for each eye. Most carnivores and birds of prey have their eyes in the front of their faces; whereas herbivores have prominent eyes, set at the sides of their faces. Eyes set at the side of the face see different aspects of the environment. Herbivores, like fish, have very large fields of vision; they need to see to both sides as well as behind, for they all serve as food to other animals. Man has only a moderately wide field of vision; but like other animals with the visual field of each eye largely overlapping, he can see stereoscopically. Men and owls only see about two-fifths of the field around them. Man probably has stereoscopic vision because tree-dwelling animals have it; it is needed for jumping from branch to branch. Stereoscopic vision bring its own problems. When the two eyes need to look at the same object, both have to be focused to get the image of the object on the fovea of both retinae.

Eyes are used not only for seeing and for looking. The light they absorb has other effects. In spring, the gradual lengthening of the day acts as a stimulus inducing secondary sexual characteristics in many species of animals, including small mammals like the ferret and birds like the pheasant. This stimulus acts on the hypothalamus (discussed in Chapter 14), which then induces the pituitary gland to produce gonadotrophic hormones, which affect the activity of the reproductive organs; and so the reception of light is an important factor in the reproduction of some species. If the duration of light is artificially altered, the whole rhythm of the reproductive cycle

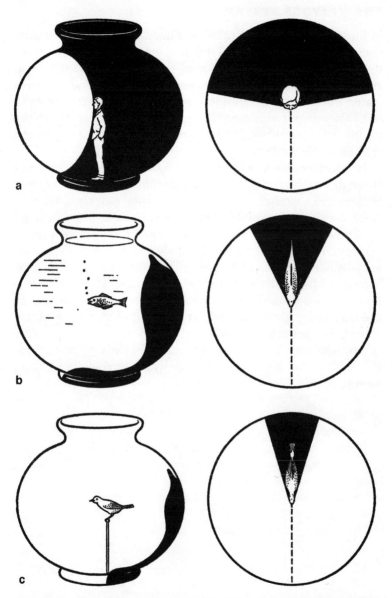

4. If a man, a fish and a bird were placed in the middle of a goldfish bowl, each one could see everything white in this diagram and nothing black. The white part is the visual field

in birds can be altered. Professor Thorpe of Cambridge slowly decreased the amount of light of the environment of greenfinches and chaffinches; he found that not only did they stop singing but that their testes had regressed to an inactive state. Then he gradually increased their daily ration of light until they were receiving sixteen hours of light per day in the middle of September. These birds were in full song in the middle of November.

In simpler kinds of animals, light is received but not through the eyes. Some have photocells scattered over their bodies. If a shadow is cast over them, they reflexly withdraw. Such a reflex is inexorable and cannot be modified or altered by learning. Earthworms have no eyes but they have a light-sensitive receptor on each side of their front ends. They arrange their position and their movements so that the same amount of light falls on both these receptors. They avoid daylight and burrow back into the earth when they are brought to the surface by gardeners. But at night when it is dark everywhere, they come to the surface of the ground. This is the time when they meet for sexual intercourse. In their preference for the dark of the night for this activity, they resemble human beings.

Chapter 4

Sound Receptors: Hearing

For his ears are so acute that they sting again.

Sound waves are waves of rapidly alternating pressures spreading out from a source like the ripples on a pond, which can be conducted in air, water and solids, but not in a vacuum. In solids, they are conducted more effectively and faster than in liquids, and in liquids, more effectively and faster than in gases. In former times, men would put their ears to the ground to listen for galloping horses, knowing that they would hear them in this way before they would hear them in the air.

In physics, all aspects of a single sound or tone are described by the frequency and intensity of the sound. From the human point of view a single musical tone has the following characteristics: frequency, intensity, timbre, growth, duration and decay of the tone, slide or portamento, and vibrato. Pitch is mainly the same as frequency, but it also includes some degree of loudness. Loudness is almost the same as intensity, though it is not quite the same, as our hearing is more sensitive to some frequencies than to others, and we hear these frequencies louder than others, although in fact they have the same intensity. The timbre or quality of a sound or tone depends partly on the frequency of the fundamental, and partly on the overtones that accompany it, and also on the intensity of the different overtones; it is also related to the envelope of the sound. This feature includes the manner of growth, duration and decay of the tone, whether it starts with a sudden full loudness or builds up, how long it remains at its maximal intensity, and similarly the manner in which it fades away. Slide or portamento is the changing frequency before the correct frequencies of the true note are attained. Vibrato is a tremor-like variation in intensity of the note (loudness-vibrato) or a tremor-like variation in the frequencies, so that the frequencies of the true note are sandwiched in between the lower and higher frequencies below and above the note.

In order to reproduce music in a lifelike way, one must have an adequate volume or intensity of sound. If it is inadequate, the frequency of the reproduced note may be correct, but the heard pitch is wrong. This is because our judgement of pitch depends on our hearing the right overtones. When the intensity of a note is insufficient, the higher overtones are lacking; and so the reproduction does not sound true. Human beings are very sensitive to differences in pitch; people good at hearing can distinguish 2,000 slight changes in pitch throughout the total range of hearing. To reproduce pitch properly, bass notes need more intensity than treble. The amplification of the sounds of music to a level to get true reproduction is what makes hi-fi listeners unpopular with their neighbours.

It is not only the ear that is sensitive to vibration; all parts of the body are. Vibrations of slow rate or low frequency can be felt, those of faster rates are both felt and heard, and those of the fastest rates are only heard; for the ear is the organ specialized to receive fast vibrations. There is no hard and fast division between tactile sense and hearing; throughout the animal kingdom the one fades into the other. The human ear is sensitive to frequencies between 20 and 20,000 cycles a second and most sensitive to those between 1,000 and 6,000 cycles a second; to hear speech, the essential range is between 500 and 2,500 cycles a second.

As the ear is developed out of the skin, it is interesting to examine the skin to find out if it has any similar properties; and it is quite easy to do this. Just get three tuning forks having frequencies of 128, 256 and 512 cycles a second. Then get a friend to set them vibrating and apply them separately to the hairs on your forearm or leg, taking care not to touch the skin itself. Keep your eyes shut and your ears blocked up, so that you do not see or hear the forks vibrating. You will find that you can tell if the fork is vibrating or merely touching the hairs without vibrating (the fork with a vibration of 512 cycles a second may cause some difficulty). You will find too that you can tell the pitch of the note from the vibration imparted to your hairs; that is to say, you will not hear a note, but you will be able to distinguish which fork it is that is vibrating; for the hairs of the skin are sensitive to the frequency of vibration of the three forks. This experiment also shows us how apt hairs are as receptors for the vibrations of sounds.

The mammalian ear is best thought of as consisting of three parts, the outer, middle and inner ear. All three parts develop in the embryo out of the surface epithelium, the covering that later becomes the skin. And so it is not surprising to find that the receptors of the inner ear are a sort of receptor used in the skin; they are pressure and movement detectors, hairs embedded in a base.

The outer ear is the part of the ear you can see – in fact what people call the ear. It is separated by a drum from a little chamber, the middle ear, and this is separated by another drum from the inner ear, which is deep inside the bone of the skull. This is the part containing the sound receptors and the nerve fibres.

The pressure waves of sound pass down the funnel-shaped passage of the outer ear to affect the ear-drum. This drum, known to anatomists as the tympanic membrane, is a flattish cone, like the cone of a loudspeaker. This membrane is connected to another membrane, the oval window, by three little bones. The oval window seals the inner ear from the middle ear. The inner ear appeared so complicated to the early anatomists that they named it the labyrinth. It consists of the cochlear apparatus, the semicircular canals and the vestibular apparatus; it is the former that is used for hearing. They are shown in Figure 5.

The middle ear is a chamber containing air, which is kept at atmospheric pressure by a tunnel connecting it to the throat. When the tunnel is blocked up, as occurs momentarily when

45

we yawn or for some days when we get a cold, our hearing is impaired. It is not absolutely necessary for the pressure waves to pass through this air-filled chamber for hearing; vibration can be conducted directly to the inner ear.

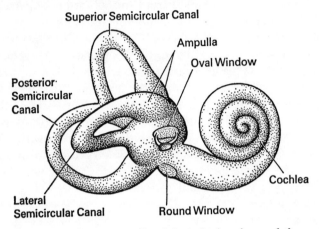

Superior Semicircular Canal

Ampulla

Oval Window

Posterior Semicircular Canal

Lateral Semicircular Canal

Round Window

Cochlea

5. The inner ear. The part on the right is for hearing and the parts on the left are for balancing and keeping the right way up

You can examine the characteristics of air conduction and bone conduction of sound in yourself by listening to your own voice. Just read aloud from a book, and in the middle of reading, block up both your ears with your fingers. You will find that when your ears are blocked up and you are hearing by bone conduction, your voice sounds deeper; conversely it sounds higher when the sound is conducted through the air to your ears. Bone conduction damps the sound of higher frequency and so the low frequencies predominate. Now continue your reading, but whisper what you read; and again, block and unblock your ears. You will find that you can hardly hear your whispered voice when your ears are blocked. The reason is the same. Whispering makes use of the higher frequencies; there are so few low frequencies used that there is almost nothing to conduct, so you hear almost nothing.

In the outer ear, the waves of sound are conducted in air;

in the middle ear, they are conducted in solids; and in the inner ear, in fluid.

That the transmission of sound waves from air to fluid does not readily occur can be observed by anyone bathing on a noisy beach or in a swimming bath. The noise around you when your head is above water goes if you put your head under the water. The air–water interface forms an effective sound-barrier, most of the sound being reflected from the surface of the water.

When the sound waves have to pass from air to fluid (and this has to happen in all animals who live in the air), a great loss of energy occurs. The middle ear contains the mechanism for compensating for this loss. This mechanism consists of the tympanic membrane, three little bones hinged together to form a system of levers, and the oval window which seals off the fluid of the inner ear. The compensation is achieved by the great area of the tympanic membrane compared to the small area of the flat footplate of little bone (the stapes) up against the oval window, and by the lever action of the three bones.

In man, the tympanic membrane is about twenty times the area of the footplate of the stapes. But as the membrane is firmly fixed all round its circumference, this whole area is not available to move. The effective difference in areas of the membrane and the stapes footplate is about 14 : 1. The lever system of the three bones collects the pressure from the tympanic membrane and concentrates it down to the footplate of the stapes; it increases the energy by about 1·3 : 1. If the force of a wave of pressure striking the tympanic membrane were 5·5 units per unit area, it would be increased to about 100 units per unit area at the membrane of the oval window. That is the order of efficiency of the compensation achieved by the mechanism of the middle ear.

In the inner ear, the waves of pressure are transmitted to fluid. As fluid is incompressible, the waves of pressure have to be allowed to play on something which will give. They are passed through the fluid to another membrane, called the round window; this bulges back and forth into the middle ear.

47

Although the cochlea is in the form of a spiral, it is simpler to consider its structure and the way it works by thinking of it uncoiled; and that is how it really is during the earlier stages of embryological development.

When the sound waves are in the inner ear, they reach a membrane called the basilar membrane. In man it is 30 to 35 millimetres long. This membrane supports hair-cells of two kinds, globular ones along the inner part and slender tubular ones along its outer part. The hairs of the hair-cells are adherent to a membrane above them, called the tectorial or covering membrane. The basilar and tectorial membranes have different mechanical properties. The basilar membrane shows the same elastic properties in longitudinal and transverse directions, whereas the tectorial membrane is stiffer longitudinally than it is transversely.

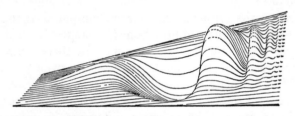

6. A wave pattern in the basilar membrane of the inner ear

When the sound waves are transmitted to the fluids of the inner ear, they send a ripple down the basilar membrane. This wave can be imagined if one thinks of the basilar membrane as a long narrow sheet, fixed at both ends and also along both sides; but fixed loosely, so that a shake given it at one end sends a wave of movement along its whole length. This wave is complicated, for the membrane is of different thickness and consistency in its different parts and it is also coiled round the snail-like cochlea. The kind of wave pattern it probably makes in this membrane is shown in a spread out membrane in Figure 6. When the membrane is raised into folds and ripples like this, the hair-cells in it are rocked about.

The tips of their hairs are embedded in the membrane above them, the tectorial membrane. There is a different movement of the two membranes when the pressure wave passes along them. For the basilar membrane is attached along both its edges whereas the tectorial membrane is attached along only one edge. Further, the two membranes have different properties of stiffness, thickness, elasticity and tautness. This difference in the movement of the two membranes displaces and twists the hairs of the hair-cells and causes a shearing movement between them and the tectorial membrane in which their tips are embedded. As the hairs are minute levers, their movements affect the hair-cells; and each hair-cell is clasped in a basket-like mesh of nerve-endings, many different nerve fibres to each hair-cell. The hair-cell converts mechanical energy into nerve impulses, which are electric current. Man uses the same sort of transduction when he uses the piezo-electric effect of certain crystals. The greatest movement of the basilar membrane occurs with high notes at the lowest part of the cochlea and the greatest movement occurs with low notes at the top of the cochlea. Thus, as the musical scale is ascended, the cochlea is descended. The change in frequency of a note of one semitone brings into activity about 400 different afferent nerve fibres; 95 per cent of the fibres conducting are the same for the two notes.

When the basilar membrane is rocked by the sound waves, it analyses and transmits to the brain two features of the sound, its frequency or pitch and its amplitude or loudness. The long axis of the basilar membrane is mainly concerned with the frequency of the sound and the side-to-side axis is concerned with its intensity. The intensity or loudness of a sound is analysed by the following mechanism. The hair-cells of the basilar membrane are arranged in two groups, called the inner and the outer hair-cells. The inner hair-cells are all along the inner edge of the basilar membrane, just at the point where the membrane becomes free from a supporting ledge of bone. They are not very mobile and so are less sensitive than the outer hair-cells. The outer hair-cells can be more easily moved and so they are more sensitive. To convey the information from these 23,500 hair-cells of each ear, there are about 28,000 nerve fibres of various sizes and rates of conduction, each of which is connected to many hair-cells.

There are also efferent nerve fibres running to the hair-cells and to the afferent nerve fibres coming in from the membrane. We assume that various parts of the brain control the sensitivity of the receptor apparatus by means of these nerve fibres, adjusting it to the total needs of the animal at the time when the sound arrives.

Electrical recording from the nerve fibres from the basilar membrane shows that each nerve fibre conducts impulses when a certain range of frequencies is sounded. The different parts of the basilar membrane react most to different frequency ranges and so the nerve fibres from each part conduct impulses to the brain when these tones occur. The intensity of the sound also affects the number of nerve fibres conducting. A very quiet note sends impulses along the few nerve fibres coming from the part of the basilar membrane that is most moved about by that sound. The neighbouring nerve fibres on both sides of these nerve fibres are also brought into activity, but they send off fewer impulses per second. When the same note is sounded more loudly, more and more nerve fibres are brought into activity. This mechanism is more like that of a *viola d'amore* than that of a violin: a loud note activates not only the string that is being bowed but also the sympathetic strings. And just as we hear the pitch of the note coming from the main string put into maximal vibration, so the central nervous system recognizes the frequency of the note from the position of maximal discharge rate of the many nerve fibres discharging maximally.

There are other mechanisms necessary for hearing as well as those we have just described; but they are not yet fully understood. We know, for instance, that some of the nerve fibres from the cochlear receptors are always transmitting impulses, even when there is silence and one would have thought there is nothing to report. From recording impulses running in these nerves, we have found that when a sound occurs, some of these nerve fibres cease to transmit impulses, others send in a greater number of impulses, and others send in fewer.

Within the cochlear nucleus, each neuron is excited by a certain range of frequencies. Above the cochlear nucleus, each neuron constituting the next link in the chain of the auditory pathway is more restricted in sensitivity, being sensitive to only a narrow frequency range. At the primary receiving area of the cerebrum, the arrangement is different. Every neuron here is activated by a large variety of tones. The mechanism described in Chapter 3 called surround inhibition occurs here. This aids the frequency analysis of the sound by accentuating contrasts. Such a mechanism also works for time as well as place, enabling us to detect rapid changes in frequency and intensity of sounds.

Hearing is not merely receiving and understanding the message of a sound. Animals which make use of hearing note both the direction from which the sound is coming and the distance of the source of the sound. We learn to do this in childhood just as we learn to estimate the position and distance of everything we see. We learn that loud and clear sounds come from a nearby source and softer and less clear cut sounds come from farther off.

Most animals, including man, which live in that mere millimetre of the universe, the surface of the earth, are only good at localizing sound horizontally. Birds who enjoy a three-dimensional life localize sounds equally well vertically as horizontally.

Animals which are around at night either have large eyes or they live by using their ears or, like the owl, they make use of both. The owl has its ears set far apart on its head; it is unique in that the structure of its two ears is different. These two anatomical features are used for localizing the little sound made by the mouse as it runs free.

The shape of the external ear is determined by the animal's need to localize sound. The passage between the ear-drum and the ear we see is funnel-shaped, with the walls making an angle of about 30° at the drum. Sounds of short wave-length should be directed into this funnel and should come from an imaginary funnel continuing the funnel of the external ear out into space. Deaf people probably turn their ears to the mouth of the speaker so as to get the sound into this funnel; they need to hear the higher frequencies of the overtones to hear speech distinctly. The old-fashioned ear-trumpet was good in this respect and it may well have been better than electric amplifiers which magnify all wave-lengths. Nowadays there are more discriminating hearing-aids which increase the amplification of the frequencies each deaf person has difficulty in hearing. The fact that higher-pitched sounds are best heard when they reach the drum within a cone of angle 30° permits a sound-localizing mechanism which is used by people deaf in one ear. The head is turned until the sound is most shrill or bright; then the source of the sound is within a 30° angle of the drum. The best position of the head for sound-localizing is to have the sound source coming straight towards one ear, the waves of greater wave-length meeting the nose-neck axis of the head like a wave against a cliff. When this happens, the further ear will be in the very worst position for hearing the sound. And so, when we are receiving a sound so that we get maximal stimulation of one ear and minimal stimulation of the other, we know from past experience that the source of the sound is at right angles to the antero-posterior axis of the head. These are not the only mechanisms for sound-localization by only one ear. The quality of a sound changes as things move off or come near. As a sound gets nearer, the bass notes get relatively louder than the treble.

If a source of sound strikes both ears at exactly the same time, the person will localize it somewhere in the middle and not in either ear. This principle is used in stereo recording and reproducing of music. When we are sitting in the correct position between the two speakers, the sound appears to come out of the wall in the middle, unless it is recorded to come from either speaker. This is so, even though most people are right-eared. Not only do they prefer the right ear, but they hear more accurately with it. But it may be that they prefer the left ear for music.

Man is not particularly good at hearing, compared with many other animals. Birds are far better at distinguishing a great many notes packed into a short period of time. Their lives are much shorter than ours, and everything about them takes place more rapidly. All animals are good at hearing the kind of sounds important for them. The chicks of penguins on their islands in Antarctica can recognize their parents from the sounds they make and so can the guillemots on our coasts. In neither case can the human ear detect any differences in the sounds made by the various parent birds. Horses, rats, mice, cats and dogs can all hear higher pitched sounds than we can. Cats hear up to 50,000 cycles a second and rats up to 90,000 cycles a second.

When the first amphibia left the Silurian Seas two or three hundred million years ago, they relied entirely on bone conduction of the vibrations for hearing; they were not equipped to hear vibrations in air, having just come out of the water. It seems that the vibrations in the earth were transmitted from the bones of their lower jaws to the bone surrounding the inner ear. In order to hear, they probably kept their lower jaws touching the ground. Whether this is the only way in which snakes hear is still under discussion. It seems quite certain that they do not hear the music played to them by snake-charmers. The real purpose of this music is to charm money out of the pockets of tourists. What elephants hear of the soothing songs from the lips of the mahouts who tend them, we do not yet know. Interestingly enough, African elephants can hear the same songs, for the Negroes of the Congo learned them from Indian mahouts brought over by the Belgians to train them before the First World War. The elephant does not use his big external ears only for hearing. He uses them to communicate, to warn us that he is threatening and will charge if we do not go away. They are also used as vanes from which to lose heat. The skin is relatively thin and it contains dilatable blood-vessels from which heat can be dissipated into the surrounding air.

Bees are able to hear by feeling the vibration in solids. Their buzzing, which to us is so characteristic of bees, is something they do not hear; they feel it. When they are standing on something solid, the vibration of the buzz is transmitted through the solid to other bees, who feel it through their legs. As well as with their legs, they hear with their antennae, on which there are receptors specialized for certain vibrations. When a bee arrives back in the hive, other bees come up to it and touch its thorax with their antennae; in this way the foraging bee can tell the others where food is to be found. This way of communicating a message allows the bees to speak to a few individuals in a crowd alive with buzzing, where another additional buzz would be lost among the noise of continuous vibration. The queen bee has her own regal speech; its fundamental note is about 300 to 380 cycles a second, and its harmonics go up to 1,500 cycles a second. The other way in which bees communicate is by dancing the message, the language discovered and interpreted by von Frisch in Munich.

Sounds in nature are used not merely for communication with one's fellow-creatures. Bats use them for echo-location or echo-ranging. They emit short bursts of sound, and these sound waves bounce off obstacles and insects; and the bats detect this echo. As Dr Grinnell of Harvard puts it: 'A bat's livelihood depends on its ability to use sound as a substitute for light in locating objects in three-dimensional space.'

Nowadays we are all familiar with this mechanism, as we hear it when we drive in a car past a row of trees or parked cars with gaps between them. In this case, the car we are sitting in produces the sound and it is reflected back from the objects along the side of the road. As trees and cars are separated by gaps that do not reflect sound, we hear a changing pattern of sound, a kind of rushing sound when there is reflection of the sound and a quieter sound when the sound is not being reflected. Auditory clues like these can be useful to blind people; with practice they can gather a lot of information about gaps in walls or doorways. They listen to the sound made by their own footsteps or to the taps they make with a walking-stick and they can hear when the sound is no longer reflected off the walls. A well-trained blind man can walk down a passage and avoid screens thrown half-way across the passage by listening to the sound of his own footsteps reflected by the screens.

That bats do not use their eyes to avoid the finest obstacles in the dark was first demonstrated by Spallanzani in 1794. He hung bells on strings in a tower and then put blinded bats in the tower. They flew around the tower without hitting the strings and sounding the bells. Five years later Jurinac, working in Geneva, produced evidence that such blinded bats are guiding themselves by means of auditory clues. Since then, it has been found that bats find their way home when blindfolded just as quickly as non-blindfolded bats. That bats can fly in the dark by emitting very high frequency sounds which bounce off objects was first suggested by Professor Hartridge in 1920. And that this really is so has been proved by the remarkable work of Professor Griffin of Harvard University. He has shown that bats, with their whorled and complicated ears, catch the echo of the sounds they themselves emit; and they do this so quickly that they have time to guide their flight, avoiding objects as thin as strings holding bells.

What the bat needs to do is to detect the faint echoes reflected off such small objects as gnats or mosquitoes, 1 to 3 mm. diameter. With regard to the physics of sound, there is quite a lot of time to do this; for sound travels in air at a speed of 34·4 cm./millisecond. But the problem for the bat is how to hear a faint echo of high frequency very soon after hearing its own emission of the orientation cry, and how to tell the one from the other. The bat copes with the problem by making its orientation cry very short – 0·3 to 10 milliseconds – so that it will not overlap its own echo. It also uses the muscles that work the bones of the middle ear to damp down the emission sound as it makes it but it does not use them to damp down the echo.

Experiments have shown that bats recover their ability to hear a second sound one millisecond after hearing a first sound; whereas the cat takes between 50 and 100 milliseconds. Human beings with practice can hear two clicks at 10 millisecond intervals, though with such a short interval the second click is heard more faintly than the first.

The various species of bats make use of a large variety of sounds. All are very high-pitched with short wave-lengths. For the bouncing of sound waves off objects, the wave-lengths must be short. If the wave-length were much longer than the object it meets, it would not be bounced back; a wave of one metre length would not be interrupted by a wire stretched in its way. This high-frequency sound must be given out in a narrow beam, like the light from a pencil-torch, so that it can be focused accurately enough to be reflected off an insect of 1 to 3 millimetres in diameter. They achieve this so well that they can tell if an insect of this size is flying towards them or away from them.

The final proof that bats do find their way about by this system of radar was obtained by Griffin and Grinnell. They jammed the bats' echo-location by high frequency noise. The result was that the bats preferred to stay at home and did not venture out.

Bats do not produce sound in the way we do, by expelling air between vibrating vocal chords; for they have no vocal chords. Some bats, such as the Egyptian bat, use vocal explosive sounds, shaped with their tongues, similar to the sounds of human speech. Others, such as the horseshoe bat, emit sounds through their noses and not through their mouths; this sound is also very high-pitched, going up to 100,000 cycles a second.

The cries of the little common brown bat are between 30,000 and 70,000 cycles a second, with most tones around 50,000 cycles a second. The highest sound yet recorded was 120,000 cycles a second, which is presumed to be the highest pitched sound made by any animal. These sounds being beyond the limits of human hearing are labelled by man as supersonic or ultrasonic. A part of the sound can be heard by most people, at least when they are young. As we get older, we lose our sensitivity to high tones and then can no longer hear the cries of the bats. When bats are caught and are frightened and struggling, they then make the same sort of squeaks as are made by rats and mice.

The common European horseshoe bat makes use of the Doppler effect. When either the source of a sound or the hearer of the sound, or both, are moving, the number of vibrations a second changes. If a whistling train comes nearer when you are standing on a platform, the number of vibrations a second increases, and it decreases as the train goes off. The result of this is that the whistle sounds higher as the train comes towards you and lower as it goes away. The horseshoe bat uses fairly long bursts of a few pure tones, almost devoid of overtones, and guides itself by this effect. It hears the note becoming higher as it approaches an object and lower as the object recedes. Some of the neurons within the animal's brain used for echo-locating are excited by sounds of rising pitch and others by sounds of falling pitch. It is obvious that for echolocating the actual pitch of a note is unimportant; whether it is rising or falling is what the animal needs to know. For on account of the Doppler effect, the rise or fall of the note tells it whether it is coming up to an object or going away.

The horseshoe bat emits its sound through its nose. The horseshoe is made up of folded skin around the nose which acts as a sort of trumpet, narrowing the sound down to a beam. To locate the echoed sound well, this bat makes much use of movements of the ears and head. All bats do this to a fair extent, and one can interfere with a bat's ability to carry out echo-location if one prevents these movements.

Bats have a sense of smell; they use this for finding their mates and not for finding food. Many bats have eyes well adapted for seeing at twilight, but even these do not use sight for finding their way about or for catching insects. Most bats live in caves into which no light penetrates and so sight is impossible.

It has been suggested by naturalists that the furry bodies and wings of moths and some other insects form a protection against echo-location. For unlike shiny bodies and wings, furry bodies absorb the sound of the bat's sonar.

In the balance of nature, those preyed upon and their hunters wage an equal battle. Whenever this was not so in the past, either the one or the other species passed away. The noctuid moths for which some bats are searching can hear the ultrasonic exploratory cries of the bats that eat them. They have only two auditory cells in each ear; these receptors are sensitive to the frequencies emitted by the bats and to no other frequencies. Professor Roeder of Tufts University in Massachusetts generated the ultrasonic frequencies of the bat's cry and photographed the tracks made by the moths in the dark. The moth first hears the cry of the bat at a distance of 35 to 40 metres away, long before the bat can get an echo off the moth. The moth then turns and flies away from the source of the sound. When the sound made by the bat is much nearer than this, the moth behaves differently: it either folds its wings and falls to the ground or it goes into a power dive. The anatomy of this moth has evolved to aid it escape from its enemy. Its ears are in the middle of its body, just behind the attachment of the second pair of wings; and the auditory nerves are closely connected to the neurons that work the flight-muscles. The distance between these nerve-cells is very short and so the impulses from the ears reach the flight-muscles very quickly.

Not all kinds of bats live on insects; some live on fruit, a very few live on fish, and even fewer live on the blood of men and horses. Fruit-eating bats rely on vision to find their way about and not on echo-location; they are around during the daytime. One sort of fruit-eating bat flies both by day and night. It uses its eyes when there is enough daylight; and when the sun goes down, it listens to the echoes of the clicking noises it makes with its tongue.

Instead of saying 'as blind as a bat', it would be better to say 'as careless as a bat'. Bats, it has been found, often pay no attention to their echo-location systems. If a new obstacle is put into a tower in which bats live, many of the bats fly into it and hurt themselves. Their echo-location systems are working perfectly; they do not bother to listen in once they have got used to the location of the objects in their accustomed environments.

Bats have existed for more than fifty million years. And as complete skeletons of that age have been found which are the same as bats' skeletons today, we may safely assume that they were using echo-location fifty million years ago. This is confirmed by the fact that the shape of their skulls indicates that the part of the brain used in hearing was very well developed. At this time, the horse was the size of a present-day wire-haired terrier.

Some other small mammals, such as certain kinds of mice and shrews, also use echo-location, for some of them are active both by day and night.

Vertebrates which live in the ground specialize in hearing the lower frequencies of sound, for the higher frequencies do not penetrate the ground. They probably make more use of conduction via the bones of their skulls. Dr Douglas Webster of New York University has studied the gerbil of Central Asia, the jerboa of North Africa and the kangaroo rat of the southern United States, and he finds that these little mammals of the desert from quite different parts of the world deal with their acoustic problems in the same way. The range of hearing of the kangaroo rat is from 1,000 to 3,000 cycles a second, and in accordance with this selective sensitivity, its basilar membrane is most developed in the apical part of the cochlea. Dr Webster has shown that the sounds made by rattlesnakes sliding heavily over the ground and also by the owls that prey on kangaroo rats come within this frequency range.

Baron von Humboldt in his wonderful book *Voyage aux Régions Equinoxiales du Nouveau Continent* published early in the nineteenth century tells us about the nocturnal birds of Peru. These birds live in complete darkness in caverns, coming out only at night to feed on fruit. The bird, called by the Peruvians the guacharo, is about as big as a hen and has blue eyes. Von Humboldt relates how the local Peruvians are afraid to go into the caves where these blue-black birds live, and they speak of dying as 'going to join the guacharos'. Unfortunately they are not frightened enough. For once a year during the summer they enter the largest cave with long poles and destroy the birds' nests. They kill the birds, as their abdominal cavities are full of fat. They then melt this fat down and use it for cooking. It has now been found that although these birds like to fly at moonlight and do use their eyes, they also find their way by using the echo from the high-pitched sounds they make. Griffin, who first investigated the realm of echo-location in nature, found that the frequency of their sounds is between 6,000 and 10,000 cycles a second and that each pulse of sound is extremely short, lasting from 1 to $1\frac{1}{2}$ milliseconds. Another kind of bird which uses echo-location is the little swift of the East Indies whose nests are stolen for bird's nest soup. They live in the same caves as bats and they use the same method to find their way about the caves; but they feed during the daytime like most birds. The sounds used by both kinds of birds for echo-location can be heard by man.

Echo-location in the sea is used by whales, seals, dolphins and sea-lions. Blind sea-lions get along quite satisfactorily. The sounds they make for echo-location are not the barking we hear at the zoo; they make a kind of pinging sound. The system of this group of animals that has been investigated most is that of the porpoise. The porpoise has no sense of smell, and so it is not by smell that it detects the fish on which it lives. Whether it uses eyesight or not, we do not know. But we do know that when the water is made so turbid that sight is impossible and when fish are silently slipped into the pool, sea-lions and porpoises invariably find them within a fraction of a second. Moreover, by their sonar system porpoises can distinguish between red mullet and other kinds of fish, and between fish 6 inches and 12 inches long.

These mammals that have returned to the water do not have the problems of air-fluid interface barriers which mammals living in air have. Arriving back in the sea after millions of years' evolution on land, they start off with the land-living ways of amplifying sound. Most mammalian systems amplify the sound twenty times before it is transmitted to the inner ear. Starting off with this advantage, one can see that they were in a good position to develop communication by echo-location. They have succeeded in increasing the lever system of the little bones of the middle ear far more than did mammals living on land; in them, the lever system increases the force of the sound thirty times.

Man is able to hear a part of the sound the porpoises emit. Kellogg reports that it sounds like a canary. The porpoise also makes clicks and clacks, like the noise of a woodpecker or the sound of a creaking door. Part of this sound is made up of vibrations in the water of 80,000 cycles a second; this is two octaves higher than man can hear. Like the bat, the porpoise increases the rate of emission of sound as it approaches an object, and it also moves its head from side to side so as to locate the echo differentially with the two ears. If you whistle to a porpoise, it whistles back.

How whales communicate and hear has been investigated since the war; though their voices were first heard, it seems, by Mr Fisher, who mentions it in his *Journal of a Voyage for the Discovery of the North West Passage* published in 1821. He describes the sound made by the white whale as 'a shrill ringing sound, not unlike that of musical glasses badly played'. Mr Fisher and his fellow-explorers heard it by keeping their ears under water. Actually they must have missed most of the sound, for most of it is in the frequency range of 50,000 to 100,000 cycles a second.

In accordance with their great size, the auditory nerves of the whale are faster-conducting than those of other animals. This is an instance of a general feature of size. The nerve fibres between any point in the central nervous system and a constant point in the body vary in thickness, which is proportional to conduction rate, in proportion to the size of the animal. A shrew, for instance, will have a slowly conducting nerve from the spinal cord to the kidney whereas the elephant has a fast-conducting nerve for this region.

Most fish communicate by sound. They serenade each other, like crickets and man. Their different calls for alarm and for aggression can now be recognized, since research work has been done on underwater recording of the sounds made by fish. It has been found out that shrimps make a great deal of noise for their small size. Fish both make their sounds and hear them by means of their swim-bladders. They cannot hear the high-pitched sounds made by the porpoises and whales which feed on them. In this respect they resemble the fly whose composite eyes cannot detect the silk of the spider's web but they are unlike the moths who do hear the shrill cries of the bats which are looking for them.

Fish developed swim-bladders to enable them to swim at various depths with different pressures. The swim-bladder is essentially an incorporated gas-bubble, and so its volume is related to changes in pressure. The pressure waves are radiated out from the swim-bladder to the surrounding tissues. The inner ear is close-by, and so it is stimulated by the waves of pressure that constitute sound. This system of sound recording cannot locate the source of the sound, for there is only one swim-bladder, and at least two ears are needed for sound-location.

As fish have the same specific gravity as sea-water, and indeed as they are largely composed of sea-water, they form no barrier to the sound-waves in the water: sound-waves pass through them as if they were not there. This is one reason why they do not have outer ears, since the sounds reach their inner ears directly.

In fish, receptors sensitive to vibration and movement are concentrated along a line running along the side, from head to tail. This lateral line sensory system contains a row of receptors which terrestrial vertebrates have lost. The receptors within this lateral line are hair-cells just like the hair-cells of the rest of the vestibular system. In fish they are stimulated either by the water directly or else by fluid in a canal running the length of the fish beneath the skin. These mechano-receptors are sensitive to the movements of water, and they are stimulated by the water swishing by the body of the fish. As the fish has two of them, one on each side, it is able to tell the direction of disturbances in the water.

While on the subject of fish, we may mention electric fish. Some kinds of electric fish do not use their electricity-generating organs as weapons, but as a sort of sonar. The discharge of the electric organ produces an electric field around the fish; objects of greater or lesser conductivities than the surrounding water can be detected within the field. The fish has electro-receptors in the lateral line organ which can detect this change in the current density distribution of the electric field. These receptors are incredibly sensitive; changes in the field of one-millionth of a volt per foot can be detected.

Chapter 5

Olfactory and Gustatory Receptors: Smelling and Tasting

Our world is so visual that even our way of expressing ourselves is visual. When we understand something, we say 'Yes, I see', not 'Yes, I smell'.

If we watch the behaviour of animals who have keen noses, we can see how all sense organs are used. A wind laden with odours passes by. The dog or the deer turns and faces the wind, pauses and sniffs. They are getting more of the odours into contact with their olfactory receptors so as to examine them in detail, to classify them, so as to know how to behave to all that the odour implies.

There is a whole world of communication, of beckoning, of warning, carried on by means of smell and all unnoticed by us. The presence of an animal's smell acts in different ways on friend and foe, just as does its visual presence. It attracts its fellows and it may repel or attract its enemies. The smell given off by the damaged skin of certain fish repels its brothers and sisters and they flee in alarm; but the same smell attracts the fish that prey on it.

It is surprising, insects being so different from us, to find that wasps and bees like the same flowers as we do. The smell of flowers developed just with the purpose of attracting insect pollinators and not to please us, though our noses may do a little pollinating as well. Insects have their olfactory organs on their antennae. In ourselves this would be equivalent to us having long mobile noses, a little like an elephant's trunk; we could then push our noses right up against the source of the smell. Von Frisch and his colleagues have discovered that some flowers have different smells in their different parts. Our crude noses note only one general smell. But insects with their little olfactory organs on their antennae can push these sense organs up against the various parts of a flower and thus can locate the different parts according to their different smells. Von Frisch has found out that in a narcissus the yellow ring is not only a different colour from the white corolla but has also a different smell. Having found that bees could easily distinguish these two parts by their smell, he then found that if the yellow and the white parts of the flower were separated, humans could also distinguish two différent smells. The bee can follow the scent of the flower according to the strength of the smell; and so the flower has arranged matters that when the bee is smelling the strongest smell, it is most likely to pollinate the flower.

Bees, ants and termites recognize the members of their own colonies by their smell. If any other insect can get into a bees' hive long enough to acquire the right smell, it will not be evicted or killed but will be tolerated, even if it spends its time raiding the eggs and honey. It appears that the drone finds the virgin queen on her nuptial flight by smell.

Smells linger in the air or water and travel long distances. And so animals use them for long-distance communication. The virgin female gypsy moth can attract the males when they are up to three-and-a-quarter miles away, according to experiments carried out in the United States. Certain ants leave trails of smell on the ground and it is these lines of smell that the other ants are following.

Fish are very good at smelling, though in their case it is difficult to separate smelling from tasting. Salmon return to the rivers in which they were born. Experiments have shown that they recognize their own rivers and streams by their characteristic smells, which they remember during their years at sea. Some fish hunt entirely by smell; these include the dog-fish, familiar to all biology students, and those fish that hunt by night, when visibility is nil. One of the schemes tried to keep sharks off bathing beaches has been to put unpleasant smells in the sea; apparently the smell of man is not revolting enough.

Some fish have such a keen sense of smell that they can detect a substance when there are only a few molecules of it in the water. Although water spreads the molecules around just as air does, the mammals who have returned to the sea from the land, such as the porpoises and the dolphins, have no sense of smell. This sense, which their ancestors used on land, has lapsed to such an extent that these marine mammals no longer have olfactory bulbs; they have lost the very nerve tracts concerned with smelling.

Snakes have a good sense of smell. For after they have

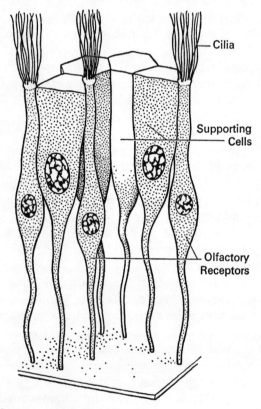

7. The olfactory receptors

bitten and injected venom into their prey, they do not always swallow it straight away. The poor frightened animal goes off and hides while it dies within the next hour. The snake has to go and find it, and it does so by smelling it out.

In vertebrates, the olfactory membrane is the part of the nasal mucous membrane containing the olfactory receptors; it is right at the top of the nose. Odours reach it by two routes; they can pass in with the air and up the nostrils, or they pass up the back of the nose from the throat. The smells of the world arrive mainly through the nostrils. The smells of the food we chew reach the membrane by passing up the back of the nose.

A diagrammatic drawing of the olfactory receptors is shown in Figure 7. The receptors are packed among columnar supporting cells. Each receptor cell ends in hair-like processes called cilia, and in the living animal these hairs move about spontaneously. There are about 50 million nerve fibres leaving the olfactory mucosa of each side of the nose. These connect up to other neurons, and from these, 50,000 nerve fibres run to the brain. Man's olfactory receptors are probably sensitive to about twenty to thirty primary odours; other odours are likely to be mixtures of these.

All substances that vertebrates can smell must have certain characteristics. The odour particles have to be transferred from air to the lipid-water interface of the membrane of the cilia. And so any substance which can be smelt has to be volatile; molecules must leave it and pass into the surrounding air. The substance must be soluble in water and lipid (fats or oil). Further, the substance must have molecules of certain sizes and shapes. If a molecule is too big, it cannot enter the pores of the membrane of the receptor. The most accepted theory of smell, the stereochemical theory, states that the silhouette of the shape of the molecule of the substance is all-important in determining whether a substance will be smelt or not, and what smell it will have. The silhouette depends on the shape of the molecule in different planes and also on its vibration frequency, which needs to be low. For a substance to be smelt, the molecules of the substance and of the olfactory receptor must have about the same shape and the same vibration frequencies. Once the molecule enters the receptor, it triggers off some process, at present unknown, that eventually sends off a nerve impulse. Substances of which the molecules are disk-shaped, for instance, have a musky smell. If chemists introduce changes into the molecule, they will alter the musky smell when they alter the shape of the molecule.

On the whole, by using this stereochemical theory of smell, chemists can predict whether a new and unknown substance will have a smell or not, and if it has, what the smell will be. Before this theory, one of the difficulties in understanding smell had always been to understand how it could be that one of two optical isomers smelt and the other did not. Optical isomers are substances having the same molecule, identical in every respect except that the one is the mirror image of the other. Why one should smell and the other not becomes clear on the basis of the stereochemical theory of smell; the one molecule having a suitable shape would pass through the pores on a receptor, but the molecule having exactly the opposite shape would be unable to do so.

Chemoreceptors have a very long history, for these receptors are probably the oldest of all. They are of most use to animals living in the sea where everything of interest is dissolved in sea water. This means not only everything of positive interest, such as food to be found and swallowed. It means also food to be avoided; for the reactions of vomiting and expelling food are laid down in the same basal parts of the brain as those of sucking and swallowing.

The chemoreceptors take up molecules of substances important to the animal. Whether to classify them as taste receptors or smell receptors is usually unimportant; only for our own species can we differentiate these two senses satisfactorily, and not always here.

All chemoreceptors developed originally within the alimentary canal. Those for smell have become separated from the roof of the mouth and are now in the roof of the nose; all others have remained in the alimentary canal. In mammals, taste receptors are situated along the surface and edges of the tongue, over the epiglottis, on the soft palate and scattered around the throat. These are arranged in little structures like goblets, called taste-buds, which are scattered in the surrounding epithelium or covering tissue. The actual receptors are narrow columnar cells terminating in little jutting out

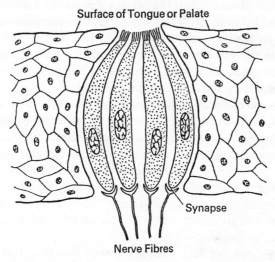

Surface of Tongue or Palate

Synapse

Nerve Fibres

8. The taste receptors within a taste-bud

processes. They are shown in Figure 8. At the lower ends of the receptors are seen the synapses of the nerve fibres, which take the nerve impulses to the central nervous system.

To be tasted, a substance has to be water-soluble. If it were not, it would not reach the tips of the taste-receptors in the taste-pores and could not pass through the lipo-protein membrane of the receptors. Doubtless too the molecules of the substance must be not too large and be lipid-soluble.

Man has an even less developed sense of taste than sense of smell, for a larger number of molecules of a substance have to be dissolved in fluid for it to be tasted than for it to be smelt.

69

A detailed investigation has been carried out in the United States on the gustatory apparatus of the blow-fly. This achievement of great technical difficulty was done by Hodgson, Lettvin and Roeder in 1955. In this fly there are within the hairs around the proboscis two kinds of taste-receptors, one sensitive to many compounds including salts, acids and alcohols, and the other sensitive to sugars. Another finding of these workers was that the sugar receptors exist to make the animal suck up the substance and the other receptors to make it avoid those other substances. The sugar-sensitive receptors may be sensitive to the stereochemical properties of the substance, similarly to the olfactory receptors described above. The same hair which ends as a taste-receptor is a mechano-receptor, being sensitive to movements and bending.

Among vertebrates, most investigations on tasting have been done on the cat. The cat is indifferent to anything sweet and it apparently cannot taste sweetness. Flies, horses, butterflies, bears and dogs, as we all know, love sweets, and so do rats and mice. Pfaffman in the United States recorded the activity of single nerve fibres coming in from gustatory receptors of the cat. He found that one kind of receptor is activated by acid tastes, another by both acid and salt tastes, and a third by both acid and quinine.

In man there are four primary tastes; whether this means that there are four different types of receptor, we do not know. These are sweet, bitter, sour or acid, and salt. We are most sensitive to the taste of bitter substances; far fewer molecules of any bitter substance give us a taste than molecules of sweet, salt or sour substances. The taste of sourness is related to the pH of the substance, though not all acids taste sour or acid. All the salts of chemistry taste salty if they are soluble in saliva and if they dissociate at least to some extent into ions; both the cation and the anion contribute to the taste of the salt. For instance, sodium bromide tastes different from sodium chloride, and sodium chloride tastes different from potassium and from ammonium chloride. But there are some exceptions to the rule that salts taste salty. Lead acetates, for instance, taste sweetish. Some metallic salts must be described as tasting metallic rather than salty. And Epsom Salts, which is sodium sulphate, tastes bitter rather than salty.

All tastes other than these primary ones are a combination of these four, with the addition of a large element of smell. The importance of smell is made clear to us all when we have a cold. At a certain stage the mucous membrane of the nose is swollen with fluid or covered with mucous or pus; then the molecules of odoriferous substances cannot get at the receptors to excite them; and so we cannot taste our food properly.

As we get older we probably lose some of the sensitivity of all our receptors. This is so for hearing and smell; and it is very marked for tasting; many of our taste-buds disappear. The acuteness of the sense of taste in children may be one of the causes for their hatred of nasty-tasting medicines.

Chapter 6

Cutaneous Receptors: Feeling

For eighthly he rubs himself against a post.

The skin is not only the covering of the body; it is also a large area of receptors, constantly examining the world and sending information to the central nervous system. Most of what is sent in is used for the automatic adjustments of the body which go on without causing conscious sensation. Some of this information is used to control the temperature of the body; some is used to aid in the control of the muscles; and some goes to alert the brain, telling it that something is about to come in, and to get ready to receive it.

By means of the receptors in the skin, the cutaneous receptors and the nerve fibres connecting them to the central nervous system, we are able to feel all the interesting things we do feel: tickling which makes us unwillingly laugh, the mere touch of a fly, the pain of a wasp's sting, or the difference between satin and velvet. Just how good our fingers are, becomes clear when we see a blind person reading Braille. In this form of writing, the little embossed dots are $2\frac{1}{2}$ to 3 mm. apart. A good braille reader can feel and interpret 2,000 to 2,500 of these points a minute when he is reading at a rate of a hundred words a minute.

The sensory apparatus of the skin has to report three sorts of information to the central nervous system. It reports the nature of the stimulus, saying: 'You have been touched, or you are being tickled, or you are being burnt.' It reports the intensity of the stimulation, saying: 'This stimulus is slightly warm; this one is very cold.' And it reports the position of the stimulus, saying: 'You have been stimulated on the top of the left little toe.'

Research workers in this field need to find out which sorts of receptors deal with what sorts of natural stimuli, which nerve fibres are conducting when these receptors respond to stimulation, and to find out how we know whereabouts we have been stimulated. The intensity of stimulation, we have already said, is signalled to the central nervous system by the rate at which impulses are sent; the greater the number of impulses nerve fibres conduct per second, the more intense the stimulus must be.

The nerve fibres of the alerting system warn certain parts of the brain that something is coming; they give the brain time to send down impulses to organize and control what is about to arrive. This goes on not only at the beginning of any stimulation but continues as long as the stimulus is present and after it has gone.

One way of investigating the subject of cutaneous sensation was done in Germany and the United States on some willing and helpful patients and on medical students. In these experiments, recording electrodes are placed beneath the nerves just below the skin and the volleys of nerve impulses passing along the nerves are amplified, shown on a cathode-ray oscilloscope, photographed and recorded by loudspeaker. In such experiments, there are three facts to be related: the kind of stimulus applied to the skin; the electrically recorded nerve impulses in the cable of nerve fibres constituting a nerve; and the sensation felt by the subject when these nerve fibres are conducting nerve impulses to his brain.

When an electric stimulus to the nerve sends impulses only along the largest nerve fibres, the subject feels sensations such as insects crawling, or gentle rubbing, tapping or stroking with cotton. When the electric stimulus is made stronger, slightly smaller nerve fibres conduct impulses as well. Then the subject feels something unexpected: he feels a sensation as if it is going to become painful. But as long as no smaller nerve fibres conduct impulses, no actual pain occurs; the sensation remains painless but with the feeling that it is going to become painful. When the strength of the stimulation is increased again, nerve fibres of smaller diameter become active. Then pain is felt. When the smallest nerve fibres of all are stimulated, the patient feels severe pain. There is a delay of two or four seconds between stimulation and sensation, and the patient cannot say exactly where he feels the pain. When the larger nerve fibres are stimulated, he can feel the sensation quite accurately, say, in the back of the heel; with stimulation of the smallest fibres, he can merely say he feels it in one or other of his lower limbs.

There are some nerve fibres from the skin which are always sending off nerve impulses, even though no stimulation is occurring. Exactly what role they play, we do not yet know. Most receptors or nerve fibres fire off impulses when a change occurs. There are some that fire off impulses as long as a constant condition is held: they are called steady-state receptors. They are used for the control of skin temperature. For example, some of them fire off impulses whenever the skin temperature is 32°C., a temperature at which one's hands or feet feel pleasantly warm.

The nerve fibres of the skin end in three different ways: as naked or freely ending nerve fibres, as complex endings, and as encapsulated endings. The freely ending nerve fibres have no specially developed structure, designed to respond to special sorts of stimuli. They are the commonest sort of nerve-ending. An example is shown in Plate 3. The cells staining dark in this photograph are the cells of the epidermis, the superficial layers of the skin. The nerve fibre is the dark wire entering this layer from the deeper regions of the skin. This photograph was made from a small piece of skin punched out of the finger tip of a man. The specimen has been killed and fixed in various solutions, and then it has been stained especially to show nerve fibres. Although the photograph gives a good idea of a twig of a nerve fibre running through the superficial layers of the skin, it does not show the dense network of nerve fibres there is throughout the skin. In reality, the close intertwining of nerve fibres is such that any natural stimulus must always excite more than one nerve fibre; it has been estimated that a stimulus of 1 sq. cm. area would cover more than a hundred nerve-endings.

The complex endings of nerve fibres show a large variety of forms. Some are coiled, some are flattish disks, some are like the little air-bladders that keep some kinds of seaweed floating, others are the ends of nerve fibres splayed out. In Plate 4, nerve fibres entering the skin from beneath it are seen. They are bending round to form a coiled structure, containing little disks. Disks such as these are used particularly for registering mechanical deformation of the skin.

Encapsulated nerve-endings consist of the nerve fibre ending within a capsule made up of layers of connective tissue. When the capsule is thick, it looks under the microscope like an onion, the nerve fibre running down the middle like the stalk of the bulb waiting to grow out. Encapsulated nerve-endings are stimulated by every sort of mechanical stimulus, stretching, bending, compression and deformation of the skin.

The hair-follicle is one variety of encapsulated nerve-ending, with a thick capsule. The hairs of these follicles are the hairs covering our skin. They act as minute levers; when a hair is bent, the nerve fibres of the capsule are excited and send off impulses to the spinal cord. The slightest touch on the tip or the shaft of the hair sets off this lever action. The hair follicles of the skin are so sensitive that one can easily feel a light touch before it actually deforms the skin. This can be tried out by shutting your eyes and getting someone to move just one of the hairs on your legs; you will find that you can easily tell when he is doing this.

Other touch corpuscles of the skin are also exquisitely sensitive. Some are excited by a deformation of the skin of the extent of 15 μ. The rate of discharge of nerve impulses from touch corpuscles is proportional to the displacement of the skin caused by the touch.

Heavier touches applied to the skin stimulate deeper nerve fibres as well. These nerve fibres are important in localizing a stimulus deforming the skin and in informing us of the position and the movements of the parts of our own bodies.

In the depths of the skin all the nerve fibres come together to form the nerves. The nerves are composed of nerve fibres running to the spinal cord to enter the posterior roots and nerve fibres leaving the spinal cord and running to muscles, blood vessels and sweat glands in the skin.

Each afferent nerve fibre, on reaching the spinal cord, divides into many branches which enter the grey matter and make connexions with other neurons. The afferent nerve fibres from the muscles run forwards in the spinal cord to connect to the motoneurons; for the motoneurons working the muscles need to be kept constantly informed about what is happening to the muscle. Nerve fibres from the viscera and from the skin both run to an intermediate layer of the grey matter, and the nerve fibres from the specialized receptors of the skin run to a more posterior layer of the grey matter.

A new lot of nerve fibres starts from these layers of the grey matter and passes upwards towards the brain. The final link in this chain is within the brain itself.

How we can tell whereabouts in the skin we have been touched or pricked depends finally on the representation in the cerebral hemisphere of the skin of the body. Putting it rather crudely, we can say that touches on the left big toe are felt in one part of the cortex, and burns on the back of the neck in another part. Different parts of the cerebral hemisphere are related to different parts of the body. And so when nerve impulses come to one part, we know that they originated in the big toe; and when they come to another part, they must have come from the little finger. The analogy with the telephone is clear. When Trafalgar 2262 rings, we know that this call comes from the sanitary engineer, or when Park 2262 rings, it comes from a family one knows living in Holland Park. But the nervous system is more complicated than this. For the message coming in from the skin does not go just to one part of the brain. In our analogy, when Trafalgar 2262 rings, the sanitary engineer rings about fifteen other offices at the same time; he delivers a message to each so that each one can take action. We are aware that we have been touched on the big toe; yet many parts of our central nervous system have also been supplied with this information, parts having nothing to do with our consciousness, sensation or perceptions.

How we localize the point of stimulation does not depend only on the nerves of the skin itself. For most touches or pricks, pinches or shoves excite the nerves deep to the skin as well. If some of the nerves of the skin have been cut through by accident, say by a knife or jagged glass, touch or pressure can still be localized fairly accurately, even though the skin itself is insensitive to very light touch, warmth, cold or burning. This is because the nerves of structures deep to the skin, of

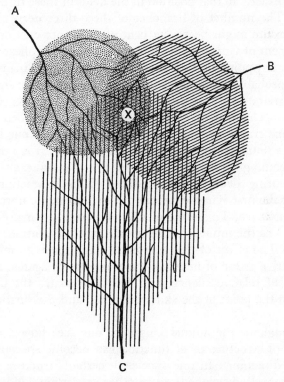

9. Diagram to illustrate how any point in the skin has a particular relation to a minimum of three nerve fibres and no other point in the body has that same relation

muscles, tendons and bones, may be uncut; and their information is adequate to tell us whereabouts we have been stimulated.

Any point in the skin is supplied by very many nerve fibres. When a point on the skin is stimulated, the nerve fibres beneath this point are stimulated unequally. For no two points on the skin come equally within the territory of all the same nerve fibres. This can best be shown in a diagram. In Figure 9, each nerve fibre A, B and C, supplies a little area of skin measuring a few square millimetres; and these areas partially overlap. If the skin is touched at point X, it is in the receptive areas of nerve fibres A, B and C. No other point in the whole body is exactly in that position in the fields of these three nerve fibres. The number of branches of these three nerve fibres it might excite might be 10 per cent of A, 20 per cent of B and 15 per cent of C. In reality, it is much more complicated than this; for any point on the skin is supplied by a great many nerve fibres, probably more like a hundred than the three shown in the diagram.

The mechanism of surround inhibition, described in the horseshoe crab's eye in Chapter 3, is used to help one localize a point stimulated in the skin. When one small group of nerve fibres coming from one point in the skin is excited, the neighbouring neurons are inhibited. This interaction takes place at the first synapse, where the arriving nerve fibres enter the spinal cord. This same mechanism occurs at many higher synapses as the input is taken up through the central nervous system. The effect of this surround inhibition is to make the most active group of neurons stand out clearly against a background of relative silence, and this accentuates the contrast between the point of the skin stimulated and the surrounding skin.

Throughout the animal kingdom, one sees how a general pattern of structure or of function can become specialized in certain directions. In one species, a certain structure is particularly well developed; in another, a certain kind of behaviour is developed, and this necessitates the development of certain kinds of receptors. In the pit vipers and rattlesnakes of

America and in Australian pythons and boas, receptors for warmth have become specialized detectors. In the New World snakes they are collected together in a pit, just below the eye, and in the Australian snakes they are in scales along the upper and lower jaws. They are sensitive to radiant energy, detecting prey by the heat they give out. A rat passing in front of the snake's face emits enough heat for the snake to be able to locate it accurately. A blindfolded pit viper will strike at a lighted electric bulb and not at a cold one; but if the facial pits are covered, it does not strike at all. The warmth of a human hand in front of the facial pit will excite the receptors in it, but if the hand strokes or touches the skin of the pit-organ, nothing happens. The pit viper has as many thermal receptors in about $\frac{1}{2}$ a sq. cm. area as we have in 200 sq. cm. of skin. These receptors are spontaneously active all the time and always sending off nerve impulses. When there is a change in the radiant energy reaching them, all that has to happen is for this spontaneous discharge to be changed in amount and in rhythm.

If a nerve running to the skin is cut and the area of skin supplied by that nerve is rendered anaesthetic, then if light touching, pinching, pricking, burning, warmth or cold are applied to the skin, no reactions follow and nothing is felt. Heavier touch may still be felt if it affects the nerves supplying the tissues deep to the skin and if these nerve fibres are intact. There are also efferent nerves running to the skin; they control sweating, the state of the blood-vessels of the skin and pilo-erection – the standing up of the skin hairs. When the nerve is cut, there will be no sweating and no raising of the hairs. Although the blood-vessels can still dilate and contract in accordance with local conditions, they no longer do so in relation to the total requirements of the body.

The skin is not only the covering of the whole body, it is not only a multiple sense-organ used for sampling and exploring the environment, it is also a great source of comfort and reassurance for the young (and perhaps the not so young). One of the advances in psychology has been made since the war

79

by Harlow in the United States. He has proved that baby macaque monkeys obtain reassurance and comfort from bodily contact with their mothers and from clinging to them; and he has shown that this contact through the skin is of far greater importance in the development of personality and character than suckling. In this case, some of Freud's brilliant guesses and deductions are wrong; sucking the nipple and passing faeces and urine are of minor importance in comparison with clinging to the furry surface of the mother (in the case of macaque monkeys), and almost certainly in the case of the human infant as well.

Chapter 7

Receptors for the Inside World

The receptors we have so far been reviewing keep the animal in touch with the outside world. There are also receptors to keep the central nervous system informed about what is happening in the inside world of the animal's own body.

All receptors are sensitive to those forces they are likely to meet and to no others. We have already seen that the receptors of the eye react only to light and those of the cochlea only to movement. It is the same with the receptors evolved to control the body. The receptors within the bladder do not respond to temperature, but they do respond to contraction and stretching of the muscle of the bladder wall. The receptors of the intestines are insensitive to temperature and to gentle touches; intestines can be torn or cut through in conscious patients without them feeling anything. But they are sensitive to stretching, to contraction and to certain chemical substances.

Position Receptors: Keeping the Right Way Up

For he can set up with gravity which is patience upon approbation.

That we stand upright with our heads above our necks and our necks straight above the trunk seems so obvious that we do not realize that this position is maintained by receptors of many kinds. Man achieves this equilibrium mainly by using his eyes. For him, the next most important receptors are the proprioceptors of the neck and receptors in the joints and skin. The third group are the receptors of the labyrinths. However, there is much individual variation in the extent to which different people rely on their eyes, their labyrinths and the input from their joints and skin.

In most mammals, amphibia and reptiles, the labyrinthine receptors are more important for balance than the eyes. In all animals they take care that when the animal falls, it lands on its feet. In those animals like ourselves who walk on two feet, they maintain the centre of gravity of the body vertically above the base formed by the two feet. This is a difficult thing to do for man, as the centre of gravity is high and the base formed by the feet is small in area.

The inner ear is not only for hearing. It is also the organ of balance. It contains receptors sensitive to movement, to acceleration and deceleration, to rotation and to vibration. The structures of the inner ear are together called the membranous labyrinth: part of the labyrinth is for hearing and the rest is for posture and balance. The part devoted to posture and balance is called the vestibule; it consists of three structures, the utricle, the saccule and the semicircular canals, of which there are three on each side, in the three planes of space. The vestibule is illustrated in Figure 5. Here the three semicircular canals can be seen, but the saccule and utricle cannot be shown as they would be on the far side. In all vertebrates, one of these canals is in the horizontal plane; its angle varies with the usual head position of the animal. In the fish, the head is in the same plane as the body and both are usually horizontal; in the giraffe, the head is usually tilted forwards and downwards, and so the position of the horizontal canal is arranged accordingly.

The semicircular canals are sensitive to rotational acceleration. The utricle and saccule are sensitive to linear acceleration, including gravity.

The centre of gravity of the body and balance are maintained by the eye, the inner ear, the joints of the vertebrae of the neck, and muscles and ligaments, all working together to form a self-stabilizing control system. All this goes on without evidence of the mechanisms involved coming into conscious-ness. If we do become aware of labyrinthine events, it is usually an unpleasant experience; for they give us the horrible sensa-tions of vertigo and sea-sickness. Deaf-mutes who are born without the central nervous connexions of the nerves coming in from the ear cannot get sea-sick.

The vestibular receptors are connected with the neurons working the eye muscles, the muscles of the neck and trunk and the limb muscles. As soon as there is the slightest disturb-ance of balance, the position of the head and eyes is adjusted, then the trunk and the limbs follow suit; thus equilibrium is restored. Every movement we make alters the centre of gravity and tends to upset our equilibrium. Compensation for the change is organized by large masses of neurons within the cerebral hemispheres, called the basal ganglia. They adjust the contraction and relaxation of the muscles to compensate for the changed centre of gravity. The chain of reflexes is started by the receptors of the utricle and the semicircular canals.

To make use of the information obtained by our eyes, we have to know when something is moving and when it is our eyes that are moving. We learn this mainly from co-ordinating information coming from the eyes and from the vestibular receptors. When this co-ordination is upset, we are likely to feel nausea and vertigo and we may vomit. Also, instead of thinking that our heads are moving, we may think it is the objects in the world that are moving: this may be so extreme that we cannot see clearly and cannot recognize peoples' faces.

Man relies far more on his eyes than on his labyrinths for keeping his body upright. In fact, we pay so much attention to visual stimuli that if we are sitting in a stationary train and we watch the train alongside move off, we get the impression that we are moving in the opposite direction. If we relied only on our accelerometers, that is to say on our vestibular receptors, we would not get this false sensation.

How it is to be without vestibular receptors, we have learned from two groups of patients: patients who received large doses of some antibiotic drugs such as streptomycin; and patients with a disorder of this apparatus called Menière's disease who have had the vestibular nerves cut. Most of these patients are able to compensate for the loss of the vestibular input. With the eyes shut, they may have difficulty with balance; but with the eyes open they can walk and run alright and ride bicycles. They are not all good at going downstairs, for this means balancing on one leg for a short time. Though these patients are not sea-sick, they may find it difficult to keep upright on a rocking boat.

In mammals, the utricle is a position-registering organ. It sends in information about the position of the head in space and it is also sensitive to linear acceleration. The semicircular canals are sensitive to rotational acceleration; they act like three spirit levels, set at right angles to each other. Unlike man-made spirit levels, they are curved, not straight, and the fluid is not spirits but endolymph, made from the fluids of the body. Incidentally, some aquatic insects actually do use an air bubble, exactly as in a spirit level. Around the bubble are hair-detectors, which are displaced by the movements of the bubble. In vertebrates, the semicircular canals report on angular acceleration and deceleration and rotation of the head. Every movement of the head stimulates at least one of these canals on each side of the head. When an acceleration becomes a constant speed, nothing more is reported than when the animal is still. If we keep our eyes shut when we are in a lift or an aeroplane, we do not feel that we are moving, once the speed has become constant.

All the receptor cells throughout the labyrinth are built on a similar pattern; they are hair-cells, the hairs being embedded in different sorts of jellies in the various receptor organs. In the semicircular canals, the hairs are embedded in firm jelly, which almost fills the canal. The receptor cells are illustrated in Figure 10. They are of two types, as can be seen in the drawing: one is cylindrical and the other is like a goblet. The nerve-endings connecting to these cells are also of two different types. The hairs of these receptors are arranged in a particular way, with one very long and stiff hair on one side and the other hairs sloping down from it. The hairs differ not only in length but also in bending strength. When the hairs are bent in one direction, the nerve fibres related to these cells are excited to send off impulses, and when they are bent in the opposite direction, these nerve fibres are inhibited.

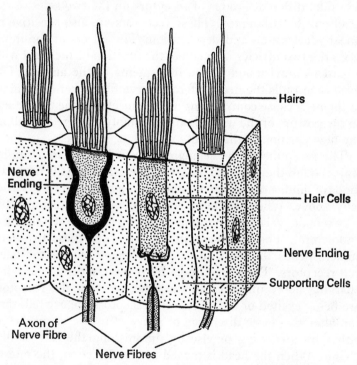

Hairs

Nerve Ending

Hair Cells

Nerve Ending

Supporting Cells

Axon of Nerve Fibre

Nerve Fibres

10. The receptors used throughout the vestibular system

In the utricle and the saccule, the jelly contains neatly arranged crystals of calcite, called otoliths; the tips of the hairs penetrate this jelly and lie among the otoliths. If lobsters are given iron filings in their water, they incorporate them in their otoliths. This discovery was made by Kreidl, a physiologist working at the end of the last century. He had the cunning idea of giving these animals iron filings; and he could then act on the otoliths with a magnet. In this way he could control the direction in which the otoliths were pulled, imitating the action of gravity. Under usual conditions, gravity excites the hair-cells by pulling the otoliths down on to them. When the head is upright, the receptors of the utricles on each side of the head will be equally stimulated. When the head is tilted to one side, different groups of receptors on the two sides of the head will be stimulated. These receptors are also sensitive to linear acceleration and deceleration. The effects of the input from the two utricles is to adjust the position of the head with regard to gravity and to the movements of the animal. The head then pulls the neck; afferent nerve fibres from the joints of the neck cause contractions of the muscles of the trunk, and so the posture of the whole body is suitably arranged to follow the new position of the head.

The receptors of the semicircular canals work in a similar way, though they have no otoliths. The canals are filled by two kinds of fluid, a rather viscous endolymph below and a covering jelly above. When the head is moved in any direction, this jelly remains relatively stationary, having more inertia than the endolymph. The difference in flow between these two substances bends the hairs and this movement excites the hair-cell receptors. The nerve fibres from these receptors are discharging nerve impulses all the time, whether the receptors are being excited or not. When the receptors are excited, they can alter this basic discharge of nerve impulses in two ways, either by increasing or else by diminishing the rate of discharge. When the head is moved in one direction, the rate of discharge is increased, and when it is moved in the opposite direction, it is decreased.

The function of the semicircular canals and the utricles is tested in patients by syringing the ears with hot and cold water and by means of a rotating chair. Hot water gives rise to currents in the endolymph of the lateral semicircular canal towards the ear being syringed, and cold water to currents away from that ear. The effects of normal acceleration and deceleration are imitated by the rotating chair. These ways of stimulating the parts of the vestibule give rise to a movement of the eyes called nystagmus. When the left ear is syringed with hot water, the stimulation of the lateral semicircular canal causes the eyes to move slowly away from the left; the patient compensates for this and moves the eyes rapidly back to the left. Stimulation of the left ear with cold water produces the opposite movement of the eyes. If the semicircular canal or the nerves connecting it to the brain are not working properly, this nystagmus will not be normal.

Muscle and Tendon Receptors

The ability to say without looking where the parts of our bodies are and in what direction we are moving them is called kinaesthesia. It depends on proprioceptors in our joints and many tissues of the body; and it also depends on receptors in the skin.

Within the muscles there are receptors needed for the automatic control of posture and movement. There is the muscle spindle, in parallel with the main muscle fibres, and the tendon organ, in series with the muscle fibres. They are shown as a diagram in Figure 11. The receptors of the muscle spindle measure the length of the main muscle fibres and also the rate of change of their length, in other words, the rate of stretch. The receptors of the spindle and tendon organs also measure tension, the pull put on the muscle or the pull of the muscle and the rate of change of tension. In Figure 11, the nerve fibres are shown as thick black lines, with an arrow alongside each one to show the direction in which it conducts impulses. The five long banded cylinders are the muscle fibres. Each one narrows down to a tendon which is fixed on to a bone. The receptors are surrounded by a connective tissue capsule, shown here by broken lines. Among the tendons of the three muscle fibres on the right, there are tendon receptors, known as tendon organs. The complicated structure between the three muscle fibres on the right and the two on the left is the muscle spindle.

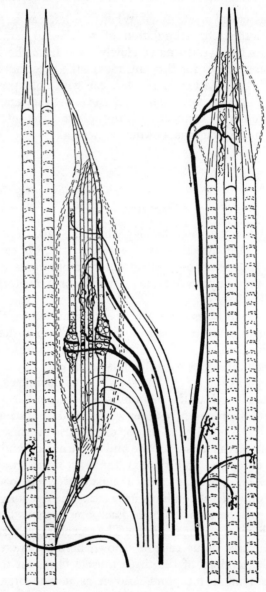

11. Muscle and tendon receptors. The direction in which the nerve fibres are conducting is shown by the arrows

In the middle there are two sorts of receptors, two globoid ones and two unthickened ones. The receptors consist of nerve fibres spirally surrounding these structures. At the ends of the muscle fibres of the spindles there are also smaller receptors. Complicated though this spindle may appear, it is in fact a simple one; most spindles would contain more receptors than this. The spindle is controlled by efferent nerve fibres, shown by the arrows pointing towards the muscle fibres of the spindle. When impulses are sent down these nerve fibres to the muscle fibres within the spindle, these muscle fibres contract and pull on the receptors of the spindle. Also when the main muscle within which the spindle is embedded is pulled upon, these receptors are pulled on.

From this rather complicated arrangement, it follows that the tension within the spindles and the tension in the tendons are not the same. Receptors within the spindles record the tension on the spindle, and receptors within the tendons record the tension on the whole muscle. The two sorts of receptors of the spindles and the tendon receptors constitute the sensing element of the servo-mechanisms used for controlling muscles.

All automatic control systems record not only the continually changing error, but also the rate of change of the error. This is necessary to avoid oscillation around the required output. For this reason the main receptor of the muscle spindle is sensitive to the rate of change of tension as well as to the amount of tension. The muscle and tendon receptors continuously send in impulses to the local region of the spinal cord. They are essential for the maintenance of equilibrium; all posture and control of the centre of gravity finally depends on the information these proprioceptors provide. They do not provide information for those parts of the brain where nerve impulses give rise to sensation. Although we can always say where our limbs and our fingers are without looking, we do not learn this from these receptors. We know it from the receptors in the joints and the skin, mainly from moving the parts of our bodies. If you were asked to say, without looking, exactly where the little finger of your left hand is now, you would probably move it a little to find out. When you move, you not only increase the inflow from the joints and skin; you also know from experience how much force you have to put into such a movement to change its position.

If all the afferent nerves coming to the spinal cord from all the muscles of a limb are cut, the person does not use this limb; it lies inert and loose, just as if it is paralysed. And yet the efferent or motor nerves are intact. The constant information coming in from the muscles, tendons and joints is so important that the spinal cord can hardly move the limb unless this continuous monitoring of movements is going on. Eventually, and with much difficulty, the person may learn to use the limb again; he then monitors its movements by using his eyes. If he is blindfolded, his movements are again wild and inco-ordinated. Not only are our purposive movements disrupted by cutting the afferent nerves but all the more automatic parts of posture and movements are equally disturbed. This cutting of afferent nerves not only may occur with accidents and with gun-shot wounds, it can also occur with certain neurological disorders. The most typical example of this is the third stage of syphilis. In this disorder, afferent nerves from the skin are cut through by the disease process, and the patients can burn themselves and stick pins into their skin without feeling it.

Baroreceptors, Thermoreceptors, Osmoreceptors and Chemoreceptors: Controlling the Internal Environment

The blood pressure is one of the variables in the body which has to be kept constant; and there are special receptors in the walls of the large blood-vessels and in the heart used to signal changes in blood pressure to the central nervous system which are called baroreceptors or pressure receptors. They are constantly discharging impulses; when the blood pressure rises, they discharge more rapidly; when it falls, they discharge less rapidly. The brain's reaction to their rapid discharge is to slow down the heart, to allow the blood-vessels of the body to dilate and thus offer less resistance to the flowing blood, and to depress respiration. When these receptors stop discharging so many impulses, the brain increases the force and speed of the heart, and sends impulses down to the sympathetic neurons in the spinal cord. The activity of this system is then increased in two ways: the sympathetic nerves to the adrenal glands make these glands pass their secretions, adrenalin and noradrenalin, into the bloodstream; and the sympathetic nerves to the smaller arteries make these blood-vessels constrict. The result is that the resistance of the blood-vessels is increased and the heart beats more forcefully, both of which tend to restore the blood pressure to its original level.

As everyone knows, mammals and birds are warm-blooded creatures. Reptiles, fish, amphibians and insects are not; they take on the temperature of the environment. Both ways of adjusting temperature seem to be successful. For insects and amphibians are found in all climates; and so are birds and most mammals, including man.

In mammals, the receptors for indicating the temperature of the surroundings are the thermoreceptors of the skin. They have already been discussed in Chapter 6. These are the same thermoreceptors as are used to tell us if an object is hot or cold. Their use for monitoring temperature is a constant and continuous one, whereas examining the temperature of objects is only done on rare occasions. There are also thermoreceptors in the mouth, throat and oesophagus, with the purpose, no doubt, of preventing the animal damaging itself by taking food that is too hot or too cold.

For the control of the temperature of the body, there are thermoreceptors sampling the temperature of the circulating blood, as well as receptors in the skin. When cooling is needed, the blood is re-distributed, much more being sent to the skin, while the blood-vessels of the skin are dilated. If further cooling is needed, sweating is started off by the hypothalamus. In some animals with thick fur, such as the dog, panting is started up, heat being dissipated from the lungs and the tongue. If the temperature is starting to fall, the blood-vessels of the skin are constricted, and if it continues to fall, the hypo-thalamus organizes the muscles to contract rhythmically in the action we know as shivering. This increases the body's heat production, and the falling temperature is corrected. When the shivering has achieved its purpose, the thermostat stops it. Here in the hypothalamus, the receptors and the effector neurons are near each other, just as they usually are in man-made thermostats.

The first and main way of controlling the body's tempera-ture, however, is the way used by all cold-blooded animals: the seeking of an environment that is comfortable so that the body neither gains nor loses heat. We are always doing this, whether we notice it or not; our newspapers are full of advertisements suggesting to us ways of keeping warm or cool.

Breathing is a fundamental activity which is arranged auto-matically and which we can also influence when we pay atten-tion to it. There are four main controls influencing automatic breathing. It is partly controlled by stretch receptors in the lungs and in the bronchial tree. It is controlled also by the feedback mechanisms and reflexes used for the control of all muscles. The depth and rate of breathing are under the influence of chemoreceptors in the medulla oblongata which are sensitive to the carbon dioxide and the pH of the blood; and they are influenced by baroreceptors in the large blood-vessels and heart.

When a gas is held in solution in a liquid, it exerts a tension or pressure; and when a solid is dissolved in a liquid, it also exerts a pressure. This pressure is called osmotic pressure. In the liquid part of the blood or plasma the salts and proteins in solution cause an osmotic pressure. In the hypothalamus and the medulla oblongata, there are osmoreceptors sensitive to osmotic pressure and they are used to keep this value constant. If the blood tends to get too concentrated, these receptors act on a mechanism in the hypothalamus that induces certain neurons in this part of the brain to secrete anti-diuretic hor-mone. This is a substance which acts on the kidneys, making them re-absorb fluid. Less urine is formed, more fluid is retained within the body, and the blood is kept at the correct osmotic pressure.

Much of the control of the internal environment of the body depends on chemoreceptors, receptors sensitive to chemical substances. Chemoreceptors for sampling aspects of the environment, those used for smelling and tasting, have been described in Chapter 5. There are other chemoreceptors in the gut. One kind is sensitive to acids and another kind to alkalis; they are used to control the digestive ferments or enzymes needed to digest the food. More important are the pH-sensitive receptors in the brain and the great blood-vessels, which are necessary to keep the acidity-alkalinity of the blood plasma between narrow limits. To keep this pH constant, there are three mechanisms. In the blood plasma there are buffers; these are salts which are partly ionized and partly non-ionized, the two forms of the salt being in equilibrium. If an acid or an alkali is added to such buffered solutions, the equilibrium is shifted; but the pH of the total solution remains unchanged, as the added acid or alkali is neutralized. The second method of controlling the pH of the blood is to excrete carbon dioxide in the breath. If carbon dioxide is retained, the pH will be lowered, as this gas goes into solution in water, forming a weak acid – carbonic acid. The third method is to excrete acid or alkaline salts in solution in the urine.

Chemoreceptors in the large blood-vessels are sensitive to the amount of oxygen and of carbon dioxide present in the passing blood. If the amount of oxygen is reduced or the amount of carbon dioxide is increased, these receptors discharge nerve impulses at a greater rate. The brain responds by increasing breathing to take more oxygen into the lungs and to get rid of more carbon dioxide; it also increases the heart rate and constricts the smaller blood-vessels.

In the hypothalamus there are chemoreceptors which record the amount of glucose in the blood; there are others sensitive to the amount of the various hormones that circulate in the bloodstream. These receptors are situated close to the neurons that control the secretion of each particular hormone. The receptors sample the amount of the hormone that reaches them; and the future amount of hormone to be secreted and passed into the bloodstream is then adjusted accordingly. For instance, the hypothalamus possesses chemoreceptors sensitive to the amount of hormone secreted by the adrenal gland medulla; and it can adjust the whole metabolism of the body and the activity of the autonomic nervous system in accordance with this amount.

Chapter 8

Nerves and Nerve Fibres

For by stroaking of him I have found out electricity.

Between the receptors and the central nervous system are the nerves. They convey the impulses sent off by the receptors. The central nervous system itself is made up of nerve fibres and nerve cells.

The nerve fibre is usually likened to a telephone wire; and the analogy is excellent. Both nerve fibres and telephone wires are electric conduction systems designed to conduct messages rapidly over long distances. In both of these systems, the message is sent as a frequency code, which is formed of pulses of activity spaced out in time; in both systems, the pulses are of constant size and they are conducted along the wire at a constant speed. In both systems, the wires have to be insulated and if the insulation gets damaged, the carrying of the messages breaks down. Here the analogy ends, for the nerve fibre is much more complicated than the telegraph wire. It is not just a passive conductor of electrical events; it is both the accumulator and the wire. In telegraphy the current is carried by solid matter – a wire made of metal; in the naturally occurring conducting system the current is carried by ions in a fluid. In telegraphy the electricity is supplied to the wire and then transmitted along it; in the living conducting system, the nerve fibre itself generates the electric signal; it is a self-generating system.

What actually happens when the nerve fibre is conducting is a problem that people have been investigating for more than a hundred years. Before the First World War, Nernst was investigating the physics of the flow of ions through membranes, and he proposed that this is the essential mechanism of the nerve impulse. This proposal turned out to be right. Apart from this, it was also important, as it put a large nail into the coffin of vitalism, the belief that the living processes of biology are different from the processes of physics and chemistry. In 1937, it was proved by Hodgkin at Cambridge that the nerve impulse is a series of travelling electro-chemical events occurring at the membrane covering the nerve axon. This membrane is made of lipid and protein and is a few molecules thick. To account for its properties, many workers consider it to be pierced by innumerable pores.

In all animal and plant tissues, there are fluids which are salt solutions. In animal tissues, these dilute salt solutions are two – intracellular fluid in the protoplasm of the cell, and extracellular fluid in the narrow channels between cells. These two solutions are kept separate by the membrane surrounding cells. Both solutions have electrical properties; they contain electrolytes and so they can conduct current. The intracellular fluid has a high concentration of potassium ions and a low concentration of sodium ions whereas the extracellular fluid has the opposite composition, a high concentration of sodium and a low concentration of potassium ions. The extracellular fluid also contains calcium ions. Both solutions have chloride ions, which are combined with the calcium, potassium and sodium.

All mobile ions carry an electric charge, cations a positive and anions a negative charge. The different concentrations of cations inside and outside the axon membrane make the inside of the nerve fibre electro-negative and the outside electro-positive. Thus there is a difference in potential between the inside and the outside of the cell. This potential difference is called the resting potential when the nerve fibre is inactive and is in a resting state. When the nerve fibre is active and conducting a nerve impulse, that potential difference is called the action potential.

How the action potential occurs is still being investigated by physicists, biochemists and biologists. Measured electrically, there is a sudden increase in membrane conductance (or decrease in membrane resistance). This change in the resting state causes an abrupt increase in the permeability of the membrane to small ions. It seems as if the barrier between the two solutions has suddenly been punctured. The two solutions with their different concentrations of sodium and potassium ions start passing through the punctured membrane: the sodium ions first rush in and then the potassium ions rush out. The sodium ions carry a positive charge and so their flow through the membrane reduces the negative charge inside the membrane to such a degree that the resting potential difference is reversed. This is again reversed by the outflow of the positively charged potassium ions. Calcium ions are essential for these changes to occur, but it is not yet known what role they play. The reduction of the resting potential difference is called depolarizing the membrane. The depolarization allows more sodium ions to flow through. Thus the changes tend to continue. These rapidly occurring events constitute the action potential, which is the electrical phenomenon underlying the nerve impulse.

Under resting conditions the membrane's property of keeping separate two salt solutions against their diffusion gradients depends on its chemical and physical constitution, on its electrical properties, and also on unknown living properties. If the membrane is damaged or if the animal dies, the membrane no longer acts as a barrier and the two solutions diffuse through in both directions. One of the factors present only in life is that the membrane itself is charged. This charge on the walls of any potential pores controls what ions can pass through. Positively charged pores would attract anions and let them pass through; negatively charged pores would attract cations and let them pass. One of the factors essential for the changes recorded as the action potential must be the changes occurring in the ionic state of the membrane itself, which allow ions to flow differently during activity from during rest.

Another factor is the mobility of the ions in the two fluids; this is related to the size of the ion. The smaller the atomic weight of an ion, the less mobile it will be and the more slowly it will flow in an electric field towards an electrode. The size of the ion depends not only on its atomic weight but also on the fact that it is hydrated. Smaller ions have larger shells of water molecules surrounding them, and the large total size means that more friction is generated when the hydrated ion flows in a solution.

What we have been considering so far is the change that occurs when the resting state of the nerve fibre becomes the active state, the change from no activity to activity, when the nerve is excited. These changes occur at an infinitely small region of membrane. When this small region goes through the changes described, an electric current flows between this spot and the immediately adjacent regions of membrane. This local circuit of current passes inwards through the active region and outwards through the neighbouring region. The current itself excites the inactive region of the membrane and this increases its conductance at these points; the increased conductance allows cations to flow through the membrane at these neighbouring regions, and so the cycle of events associated with increased permeability takes place again here. Thus by infinitely small steps, the electric current spreads along the membrane of the nerve fibre. This process of continuous spread of depolarization takes place in one direction only – ahead of the region of membrane which has just been active. The reason for this is that the membrane cannot be depolarized until it has been repolarized; the electrochemical changes cannot be repeated until they have finished taking place and the resting state has been re-established. And so the little patch of electrochemical changes finds membrane in front of it free to be affected and membrane behind it not free to be affected as the changes have not quite finished taking place. This makes it inevitable that these electrochemical changes will pass along the membrane only ahead of the impulse to the part of the nerve fibre that has not yet been activated.

There is another consequence of the fact that the electrochemical changes take a definite though very small amount of time to occur. One nerve impulse cannot follow another until these events have finished. This time-lag fixes the number of impulses that a nerve fibre can carry in a given time.

These electrical events are always of the same extent, producing the same amount of current whenever they occur in one and the same fibre. A strong stimulus does not set up a big nerve impulse and a small one a small impulse; in any nerve fibre the size or amount of the nerve impulse is always the same.

Once the electrochemical changes taking place at the membrane of the nerve fibre have been started, they spread along the fibre to its end. They are self-propagating, and they cannot be stopped on the way. This fact – that the nerve impulse once started is inevitably conducted throughout the length of a nerve fibre without being altered on the way – is an example of what is called the all-or-none principle. This principle states that an event either takes place or it does not; if it takes place, it is the same on all occasions and it cannot be altered in amount. One consequence of the all-or-none principle of impulse conduction in the nerve fibre is that when an alteration has to be made to a message, it cannot be made during its passage along the nerve fibre. All changes to messages in the nervous system have to be made at the places where neurons meet, where the message is passed from one neuron to the next. And a corollary of this is that when it is important to take a message from one place to another unchanged, one nerve fibre is used. When it is important to influence the message, to let messages interact, then short chains of nerve fibres are used, so that at each junction or link in the chain, modifying influences can be introduced.

As we have seen, one of the important characteristics of a nerve fibre is the number of impulses it can send in a certain time; another is the rate at which it transmits each nerve impulse. The manner of conducting nerve impulses we have described so far is rather slow; in mammalian nerve fibres the rates are from $\frac{1}{2}$ to 2 metres a second. This is the mode of conduction of the non-myelinated nerve fibres. Larger nerve fibres, which have a myelin sheath, conduct much faster, the rate being related to their diameter. Myelinated nerve fibres do not have a continuous covering of myelin sheath throughout their lengths; the myelin stops at little regularly placed gaps, called nodes. In these myelinated fibres, the nerve impulse jumps from one node to the next. This method of nerve conduction is called saltatory conduction. As the nerve impulse jumps from one node to the next, it can be conducted much more quickly along myelinated than along non-myelinated fibres. The myelin sheath is an insulator and so it prevents the leakage of current from the axon to the extracellular fluid in the region of nerve fibre between nodes. The electrochemical events described above thus occur only at the nodes in the case of myelinated fibres. The nodes are surrounded by Schwann cells which will be mentioned in the next chapter; they supply energy to the nerve fibre to enable the changes to take place that restore the nerve fibre to its former state after conducting an impulse, sodium being removed and potassium taken up.

In myelinated nerve fibres, the electric circuit is from the activated membrane of the already active node, longitudinally along the axoplasm, out through the membrane of the next node, and back to complete the circuit in the extracellular fluid. If the intensity of current is sufficient for it to flow a relatively long distance between nodes, then a nerve fibre with a long internodal length will conduct impulses faster than one with a short internodal length. There are some other factors influencing the rate of impulse conduction. For instance, nerve fibres of larger diameter can conduct faster than fibres of smaller diameter because electrical resistance of the axoplasm through which the current has to flow is lower the larger the diameter of the cylinder of axoplasm. The rate of conduction of impulses in myelinated mammalian nerves is over a range of 2 to 120 metres a second.

Volleys of nerve impulses passing along nerves can be detected with suitable apparatus by means of electrodes on the skin, and so one can find out if the nerves are working properly or not. A tap on the nail of a finger causes a volley of nerve impulses which can be followed up the limb as far as the arm-pit, and it can again be detected when it reaches the cortex of the brain on the opposite side.

The electrochemical events described so far are not the only changes that occur when a nerve fibre conducts impulses, but they are probably the essential ones. As a nerve impulse passes along the nerve fibre, the nerve fibre uses a minute amount of oxygen, it gets rid of a minute amount of carbon dioxide, there is a slight local increase in temperature, and there is a change which is visible with a strong microscope. The slight rise of temperature and the visible change are probably accompaniments of the essential changes of the nerve impulse; the gaseous changes probably accompany the return to normal conditions after the nerve impulse has passed.

The very fastest conducting fibres are used as the afferent fibres of the essential reflexes of movements and posture. Similar fast-conducting fibres are used within the spinal cord to report to the cerebellum (discussed in Chapter 11) how movements are progressing. The next largest and fastest conducting nerve fibres are the efferent fibres running to the muscles. Thus this system of receptors from the muscles to the spinal cord and fibres back again to the muscles to make them work, is run on the fastest conducting nerves of the body; all posture, standing and movement depend on it. Nerve fibres used for conveying sensory information to the brain and spinal cord cover the whole range of conduction rates, with non-myelinated fibres conducting as slowly as half a metre a second and myelinated fibres conducting by saltatory conduction at 120 metres a second. The nerve fibres within the autonomic system and all nerve fibres to and from the viscera are small and slowly conducting. When we blush, we do not do so as suddenly as we jump when we step on a sharp stone. It is unnecessary to signal to our fellows our embarrassment or humility with speed, but it is important to get our foot rapidly off the cutting edge of a stone. And so fast-conducting nerve fibres are used for this and slow-conducting ones to dilate the blood-vessels of the skin of the face.

If we liken nerve fibres to telegraph wires, the actual nerves in the body are bundles of telegraph wires; they are cables. In a large nerve composed of thousands of nerve fibres, such as the sciatic nerve of man, there are impulses passing at all speeds between $\frac{1}{2}$ m./sec. and 100 m./sec. (225 miles per hour).

As the rate of conduction of the impulse along any nerve fibre is fixed, there is only one variable that can be altered: the number of impulses conducted within a certain time. The only message carried by the nerve, so far as we know, is the electro-chemical change just described. All dealings with the world and with the body itself have to be translated into this coinage; there is no other sort of tender. This is similar to a computer. All the data fed into a computer have to be translated into its code and when the machine has finished its calculation, they have to be translated back from its code into the language of statistics, mathematics or everyday speech.

An analogy here is the taximeter. All the passenger is interested in is the amount of money the journey is costing. The taximeter automatically translates all events into these terms. Whatever transpires on the journey, rushing along here, stopping twenty minutes in a block there, slowing down for your driver to exchange a few well-chosen words with the driver of another vehicle is all presented to the passenger in terms of money. So it is with the nervous system and its journey through the world. Whatever happens both inside and outside the body, the nervous system is presented with a record of electrochemical pulses and from this it must construct the world.

Chapter 9

Communication within the Central Nervous System

Neurons

The investigation of the nervous system by means of the microscope began about a hundred years ago. When the anatomists looked down their microscopes, what they saw was a thick tangled mass of fibres. As they made thinner sections and teased nerve fibres out until only a few were there at a time, they came to realize that they were dealing with two sorts of cells: there were neurons; and there were other cells, the function of which is to look after, feed and repair the neurons. Once all workers had come to this conclusion, a controversy arose whether neurons are continuous throughout the central nervous system, forming a vast and complicated network, or whether every neuron is separated from every other one, with a gap between them where they meet. This latter view is now recognized as being the correct one. It was the view of Cajal, the founder of the Spanish school of histologists. One of the ironies of history is that the contrary and erroneous view was supported by Golgi who invented the method of staining the nervous system for microscopical investigation, which Cajal used to establish the correct view, a view Golgi bitterly opposed. And Cajal and Golgi shared the Nobel Prize the same year for their respective contributions to knowledge of the nervous system.

Neurons are by far the largest cells in the body; their axons are often more than a metre long. The very longest ones reach from the tip of the toes to the top of the spinal cord. In animals like the giraffe or the whale, one realizes how enormous such a cell can be. But not all neurons are that large. The surface area of the largest is a thousand times greater than that of the smallest neuron.

A photograph of a neuron of the spinal cord is shown as Plate 5. In the centre is a clear space; this is the nucleus containing the nucleolus. On the surface of the cell are the nerve-endings of nerve fibres, making connexion with this cell. They form little bulbs on the cell membrane. On the right, the cell-body continues into a dendrite, which is also covered with nerve-endings. Each one of these nerve-endings is forming a synapse with the large neuron. This photograph was taken from a very small piece of a very thin slice of the spinal cord. The knife cutting it has passed clean through the centre of this neuron so we can see the nucleus in the middle and the outside of the cell like a wall. The actual membrane surrounding the cell is too thin to see with the light microscope. It probably consists of a layer of lipid two molecules thick, covered on both sides by a layer of protein. One has to think of the neuron in three dimensions and not flat as it is inevitably shown here. The surface is rough and wrinkled, so that it provides a large area for the reception of nerve-endings from other neurons.

The dendrites of the neuron are also covered by nerve-endings. In many neurons, in particular those of the cerebral cortex, the dendrites are covered with spines. They resemble the branches and spiky leaves of a gorse bush. The larger the neuron, the more spines there are on its dendrites.

One should think of the surface of the cell-body, dendrites and spines as looking like a mosaic. The little blocks of glass and stone of the mosaic would be the knobs of the nerve-endings on the surface of the neuron, and the cracks between the blocks would be narrow lines on the surface that are not covered by nerve-endings of connecting nerve fibres.

The area of a cell-body with its dendrites offering an anchorage to nerve-endings is very large. It has been worked out that on some neurons of the cat's spinal cord, there are about twenty-two of these nerve-endings per 100 sq. μ. of surface of the dendrites and cell-body. This works out that on an average-sized neuron of the spinal cord there are about 800 nerve-endings and on a large neuron supplying a nerve fibre to muscle fibres there are about 10,000.

The cell-bodies of neurons are of various shapes; some are more or less spherical, some are star-shaped, some are pyramidal, some look like baskets, others look like ferns. A fern-shaped neuron is shown as Plate 6. This sort of cell is called a Purkinje cell, named after the eighteenth-century research worker who first described it. The cell-body is in the lower part of the photograph; the axon cannot be seen as it is not on the plane through which this cell was cut for microscopical examination. The spines on the dendrites are not shown in this preparation, as a different stain is needed to show them. Purkinje cells occur only in the cerebellum (discussed in Chapter 11), and in man there are about ten million of them. On each one of them it is reckoned that about 300,000 nerve-endings terminate and can deliver impulses.

The neuron is more complicated than its general appearance suggests. In order to pass the message on to the next neuron, it has to secrete a chemical substance at its nerve-endings. For it is not only an electric wire, it is also a factory producing chemicals. The nucleus and the cell-body produce the protein of which the neuron is formed and they also make the precursors of the chemical substance secreted by the nerve-endings. These substances are continually flowing down the nerve fibre. When a nerve fibre is cut across, the flow of the protoplasm out of the cut end can be seen with a microscope. This flow into the surrounding tissues constitutes the growth and repair process of neurons; for when nerves are cut through, as occurs with accident and disease, they grow in this manner and slowly repair themselves.

Whether under normal circumstances any of this protein passes out of the axonic membrane to have an influence on cells in the immediate neighbourhood is not yet known. Some research workers consider that it does so and that the protein has an influence on the cell-body or the dendrites on which it ends.

Neurons, being such long cells, are always accompanied by supporting cells which provide them with food and energy. In the central nervous system these cells are called the neuroglia; in the peripheral nervous system they are called Schwann cells, after the nineteenth-century anatomist who first described them. If a neuron becomes separated from its Schwann cell for a distance of more than a few μ, it dies.

A neuron within the central nervous system might be thought of as being like a funnel. It collects information from a large area and sends it on through a narrow channel. The mouth of the funnel is equivalent to the whole surface of the body and dendrites of the neuron; the narrow neck is the part where the axon arises; the outlet of the funnel is the axon itself, which takes away the nerve impulses from the cell-body.

Passing the Message from Neuron to Neuron

Up till now, we have been discussing afferent nerves bringing information to the central nervous system and efferent nerves running from the central nervous system to muscles, receptors and glands. The cell-bodies of the afferent nerves are just outside the spinal cord, being buried in the bones of the vertebral column. The cell-bodies of the efferent nerves are within the grey matter of the spinal cord and brain. Apart from the autonomic system, all other neurons, axons and nerve fibres are within the central nervous system; in fact, they are the central nervous system.

All neurons conduct impulses in one direction only. This direction in the brain and spinal cord is always from the cell-body down the axon to the nerve-endings. The kinds of connexions made in the central nervous system between neurons are of many sorts. One finds one-to-one linkages, with one neuron sending its axon and its little branches only to one other neuron, and this neuron receiving only from the first neuron. But this simple pattern is rare. Far commoner is the kind of organization in which one neuron sends its axon out to form connexions with hundreds of other neurons. Looked at from the standpoint of the receiving neuron, it may receive axons originating in one or two neurons or it may collect them from hundreds of neurons, the cell-bodies of which may be a hundred centimetres away or more.

Between a nerve-ending and the next neuron on which it ends, there is a gap, called the synaptic cleft. It measures 200 to 300 Å wide. Events and structures are usually named in relation to this gap, which is the synapse. Those coming before the synapse are called pre-synaptic and those after it post-synaptic. These are convenient terms and will be used from now on to allow us to dispense with unclear terms such as the next neuron or the previous neuron which we have had to use till now.

At synapses, alterations can be made to the message being passed on. A nerve impulse cannot be changed once it is in the nerve fibre, for once it has started, it must go on to the nerve-ending. The synapse is an arrangement for diminishing or increasing the arriving messages, for spreading them far and wide or for channelling them down into a few or only one pathway. The more synapses there are on a pathway, the more modifications can be brought into the responses to stimulation and into behaviour. A similar situation would arise if there were only one road between Manchester and London with no possibility of turning off, or if there were a road with many crossings. If there is only one road the journey is quicker as there is no stopping at the cross-roads; but it is also un-modifiable. Once on the road, you have to continue to the destination. If there are cross-roads, the journey is slower; but all sorts of modifications and ways round can be made.

How the message is passed across the synaptic gap from one neuron to another will be discussed in the rest of this chapter. This field of inquiry has been explored by Sir John Eccles and many physiologists who have worked with him at the National

University of Australia at Canberra. One of the ingenious techniques they have worked out is to make pipettes and electrodes of microscopic size, so small that they can be introduced into the cell-body or even a dendrite of a neuron. With these, they can inject ions or chemical substances into various parts of the cell and they can record spontaneous and induced electrical phenomena.

When a nerve impulse arrives at the synaptic gap, it delivers a certain amount of excitation to the post-synaptic neuron. Whether this excitation suffices to make the post-synaptic neuron fire off impulses or not depends on the nature of this neuron and on its state of excitability at the time. When several impulses arrive simultaneously, the amount of excitation delivered to the post-synaptic neuron is the sum of all arriving impulses. If only a few nerve impulses arrive and they come spread out in time, their sum may never be enough to fire off the post-synaptic neuron. For the excitatory state induced by the arrival of an excitatory impulse lasts only a very short time. This is because the membrane of the post-synaptic neuron is a capacitor which can keep its charge only for a few milliseconds. The current delivered to the membrane of the post-synaptic neuron leaks away as it spreads, because the membrane is a poor conductor. When a nerve impulse arrives at one of the large motoneurons of the cat's spinal cord, the resulting increase in excitability lasts 5 milliseconds. A nerve impulse arriving at a Purkinje cell of the kind illustrated in Plate 6 raises its excitability for 100 milliseconds. Thus we see that the time at which subsequent nerve impulses arrive is one of the important factors determining whether a post-synaptic neuron will fire off or not. If many impulses arrive at almost the same time, the chance is increased that the current will not leak away but will spread along the cell-body to the axon-hillock. That is the region where the new nerve impulse of the post-synaptic neuron starts off; it is just at the place where the axon leaves the cell-body.

Every nerve-ending delivers a constant amount of excitation per impulse to the post-synaptic neuron, for it works on the all-or-none principle. The cell-body and the dendrites of the post-synaptic neuron do not work on this principle; they react to excitation in a graded or quantitative way. The post-synaptic neuron is a mechanism for adding up excitation. Its output is related to its input, but the relation is not usually a simple linear one. The cell-body of the neuron is subjected to greatly varying influences, depending on what it receives from the many nerve-endings on it. The interaction of these many influences at the post-synaptic neuron is the fundamental mechanism of the central nervous system.

Equally important is the geometrical arrangement of the inputs. Nerve impulses arriving at different places on the post-synaptic neuron add their excitation. Further, an input arriving at a certain place on the post-synaptic neuron can alter the effectiveness of an input arriving at another place. It may increase it or it may annul it. Not all parts of the post-synaptic neuron are equally excitable. The parts of the dendrites farther away from the cell-body are less excitable than the cell-body itself. Excitation delivered far out on a dendrite may be insufficient to fire the neuron, but it may be enough to increase its excitability; then, further impulses arriving become more effective, until sufficient excitation is added up to make the neuron fire. Thus the shape and size of the dendrites, whether a dendrite is broken down into innumerable branches or whether it consists of just one or two short twigs, these are factors of importance in the functioning of the nervous system. This geometrical aspect of the neuron is now being studied with regard to its effect on function. As an example we can mention how nerve fibres coming in from the skin end far out on dendrites of a motoneuron; nerve fibres coming from the brain end either on dendrites just near the cell-body or on the cell-body itself. This arrangement shows us that the brain is in a better position for influencing this motoneuron than the skin.

All neurons are not equally excitable and they are not in the same state of excitability all the time. Some are spontaneously active, sending off impulses regularly without waiting to receive an input. Others, once they have fired off, continue to fire without waiting for a further input. A neuron in which very slight changes in the input cause large changes in its output is a sort of amplifier. It is probable that some neurons have the function of adjusting the excitability of other neurons. By firing off, they keep the excitability of the other neuron at just the right level, so that when further impulses arrive, this neuron will then fire. We know exactly how often certain neurons will fire off impulses in relation to their input. The Purkinje cell, illustrated in Plate 6, will fire four times on receiving one impulse from the neurons of a structure in the medulla oblongata called the olive. These olivary neurons will fire impulses at the rate of a 100 a second, and the Purkinje cell will fire off 400 times a second in response to this excitation. The fastest rate in the mammalian nervous system is 1,000 times a second. There are some neurons which are left in a hyper-excitable state for 10 seconds after they have received many impulses. On the other hand, there are neurons which need to receive a great many impulses before they will fire at all, and then they fire off only a few impulses. There are other neurons always kept in a state of excitability so that they are always just about to fire off. In this case, the arrival of only a few more impulses fires them off.

As the excitability of neurons varies, the amount of excitation needed to fire a neuron is different at different times. At one time a certain amount of excitation will fire it off; half a second later, this amount will merely raise its excitability. This is clearly seen in the case of the motoneurons working the respiratory muscles. These motoneurons show rhythmical changes in their potentials in phase with respiration. If some nerve impulses arrive at one of these motoneurons, they may or may not fire it off, depending on the phase it is in. If its excitability is already great, the arrival of a few more nerve impulses will make it fire; if its excitability is falling, these few impulses will have no effect.

The behaviour of a neuron, living singly and uninfluenced by impulses arriving from other neurons, can be examined in two situations; it can be cut out of the nervous system by micro-dissection, or it can be removed from the mass of neurons and grown in tissue-culture. Most neurons examined like this send off impulses spontaneously. All neurons fire off rhythmically. For when its threshold for firing is reached the neuron fires off an impulse. It cannot fire off another one until it has recovered; it has to wait for its threshold to be reached once again. And so it fires, waits for a fraction of a millisecond, and then fires off another impulse.

So far we have been considering only nerve fibres that excite other neurons into activity. But there are also inhibitory nerve-endings. They tend to prevent the next neuron from firing off impulses; thus their action opposes that of the excitatory nerve-endings. Both sorts of nerve fibres work in the same way: a sufficient number of impulses has to arrive at the post-synaptic neuron within a brief period of time. Excitation and inhibition tend to cancel each other out. The inputs to the post-synaptic neuron of inhibition and excitation add up; and this algebraic summation produces the output of the post-synaptic neuron in the form of a certain number of impulses per second.

All branches and divisions of a neuron and its axon always cause the same effect; they all inhibit or they all excite. There is no such thing as a neuron being excitatory at some of its nerve-endings and inhibitory at others. Inhibitory neurons are themselves excited into activity by excitatory neurons, and they can be inhibited by other inhibitory neurons.

We have now described excitation and inhibition occurring at synapses on the post-synaptic neuron. There is also another kind of inhibition – pre-synaptic inhibition. Here the excitatory nerve-endings are inhibited before they can deliver their excitation to the post-synaptic neuron. Pre-synaptic inhibition works by preventing the excitatory nerve fibre from adding its quantum of excitation at its synapse on the post-synaptic neuron. This kind of inhibition is more effective and longer-lasting than that of the inhibitory neuron acting directly on the post-synaptic neuron. It can suppress the excitatory effect of an active neuron, turning this neuron off and stopping it transmitting its impulses. Pre-synaptic inhibition is used by many of the nerve fibres from the skin, from the muscle and the tendons. And these nerve fibres themselves can also be pre-synaptically inhibited by other nerve fibres from the skin, muscles and tendons. Thus many of the impulses coming into the spinal cord can be suppressed. The full details of the organization of this input are still being worked out. More recently still, pre-synaptic excitation has been discovered.

A simplified picture of these events at a neuron is shown in Figure 12. For the sake of simplicity and unlike reality, only one inhibitory and one excitatory nerve-ending are shown. On the excitatory nerve-ending there is also shown an inhibitory ending, which inhibits this nerve fibre just before it ends by pre-synaptic inhibition.

Up till now the description of what must be taking place in the central nervous system has been much simplified. For neurons in reality are hardly ever connected in a one-to-one way. They work together in clusters, chains and rings. Impulses are delivered into these groups of neurons and many nerve fibres lead out of them. These groups have their own rhythmicities and this spontaneous rhythm is changed by nerve impulses coming from other groups of neurons. It is probable that many of the rhythmical activities of the body are organized in this way. This sort of modifiable spontaneous activity may be the basis of the rhythms of the heart-beat, of breathing, of stepping and running, of flying and swimming.

What is wonderful and amazing is that these simple elements – neurons delivering excitation or inhibition in fixed amounts – enable us to do everything of which we are capable. For any neuron has only two ways of behaving: it either fires off an impulse or it does not. With these two possibilities, innumerable variations of rhythm are possible. The effect on a post-synaptic neuron is likely to be different according to whether impulses arrive at regular or irregular intervals. For example, impulses arriving in groups of three at the onset of every half second will have a different effect from three im-

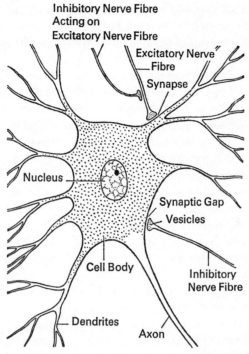

Inhibitory Nerve Fibre
Acting on
Excitatory Nerve Fibre

Excitatory Nerve
Fibre

Synapse

Nucleus

Synaptic Gap

Vesicles

Cell Body

Inhibitory
Nerve Fibre

Dendrites

Axon

12. A neuron on which an excitatory and an inhibitory nerve fibre are ending. On the excitatory nerve fibre, there is an inhibitory nerve fibre

pulses arriving regularly spaced out throughout the half second. When a neuron fires off impulses with a rhythm of pop-dash-pop-dash-pop-dash-pop-dash continually, this contains – as with morse code – quite a different message from one of pop-pop-pop-pop. Whatever rhythm occurs, there is only one variable – the number of impulses sent in a certain length of time.

As far as our knowledge of the central nervous system goes, there are only two conducting elements: the neuron and the junction between neurons, the synapse. These two elements work on different principles. Once the neuron has been adequately excited, it fires off an impulse, and the impulse continues without diminishing down to the nerve-endings; here we have an all-or-none system. At synapses we have a graded system, the principle being one of algebraical summation. When the excitation of the neuron is sufficient, the neuron fires off an impulse.

The following factors act at a synapse. There is the number of nerve-endings on the post-synaptic neuron, and of this number one has to consider how many of them are active at any time. These nerve-endings are either inhibitory or excitatory. The timing of their inputs to the post-synaptic neuron is all-important, for the effect of any nerve-ending is only very brief. Further, the position of every nerve-ending is important, for its effect depends on whether it is far out on a dendrite or on the cell-body. And finally there is the biochemical environment of the post-synaptic neuron, which determines its degree of excitability. Thus every neuron in the central nervous system is an integrating mechanism. It combines all it receives, excitatory and inhibitory, with its own state of excitability; it adds up its input, and the sum is either sufficient to make it send on new impulses or it is not. One might think of the synapse in the following way. Suppose someone is trying to lift a weight with his outstretched hand. The weight is the post-synaptic neuron and his hand is the exciting neuron. If you add your lifting power to his, then together you may lift the weight, whereas alone he could not do it. In this case you are an excitatory nerve-ending adding your input of excitation to his. But suppose you push the weight down as he tries to lift it. Then you are an inhibitory nerve-ending. Whether the weight is lifted or not depends on the relative power of his lifting and your pushing it down. But say instead of pushing the weight down, you pushed his wrist down, so that he could not lift the weight up. Then you are exerting pre-synaptic inhibition. What happens to the weight is the result of all these events.

When physicists and computer engineers learn how the central nervous system solves its problems, they are impressed by the similarities to instruments they design, such as the calculating machines nowadays called electronic computers. For the performance of the two sorts of machines is very similar in some ways. Dean E. Wooldridge, an electronic engineer, discusses some of these similarities and differences in his book *The Machinery of the Brain*. He writes:

The neuron possesses not only some of the characteristics of an on/off switch, but also other properties. . . . The body of the neuron, in electronic terms, is like a summing amplifier that adds the effects of a number of inputs and compares the sum with a threshold value to determine whether the axon is to fire, and, if so, what is to be the frequency of its output pulse train. . . . The secret of the power of modern computers resides in the discovery that extraordinarily complex operations can be broken down into steps that can be handled by very simple processing elements. In mathematical calculations, any operation that the mathematician has invented can be broken down into such elemental steps and caused to control the generation of the voltages representing the output numbers. And in logical problems, the computer can deduce new conclusions from given propositions by the application of the rules of logic, which can be broken down into the same simple processing steps as those used in mathematical computations.

The material out of which the two machines, the calculating machine and the central nervous system, are made is quite unimportant. For both achieve the same results, one purely electrically, the other electrochemically.

Physicists have now imitated the behaviour of neurons by constructing electric circuits to behave as neurons do. From transistors, semi-conductor diodes, capacitors and resistors, they can reproduce the resting potential and action potential of the post-synaptic neuron. Spatial and temporal summation in the neuron can be faithfully imitated; excitatory and inhibitory inputs to the post-synaptic neuron can be made by using two summing amplifiers with a common output. Finally such man-made neurons can be connected in chains, using the output of the one as the input of another, on the plan of a simple nervous system.

Digital computers break down all decisions into yes or no,

to fire off an impulse or not to do so, at every switch or junction. But they do not have to be built on this principle; they can also incorporate analogue systems. Dean Wooldridge believes that such computers will come to supersede digital computers for some purposes. He writes:

There is, for example, probabilistic logic, in which the basic elements are not positive yes/no answers, but estimates of the probability that the answer is yes or no. Simple on/off switches can be used as the components of computers based upon such logical schemes, but they are inefficient. . . . When we are wiser about these matters, it seems certain that we shall want processing elements for our computers that provide greater versatility in their performance characteristics than do simple on/off devices. In fact, the exploratory work now under way in various laboratories on different types of 'electronic neurons' with variable-summing and adjustable-threshold features is probably a forerunner of this ultimate broadening of the spectrum of the elemental processing components that will be used by the computer circuit designer.

And he concludes:

. . . Is there some characteristic of electronic digital computers that possesses fundamental significance? There is indeed one such characteristic – the discovery that complex computational and logical operations can be broken down into steps that can be handled by very simple processing elements. . . . This would also appear to be a valid description of the essence of brain function.

Chemical Contributions to Transmitting the Message

In the previous chapter, we described how changes in the permeability of the axonic membrane give rise to the electric current which is the nerve impulse. Similar changes in permeability are brought about by the arrival of the nerve impulse at the synapse on the post-synaptic neuron.

Nerve-endings are very small in relation to the neuron on which they end, and each one can supply only a very small amount of current. Further, much more current is needed to depolarize the membrane of the post-synaptic neuron than is needed to depolarize the membrane of the axon. Also, the electrical resistance of a gap of 200 Å wide means that more current is needed to affect the post-synaptic membrane. Altogether, these factors have the result that insufficient current is available from the nerve-endings of nerve fibres to depolarize the post-synaptic membrane; and so a different mechanism has to be used. Use is made of special substances called transmitter substances. These are thought to be stored in minute vesicles in the nerve-endings.

Early in the present century it was realized by physiologists that the effects of injecting adrenalin on certain tissues was the same as stimulating the sympathetic nerves. And so they thought it likely that the sympathetic system works by the local injection of these substances. Much research work has gone to prove that this is so. That the parasympathetic system works by secreting a chemical substance was shown by Loewi. In 1921, he thought of the crucial experiment in the middle of the night. He jotted it down, but in the morning he could not read his writing. Fortunately the idea returned on another night. Immediately he got up and went to his laboratory and did the experiment there and then. He collected the fluid out of a heart after he had stimulated the parasympathetic nerves running to the heart. He then transferred this fluid to another heart. This fluid had exactly the same effect on the second heart as the stimulation of its parasympathetic nerves would have had. The substance poured into the fluid from stimulation of the parasympathetic nerves was later identified as acetylcholine. Later he showed that stimulating the sympathetic nerves to the heart releases a different chemical substance, causing the heart to accelerate. This was later shown to be noradrenalin.

These exciting discoveries opened up a new realm in physiology and pharmacology. It was soon found that the transmission of the nerve impulse to the muscle is also carried out by acetylcholine secreted at the motor nerve-endings. The sympathetic nervous system works by secreting noradrenalin at its nerve-endings. The discovery that the two parts of the autonomic nervous system work by secreting chemical substances naturally led research workers to look for the secretion of the same or similar substances within the central nervous system. This has been a much harder thing to discover.

As far as our knowledge goes, neurons belong to groups, those that secrete acetylcholine and those that secrete monoamines; the former are called cholinergic and the latter monoaminergic. The monoamines are dopamine, noradrenalin and adrenalin. There is also a purely inhibitory transmitter substance, γ-aminobutyric acid. It is not known whether there are other transmitter substances still to be discovered.

The transmitter substances are stored in the nerve-endings in an inert form; they have an effect only when they reach the membrane of the post-synaptic neuron. When the nerve impulse reaches the nerve-endings, it causes the expulsion of the transmitter substance into the synaptic gap. How these substances act on the membrane of the post-synaptic neuron is not yet known; it is presumed that they are able to alter its permeability characteristics for a very brief period of time. The events occurring at the membrane of the post-synaptic neuron are similar to those occurring with the excitation of the nerve fibre. There is a flow of cations through the membrane at the spot covered by the nerve-ending. This spot becomes electro-positive, and that sets up a local current. This current excites the adjacent areas of surrounding membrane. When these changes take place over a large enough area of the membrane, depolarization spreads till it reaches the axon hillock; from here it spreads down the axon; then an impulse has been generated.

Inhibition is thought to result from an increased permeability of the membrane, which allows chloride ions to pass. When sodium ions pass through the membrane, depolarization occurs and the post-synaptic neuron is excited; when chloride ions pass, hyperpolarization occurs and the post-synaptic neuron is inhibited.

It appears to be that the chemical constitution of the trans-mitter substance, though it must be important in some ways, is not the main determinant of excitation or inhibition. The membrane of some neurons has been found to possess dif-ferent physiological properties in its different parts; some regions when activated give rise to excitation and others to inhibition. Recently it has been discovered that a neuron secreting one sort of transmitter substance can excite one neuron and inhibit another; this example makes it clear that the character of the post-synaptic membrane is more important than the nature of the transmitter substance. Noradrenalin and acetylcholine can each have excitatory and inhibitory actions. We now know that one neuron will react in one way to all of these substances and another neuron in another way. Other neurons are unaffected by all the transmitter substances

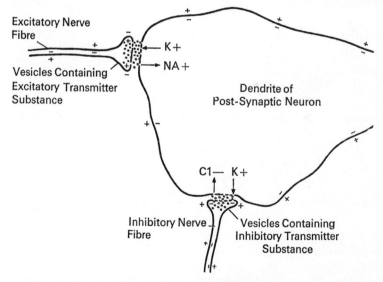

13. An excitatory and an inhibitory nerve fibre ending on the dendrite of a neuron. The charges are shown on the membranes and the ionic changes at the endings are indicated

known. It is clear that this territory is just being opened up and that advances in our knowledge are likely to be made soon.

Figure 13 is a diagram showing in enormous magnification changes occurring at the membrane of a post-synaptic neuron. There is a negative charge inside the membrane and a positive charge outside. An excitatory and an inhibitory nerve-ending are shown, each containing vesicles, which probably contain the transmitter substances. The vesicles on the arrival of the nerve impulse pass through the membrane of the nerve-ending into the synaptic gap and unite with the post-synaptic membrane. Here they affect the membrane so that ions pour through it, chloride ions at the inhibitory endings, sodium ions at the excitatory endings, and potassium ions at both.

Chapter 10

Selection of Incoming Information

For from this proceeds the passing quickness of his attention.

If we were to imagine how a nervous system might work, we would probably think that everything happening in the environment would have to be reported to the brain. In actual fact, that is not how it is done. Roughly a hundred million nerve impulses are reckoned to reach the central nervous system every second. We cannot attend to this vast mass of incoming messages all the time. If we were fully aware of everything reported to the central nervous system, we would be incapable of action and also incapable of repose. If this input were not reduced, there would be an overloading of the lines and the various end-stations would be clogged up. And so the input to the brain has to be selected and controlled by the brain itself. Of all these millions of arriving nerve impulses, only a small number reach the brain, and of that number, a far smaller number eventually reach the parts of the brain where they give rise to conscious awareness.

By using a tape-recorder, we can easily observe just how well the nervous system selects what it is interested in. When we play back what we have been recording, we will be astounded to hear a clock strike in the middle of it. We would willingly have sworn that the time we were recording, no clock struck; and yet there it is, on the tape. The tape-recorder does not select its input; it records everything indiscriminately.

The problem facing an animal is how to discriminate the meaningful signals from the chaotic mass of background noise. For only certain aspects of our environment interest us. If we are thirsty, we have to be looking out for water; if we are hungry, we must be searching for food. Our attention and our interests are directed by our needs; and the need that is predominant at any time will make us attend to those aspects of the environment that are likely to satisfy it.

Even when an animal is asleep, it must still be alive to danger, for predators are out looking for it. The young must be looked after and succoured at all times. The cry of a baby in the night may not be loud but it must waken its mother, while the radio blaring across the street must not, otherwise she will be tired and fretful in the morning. Even animals as large and important as elephants are very sensitive to anything happening at night. Hediger, who has studied the behaviour of elephants in zoos, circuses and in their natural environment, has related how difficult it is to observe their sleeping habits. He could never creep about even on tiptoe without waking them. When elephants sleep, they put their heads on the bodies of their comrades and even rub their hind-quarters hard against each other without waking each other up; but they would always wake immediately a human being made the slightest noise.

To bring the input to controllable dimensions, it first has to be reduced. Secondly, this reduction has to be arranged properly, allowing information of possible importance to come in while irrelevant matter is kept out. And finally, all the information that comes in has to be distributed correctly and sent to the right parts of the central nervous system for appropriate action.

Selection is necessary, as so much is always going on in the animal's environment. The sun is shining, there are long shadows on the far side of the wood, there are pine-needles on the ground, and a robin is being aggressive just inside his territory. But none of this is relevant to the deer, sniffing the wind and pricking up its ears. It selects only the unexpected, such as a new smell arriving on the wind, and it listens for the sounds that may come with it. The animal is alert and seeking information. It is very busy neglecting the great bulk of stimuli affecting it and selecting only those of interest.

When something interesting happens, the central nervous system becomes alert and the receptors are adjusted to examine the various stimuli. Interestingly enough, many different receptors are adjusted for each sort of stimulus. For instance, a sudden sound will increase the sensitivity not only of the cochlear receptors of the inner ear but also the photoreceptors of the retina.

Alerting the brain appears to activate a central part, the reticular formation; from here, excitation is passed on to the cerebral hemispheres. For instance when something catches the animal's eye, impulses pass rapidly into the reticular formation and then the whole brain is prepared and the animal becomes vigilant. The visual input is also sent to the visual receiving area of the cerebral hemispheres to give the animal a picture of what is happening in front of its eyes.

Take another example. If we tread on a nail, one level of our central nervous system causes us to feel pain, to make us have an unpleasant emotion, and to localize the pain to the lower surface of the foot. Other levels receive the message and deal with it according to their needs, interpreting the information as demanding action, such as raising the blood pressure, constricting the blood-vessels of the upper limbs, stabilizing the body on the unpricked limb and withdrawing the pricked limb from the ground. At a higher level in the central nervous system, the input arising from treading on the nail has more complicated effects. It not only is sent on to parts of the cerebral cortex for further analysis, so that the animal feels pain in the foot and can try and work out what has caused that pain. It is also sent to sensory areas for other inputs, hearing, vision, vestibular sensation. It may inhibit these other inputs, so that attention is focused on the foot; or it may heighten these inputs, so that all afferent channels become more important, so that attention is focused on every sort of sensation.

The distribution of the input within the central nervous system needs to be a changing one, continually capable of being re-distributed. For instance, the passage of food along the alimentary canal does not usually need to occupy our consciousness; our consciousness – what we call 'we' – must be left free to enjoy music. But if something goes wrong, if there is a traffic block in the alimentary canal, an obstruction, then the usual afferent impulses coming in from the canal are reinforced and finally the neural substratum of consciousness is made aware of what is happening. If we then get colicky pains, we can use the tools of consciousness – knowledge, reasoning, planning – to take steps to get rid of the obstruction.

One of the purposes of increasing, decreasing or completely suppressing the incoming messages is for the central nervous system to select. It needs to control its input, to play up one form of input and play down another. It may suddenly be important to the animal to pay particular attention to what it is looking at and to neglect a background noise. Then, the activity of the visual receptors of the retina has to be emphasized and that of the cochlear receptors of the inner ear reduced.

There are certain mechanisms used by the nervous system for increasing one input and decreasing another, for making one input the important one for a time and fading others into the background. Inhibition reduces the number of nerve impulses; it can when necessary be so complete that the message is totally obliterated. Facilitation increases the message; it can spread it far and wide in the nervous system, it can give it priority to run along certain pathways, and it can increase or double the number of impulses at any synapse.

Vertebrates are inquisitive; once their basic needs have been satisfied and they are replete, they like to go out and explore the world. Even the timorous herbivores, antelopes and deer, do this, exposing themselves to danger. The question that occupies the animal is – what is this? To answer the question, it seeks information from all possible sensory channels. There are certain mechanisms we are beginning to learn about that are used at various places within the nervous system. For instance, surround inhibition is used to bring out contrasts and edges, so that objects stand out against backgrounds. Movement must stand out from stillness, a slight noise must suddenly appear as a contrast to the silence behind it. In the parts of the cerebral cortex occupied with vision, there are neurons that are stimulated by a contour, by an edge of something seen. It was explained above how contrasts are accentuated at many levels of afferent systems by surround inhibition. This mechanism highlights a central region of maximal stimulation by inhibiting the surrounding receptors. Negative feedback also serves to accentuate what is important. It suppresses excitation wherever it acts. It can be set at a certain level, so that maximal excitation is allowed to pass, and only the weaker excitation is suppressed. The effect of this is like a camera shutter, removing the surrounding region of potential excitation.

Selection of what appears interesting starts at the receptors themselves. We are all familiar with the first control of the visual sense organs, our eyelids. They are the first element of selection in the visual input. We can cut off this input merely by shutting our eyes. Marsupials can do the same with their ears; they have a muscle which closes their outer ears when they go to sleep. Hippopotami can also close their ears like this and they use these muscles when they go under water. All mammals control the amount of sound reaching the inner ear by relaxing and tensing the muscles acting on the little bones of the middle ear.

Most receptors are controlled by nerve fibres sent to them from the brain and spinal cord. There are controlling nerve fibres running to the retina, to the cochlea, to the receptors of the vestibule, to the olfactory receptors and to the muscle spindles; similar fibres to the skin and to taste receptors have not yet been found.

Before the afferent nerve fibre ends at its first synapse, it can be subjected to pre-synaptic inhibition. There is further control at the synapse itself, where the input can be modified in many ways. When a stimulus affects the skin, a burst of impulses is sent along the fastest conducting nerve fibres to go to various parts of the brain. These regions are alerted to further impulses coming in. The first neuron on the afferent pathway within the central nervous system can be inhibited by an inhibitory neuron under control from the brain; further-more, this inhibitory neuron can also be made active by a branch of the incoming neuron itself. A simplified version of this scheme is shown in Figure 14. Inhibition arranged in this

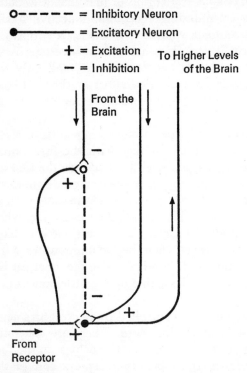

14. Scheme showing the descending control of the input at the first synapse on an afferent pathway

way can be so effective that the incoming nerve impulses can be completely suppressed. There are also descending nerve fibres from the brain which keep the next neurons at the first synapse continually firing off impulses. When further impulses come in from the skin receptors, the amount of this activity can be doubled. This is a way of keeping the sensory system always at the ready and sensitive to the changes occurring in the environment.

An important advance in physiology was made in recent years by Hernández-Peón, working in Mexico and California. When a light is flashed in front of a cat's eyes, the nerve impulses passing along its optic nerves can be recorded by electrical techniques. They can be found at all points on the afferent pathway, including the primary visual area of the cerebral cortex. Hernández-Peón found that if an animal's attention is distracted from one kind of stimulation and it is turned to another kind, the size of the electrical response being recorded is decreased. One of the first experiments he published was done in this way. He recorded the nerve impulses coming along the visual pathway while a light was repeatedly flashed in front of the cat's eyes. Then he brought a tin of sardines up to the cat's nose or else he whispered something in its ear. When he did this, he found that the nerve impulses coming in from the flashing light ceased to arrive at the visual region of the cerebral cortex. When the smell of sardines was removed or the whispering was stopped, the nerve impulses due to the flashing light returned to their original number. From some further experiments he concluded that the suppression of the visual input was taking place at every synapse on the visual pathway. These experiments could also be done the other way round, the visual, odorous, or painful stimuli obliterating the auditory input. When Hernández-Peón showed the cat the sardines or a live mouse in a glass, the auditory input from repeated clicks was suppressed. It was also suppressed by the smell of the sardines or by a painful stimulation of one of the paws.

From these experiments it has been concluded that when a cat's attention is focused on one sort of stimulus, a regularly repeated and unimportant stimulus into another afferent channel is not permitted to reach the primary receptive area. This suppression of information which has become unimportant occurs at every synapse on the afferent pathway and also at the receptors themselves.

Hernández-Péon has now carried out in man some of the experiments he first did in cats. He finds that the nerve impulses coming in from the eyes are greatly reduced when the person is engaged in conversation, when he is solving an arithmetical problem or when he is asked to remember something. And what is more interesting, he finds that when he suggests to the person that the brightness of the flashing light is being altered, the action potential he is recording from the brain is correspondingly altered. If he says the light is being made brighter, the action potentials get far bigger and when he suggests that the intensity of the light is being reduced, the response becomes less. All this was done without actually changing the intensity of the light. Similarly it is found that the inflow arriving at the primary tactile area or primary auditory area can be substantially reduced by getting the subject to solve mathematical problems or just by engaging him in conversation. It has also been shown that the number of nerve impulses arriving at the higher centres of the brain diminishes as the stimulus is continued regularly and becomes monotonous, as had previously been observed in the cat.

When an event stops being new, it becomes less important and it loses priority; the lines must be cleared for new events. For the nervous system, an event is new if it is changed in any way. If a click is repeated, the nerve impulses caused by each click gradually fade away. But if the pitch of the sound of the click is raised or lowered, if the click is suddenly made softer or louder, then the response in the cochlear nucleus is immediately brought back to its original size. For this is different from the previous input. It may be important; and so it constitutes the kind of information the brain wants. When this occurs at the higher levels of the central nervous system, it is familiar to us all. A monotonously repeated sound may not keep us awake and it may even help us sleep; we soon cease to hear it. But if it changes in any way – by dropping a beat, or by changing its pitch – our attention is involuntarily turned to it again.

We have learned from Hernández-Peón's work that our

ability to pay attention to one event and to neglect another is not a purely psychological phenomenon. It depends on descending control of the inflow from the various sensory inputs. Similarly, we can pay attention to something going on in our minds, to the activity of the highest levels of the brain, and fail to notice something happening in the world without. In this case, we are able to play down a sensory input and play up the activity of the cerebral cortex.

With practice one can learn to neglect one sensory input habitually. Everyone who uses a microscope learns to pay no attention to the input coming in from the eye not looking down the microscope although one does not close that eye. I have already mentioned how one does not hear extraneous noises when recording something with interest. Similarly one can learn with practice to neglect a lot of nearby noise and to attend to what one is doing. Ballet dancers learn to suppress the input coming from the vestibular apparatus when they do rapid pirouettes. They use their eyes instead and avoid a conflict between the inputs from the vestibule and from the eyes and in this way they cease to feel giddy or to have nausea.

Under certain circumstances, of which suggestion under hypnosis is one and hysterical insensitivity is another, the volleys of arriving nerve impulses can be recorded from the cerebral cortex without the subject experiencing any sensation. We conclude that sensation is not only a matter of exciting the appropriate regions of the thalamus and cortex. What further mechanisms are needed we do not yet know.

Up till now, we have talked of descending control of afferent pathways to the higher levels of the brain without saying what parts of the brain exercise this control. There are several different parts that do so – the cerebellum, parts of the midbrain, parts of the reticular substance, and the cerebral cortex.

Each primary receptive area of the cerebral cortex is able to control its own input, its own afferent pathway. For instance, the visual area of the cortex can control the retina and the relays on the visual pathway, and the auditory area of the cortex can control the inner ear and the relays on the auditory pathway; the part of the cerebral cortex primarily receiving somaesthetic sensation controls the input at the first synapse on the afferent pathway from the skin.

As was mentioned above, one of the most important regions organizing the control of the inflow is a part called the reticular substance. This is in the core of the hind-brain and the mid-brain; below, it reaches into the spinal cord, and above, it becomes part of the hypothalamus and the thalamus, both of which will be discussed later. It consists of a vast number of neurons, each one of which makes a great many connexions with other similar neurons. Many of the axons divide into two or three branches. It has been estimated that one reticular substance neuron can make connexion with 30,000 other ones. The reticular substance is a mass of synapses; and a great number of passing nerve fibres, both those ascending to higher levels of the brain and those descending to the lower levels of the brain and to the spinal cord, send in branches to these neurons as they pass.

The reticular substance is not a single entity, and so the different parts of it have many functions. There are parts important for assigning priorities to the input, for selecting and filtering it before sending it on to the higher levels of the central nervous system. For this function, the reticular substance receives nerve fibres coming in from all afferent pathways. The incoming messages are distributed in two ways to neurons of the reticular substance: one lot of neurons receives only specific afferent nerve fibres, one lot for touch and another lot for vision, and so on; and another lot of neurons receives nerve fibres from every input, one neuron being excited by auditory, labyrinthine, visual and tactile input. One surmises that the general activation of certain neurons is concerned with making the animal attentive to everything happening or likely to happen around him, and that the specific activation of the other neurons is concerned with making the animal attend to a particular kind of sensation. These two activities, alerting the whole brain and preparing certain sensory regions of the cerebral cortex to receive an input, must be important neural mechanisms underlying the psychological function of paying attention.

Certain parts of the reticular substance awaken the animal from sleep, keep it awake and maintain vigilance. Other parts have the opposite function: they bring about relaxation and repose, and prepare the animal for sleep. These two systems work reciprocally. An increased input to the brain increases the activity of the alerting system, and a decrease in the input excites the reposing system. The alerting system of the reticular substance has inputs from all sensory channels, except that of smell. This part of the reticular substance also receives an input from above, from the cerebral hemispheres. Presumably, ideas and thoughts also alert this system and make the animal attend to whatever may be happening.

When the alerting system of the reticular substance is active, impulses are rushed down to the spinal cord. They go to the motoneurons of the muscle spindles and make all the spindles tense. This is like tuning the strings of a violin. They are then ready to be played upon.

This action of the reticular substance on the muscles of the body is present throughout waking life and also to a certain extent during sleep. People who are psychologically tense unconsciously keep their muscles active and tense; and those who are relaxed allow their muscles to relax. The activity of muscles in people about to be executed has been examined in an investigation done in the United States. As would be expected, these people have most of their muscles actively contracting. Many anxious people are in the same state all the time. They feel that most conditions of living threaten them; and they react like those facing death, being frightened and apprehensive.

Chapter 11

Standing and Moving

> For God has blessed him in the variety of his movements.
> For, tho he cannot fly, he is an excellent clamberer.
> For his motions upon the face of the earth are more than any
>   other quadrupede.
> For he can tread to all measures upon the musick.
> For he can swim for life.
> For he can creep.

Plants are merely moved; animals move. Movements are brought about by muscles; and muscles are made to work by the nerves coming from the central nervous system. Before considering how animals move, we will discuss how nerves make muscles contract.

The Nerves Work the Muscles

Throughout biology one sees a few mechanisms and a few structures being used in many different ways; there is a general pattern and then there are variations on it. We have already seen how some of the characteristics of membranes surrounding cells are developed and used in different ways. The membrane's selective permeability is made use of to allow molecules of only certain shapes to pass through the receptors in the olfactory mucosa; the passage of ions through the membrane, some passing easily and others with difficulty, governs the mechanism of the nerve impulse; and at synapses this selective permeability to ions is used to excite and to inhibit the post-synaptic neuron.

An example of this variation on a basic theme can be seen in the way nerve impulses are delivered at the neuro-muscular junction. For here, where the motor nerve reaches the muscle, there is a modified synapse, similar to those used within the central nervous system.

When nerve impulses reach the end of cholinergic nerve fibres, they release acetylcholine. This substance then passes across the minute gap between the two membranes and unites with the membrane of the post-synaptic neuron. In the case of the nerve and muscle, there is a similar gap between the nerve-ending and the membrane of the muscle fibre. This junction area between the nerve fibre and the muscle fibre is called the neuro-muscular or myo-neural junction. It is like an enormously enlarged synapse, the region of junction being thrown into folds. The nerve-endings are similar to those of the central nervous system, though they are larger, and contain the minute vesicles in which the acetylcholine is stored. The nerve impulse arrives at the nerve-ending and causes the expulsion of a very small amount of acetylcholine into the gap; the actual amount at the motor-end plate gap is 10^6 molecules. It combines with the protein of the motor-end plate of the muscle fibre, increasing its permeability. With increased permeability, the membrane allows the passage of sodium and potassium ions, which depolarize this membrane in the same way as was described for the synapse. Each nerve impulse arriving at the efferent nerve-ending makes the muscle fibre contract just once, though there is an exception to this in the muscles of some insects.

Many drugs have been discovered in nature or made by man which stop the activity of cholinesterase, the enzyme which breaks down the acetylcholine into its two derivatives, choline and acetic acid. When they are given, the acetylcholine remains present and accumulates. Some of these substances have been used as insecticides and the war departments of most countries have large stores of them to use as homicides; they are called nerve-gases.

In general, the musculature of the viscera is controlled by

adrenergic and not cholinergic mechanisms; the chemical transmitter is adrenalin or noradrenalin. In invertebrates other substances are used: serotonin is the transmitter to some muscles of the snail.

From the neuro-muscular junctions of the skeletal muscles, depolarization spreads in both directions along the surface membrane of the muscle fibres, and it makes the myofibrils of the muscle fibre contract. How the muscle turns chemical energy into mechanical work – the mechanism of how the muscle fibres contract – lies outside the territory of neurology. For when we leave the end of the nerve-terminals after they have had their effect on the proteins of the muscle fibre membrane, we have come to the end of the peripheral nervous system.

Reflexes of the Spinal Cord

For thirdly he works it upon stretch with fore-paws extended.

We all know that the commonest things are not necessarily the easiest to understand and they may be the hardest to investigate. Although an enormous amount of work has been done by biochemists, physiologists, anatomists and neurologists for a hundred years or more, we still do not know much about how animals make movements out of muscles.

Neurologists think of the moving of vertebrates as being organized at different levels of the central nervous system. The lowest and most basic level is the spinal cord; the next level consists of the structures of the oldest parts of the brain; above these are structures within the fore-brain; and the highest level consists of the two cerebral hemispheres. This view of neurology was taught by Hughlings Jackson in the last century; it is based on the fact that the central nervous system develops and comes to function more or less in this order and that in senility it declines in the opposite order. When the foetus is still in the womb, the spinal and lowest level brain reflexes are present. After birth, higher level reflexes are added, till the cerebral hemispheres crown the simpler reflex activities. When we become senile and deteriorate, this course of evolution is reversed; the highest levels no longer add their contribution, and finally the senile person passes beyond second childhood and has only the simplest reflexes, such as those of sucking, swallowing, coughing, sneezing and yawning, standing and walking.

The reflexes needed for standing and walking are subdivided in many ways. There are two intertwined systems, the one concerned with stability and posture and movements of the trunk, the other concerned with movements of the limbs.

The simplest reflexes usually consist of three elements: an afferent nerve fibre, an efferent nerve fibre, and intermediate neurons between them. The essential reflex of posture and movement is a servo-mechanism called the stretch reflex. When a muscle is stretched or pulled upon, the stretch excites the receptors of the muscle spindles; they send off nerve impulses to the spinal cord via their afferent nerves. These are the largest nerve fibres in the body and they conduct the fastest. They end on the motoneurons supplying the muscle fibres among which these spindles are situated. The number of nerve impulses per second they bring to the motoneurons is directly proportional to the amount of stretch put on the muscle spindle. By sending in impulses to the motoneurons, they stimulate them to fire and make the muscle contract. Thus stretch of the muscle makes the muscle contract. When the muscle contracts it takes the load off the spindles; they cease to send in impulses to the motoneurons and they cease to fire and the muscle relaxes. This mechanism is called the phasic stretch reflex, and it seems to be used for any sudden rapid adjustments. It is illustrated diagrammatically in Figure 15. This reflex consists of only two parts: the afferent part consisting of the receptors in the middle of the spindles and the nerve fibre from them running to the motoneurons; and the efferent part, consisting of the motoneurons supplying the muscle fibres. Between the two parts there is one synapse. As there is only one synapse between the afferent and the efferent nerves, the time spent in crossing from one to the other is only about a thousandth of a second. If this reflex took too long, our muscles would take an appreciable time to adjust to changes in posture and movements. There is also a tonic

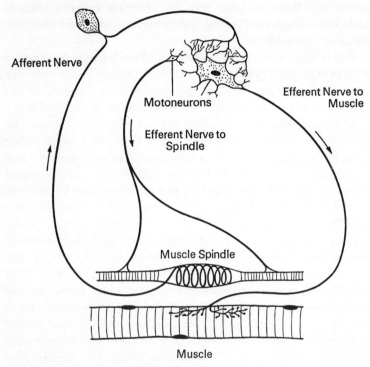

Afferent Nerve

Motoneurons

Efferent Nerve to Muscle

Efferent Nerve to Spindle

Muscle Spindle

Muscle

15. Mechanism for control of the muscles of the body

stretch reflex. This is probably the reflex used for all the adjustment of muscles that does not need to be done very quickly. As the reflex has more than one synapse between its afferent and efferent limbs, it can be played upon by other influences.

Every stretch reflex has effects on neighbouring muscle fibres and also on muscles other than the ones actually stretched; in fact one muscle is never stretched all alone. The afferent nerves coming in from any one muscle of a limb not only have effects on other muscles of that limb but also on muscles of the opposite limb. For all reflexes must be co-ordinated harmoniously and they must be arranged to work in a correct order.

When the muscle contracts or is pulled upon, another receptor is excited, the tendon organ (described in Chapter 7). A pull on the tendon organ has the effect of quietening the activity of the muscle connected to the tendon and of the muscles working with that muscle; a pull on the spindles increases the activity of the muscle and quietens the muscles opposing the action of this muscle. In the competition between these two receptors, the spindle receptor is the more powerful one.

There are some muscles of the body that have to be kept contracted all the time. Examples are the muscles that close the anus and the urethra and the large sheet of muscle forming the lower wall of the abdominal cavity. The stretch reflex is an excellent way of keeping them properly contracted. But for muscles that are used for movements, the unmodified stretch reflex would be useless. Whenever a movement took place, all muscles would rigidly contract, keeping the limb in the original position.

In biology and in engineering there are at least two classes of self-regulating systems: there are stabilizing systems and tracking systems. Examples of stabilizing systems we have considered are the admission of light to the retina, the balance of the body and the automatic compensation for changing load of the stretch reflex. We now come to movements of the parts and of the whole of the body; these are organized by tracking systems. In a stabilizing system, the output has to be maintained at the same level as a stable, constant pre-set input. In tracking systems, the pre-set input is always changing. In movement, the direction, the force, and the speed are always changing.

We still do not know how movements are started. The stretch reflex tends to keep the muscle at a fixed length. This length will be maintained whatever pull is put on or taken off the muscle; for the reflex opposes any change in the load. Clearly this stable system has to be broken through when movements are needed. Most investigators think that impulses are sent to the muscle spindles to set them at the required length. Then the main muscle shortens to the same length as the spindles. But it takes a certain amount of time for the muscle to follow the length set by the spindles; and so this system has a time-lag in it. As may occur in all negative feedback mechanisms, the time-lag causes overshoot. The main muscle fibres adjust to a condition that has just passed. This defect is met by making the receptor in the spindle sensitive to the rate of stretch as well as to the amount of stretch. In this way, the time-lag in the system is corrected by introducing time into the adjusting mechanism. The faster the spindle is made to contract, the more rapidly its receptor sends off impulses to the main motoneurons. The motoneurons have their rate of sending off impulses adjusted to the rate of spindle contraction and relaxation; this compensates for the time-lag, and it also automatically adjusts the rate of any movement.

If something very hot touches you, you will find that your hand is pulled away so quickly that it has all happened before you know anything about it. By means of electrical recording it is possible to time the events in this reflex to an accuracy of a thousandth of a second. It can then be calculated that the hand is pulled away before any information reaches the cerebral cortex to tell you what has happened. If you tread on a thorn, it takes about a twentieth of a second for the nerve impulses to get to the spinal cord and back to the muscles, pulling your foot away, but it takes a fifth of a second, four times as long, for the impulses to get up to the brain and back to the muscles of the limb. In a giraffe it takes even longer; it would take a third of a second for impulses running in the fastest-conducting fibres to reach the brain from one of its feet.

The organization of the total response to this painful stimulus follows the usual pattern employed among the higher mammals. At first, there is an emergency response, effective, possibly too crude. Then the event is reported to the higher parts of the central nervous system where it can be considered and integrated with all that is going on at that moment. Further action is then taken. This takes longer, but it has the advantage that it fits in better with the total situation of the animal at the time.

Not all reflexes are designed to pull the part of the body away from things likely to injure it. For instance, the scratch reflex is designed to remove irritating insects from the fur. Its pathway within the spinal cord can be a long one, for something irritating the animal at the back of the head brings the hindlimb forward to scratch this bit of skin. The scratch reflex can easily be produced in dogs by tickling the skin of the back or sides; you often get it by tickling them just behind the shoulders. Then the dog stops what he is doing, distributes his weight on three legs, and he has to go on scratching for as long as you go on tickling him. It is interesting to note that all breeds of dog, from the little hairless dog of Mexico to the big St Bernard, scratch at the same rate, at about five scratches a second.

Muscles taking part in most movements may be classified as protagonists, antagonists, synergists and fixators. The protagonists are the muscles making the limb or the part of the limb move in the direction in which it is intended to move. If you need to scratch your face, the flexors of the arm and the forearm are the protagonists. The muscles on the other side of the limb are the antagonists. They tend to oppose the action of the protagonists; in this example, they are the extensor muscles. The synergists are the muscles working together with the protagonists. In this example, the synergists would be the neck and trunk muscles bending your head down towards the upper limb. The fixators are the muscles holding a part still so that another part can use it as a firm base from which to move. In this example, the fixators would be most of the muscles of the trunk, of the thoracic cage, and the abdominal wall. They hold the trunk in position and the spine upright, so that the upper limb and head can move.

In order to move, one activates the protagonists and usually inhibits the antagonists. The mechanisms underlying these reflex arrangements were worked out by Sherrington, who named the general principle reciprocal innervation. For instance, to bend your elbow, you must activate the flexor muscles, those that cause flexion of the limb, and inhibit the extensor muscles, those that straighten it.

Reciprocal innervation is easily understood in the case of the movements of our eyes. In order to look to the left, we have to activate the lateral-pulling muscle of the left eye and at the same time inhibit the medial-pulling muscle. If this were not done, there would be a tug-of-war between the two muscles, each pulling in opposite directions. As our two eyes work together, looking to the left in fact needs activation not only of the lateral-pulling muscle of the left eye, but also activation of the medial-pulling muscle of the right eye. Reciprocal innervation is organized among the neurons that work the eye muscles; and so this detailed organization does not have to be arranged by the parts of the brain that send down a message saying 'Look left'.

There are other elements of reciprocal innervation apart from the reciprocal inhibition of the antagonists. Certain reflexes reach across the body, the afferent part being in one limb and the efferent part in the other. For instance, when one lower limb is flexed, there is a reflex extending the opposite limb. When this reflex occurs alternately, first in one limb and then in the other, one has the basis of stepping, and this is one of the reflexes underlying walking and running.

There are also many reflexes connecting the fore- and hindlimbs in quadrupeds. The pathways for most of these reflexes are more complicated than one would have thought. For they are not only between the fore-limb and hind-limb regions of the spinal cord; they include chains of neurons in the lower parts of the brain. All these reflexes are, in the words of Sherrington, 'fragments of an act, not an act'. Each level of the central nervous system adds its own contribution till finally there is an act appropriate for the situation.

The spinal reflexes are better developed in vertebrates of lower orders than mammals. Mammals in which the spinal cord has been cut across cannot stand. But chickens which have had their heads cut off can run around the farmyard minus a head; their legs work perfectly, their wings flap in conjunction, and even their balance is adequate. The movements continue until all the blood is pumped out of the carotid arteries, and the loss of blood brings these reflex movements to an end. Snakes continue to perform their serpentine movements after their heads have been cut off and move along the ground. Beheaded eels are capable of all the movements of which eels are capable when possessed of heads. If a frog or toad is decapitated while it is copulating, its headless trunk continues to clasp the female, faithful beyond death.

Neither two-legged nor four-legged animals can stand when the spinal cord has been divided from the brain. But if in cats and dogs the lowermost parts of the brain are left in connexion with the spinal cord, things are different. The reflexes making the extensor muscles contract are reinforced. When this occurs, pressure on the under-surface of the foot makes the extensor muscles of the limbs contract. These muscles then oppose the pull of gravity, and the animal stands.

When the spinal cord is cut across in the South American sloth, this animal can still maintain its normal posture of hanging, belly upwards, from the branches of a tree. With the spinal cord divided from the brain, all the flexor and adductor muscles of the limbs are in constant activity and the animal will continue to hang satisfactorily, though unable to move.

In man, the spinal cord may be cut through and separated from the brain by wounds, accident or disease. A bullet may be shot right through the spinal cord. This leaves the patient with two separated central nervous systems. He has his brain and a certain length of spinal cord above, and the rest of the spinal cord below; and there is no neural connexion between the two. If this injury occurs in the neck, death comes soon; for breathing ceases.

After such injuries, the spinal cord at first ceases to show any activity; this is the stage of spinal shock. During this stage, none of the muscles supplied by nerves below the level of damage to the spinal cord contracts. The reason for the inactivity of the neurons working these muscles is that when the inflow from a large number of neurons of the brain is suddenly removed, neurons dependent on this inflow become so inexcitable that they no longer work. It takes time for them to adapt to new conditions and start working again without this habitual inflow from the brain. When they do recover, the correct balance of excitability is never achieved again; the stage of inactivity is followed by a state of excessive activity.

After the spinal cord has been cut across, the lower part eventually works automatically on its own. At this stage the reflex movements that are built into the spinal cord can be studied; for the brain can no longer influence its activities. In such patients the flexor withdrawal reflex becomes overpowering; any harmful stimulus to the lower limb causes this limb to withdraw: the limb is flexed at every joint and so it is pulled away from the stimulus. The other lower limb may be flexed or it may be straightened out. This flexion of one limb with straightening out of the other is the basic movement needed for removing one lower limb from anything harmful and putting the weight on the other limb at the same time, a protective reflex to avoid damaging the foot. Another reflex is seen when firm pressure is put on the sole of the foot; it usually makes the limb extend so as to take the weight; this is one of the essential reflexes for standing.

When the spinal cord has been cut across, there is one kind of spastic paralysis. In this paralysis, the affected part is stiff, because most muscles, protagonists and antagonists, are contracting at the same time. Although this is not the main cause of the paralysis, it alone makes movements difficult. The main reason why the patient cannot control his movements is that the motoneurons are no longer in connexion with the brain; and it is the brain that makes purposeful, non-reflex movement. In spastic paralysis, the lower limbs and the abdominal wall are liable to go into violent spasms: the two lower limbs are often firmly wedged together, either straight out or flexed. In these patients the bladder and bowels work automatically, the patient being unable to control them. They carry on independently, as in a baby. When the central nervous system is intact, this control is organized by many parts of the brain. The front parts of the cerebral hemispheres are the region of most importance for voluntary control. When we wish to sit through a play or a concert, this part of the brain prevents reflex emptying of the bladder. Like all skilful movements, this control has to be learned and practised. Using this region of the brain, we also make the bladder or rectum empty when we decide it is a convenient moment. Many other animals have acquired these skills. We may observe this in the dog. This animal uses urine to map out his territory; and as we all know he has difficulty in passing a tree or lamp-post without leaving his mark. The quantity of urine secreted is insufficient for this social use; and so we see the male dog cocking a leg and going through all the movements of emptying the bladder, even though there is no urine to pass.

Changes in Reflexes

Reflexes are not inevitable and fixed; but the very first part of a reflex may be difficult to change. They can be controlled, diminished, obliterated, suppressed, amplified and developed. This can be done by all those factors that we call mental, emotional or psychological, including suggestion and hypnosis. The more neurons and synapses there are in a reflex pathway, the more modifications there can be introduced into the reflex. We can do very little to change the knee-jerk and nothing to alter the pupil's reaction to light and dark. But we can train ourselves to suppress the gag reflex, the reflex that makes us retch when something touches the back of the throat. The reflex watering of the mouth, on which Pavlov concentrated, depends largely on training. A convinced vegetarian's mouth would probably not water when he smells steak cooking, whereas most other people's would.

At the lower levels of the central nervous system, the more stereotyped and simple reflexes are organized. They consist of three or four neurons with two or three synapses in between. Above this, further interneuronal pathways are available, the time for the reflex effects taking a little longer and a greater variety of effects becoming available. At every synapse variation can be introduced. Above the spinal cord, the different regions of the brain can be brought into the reflex cycle. Further modification of the effects is achieved. And finally the whole brain including the cerebral hemispheres can add their contribution. In this case, we no longer talk of reflexes. But nothing essentially different has occurred. Further and further pathways and synapses have been introduced into the cycle so that more modifications to behaviour can be achieved.

For example, the movements of the legs in running are organized by the lower levels of the spinal cord. This simple and stereotyped movement is then altered so that it becomes the skilled movement of running over uneven ground, jumping over a puddle, and continuing to run while looking back over the shoulder. Swallowing is a simple stereotyped movement organized by the lower level of the brain. It becomes the final part of the more complicated movements of eating, tasting and considering the food.

The more complicated and delicate the movement, the more learning is used, and the greater the part played by the highest levels of the brain. We can also control by means of the highest levels of the brain many simple reflex activities. The control of otherwise automatic reflex functions is a speciality of Indian fakirs and those adept in Yoga. By means of it they impress the multitude and European visitors and themselves most of all. Reflexes can also be altered and controlled at spinal level. When the spinal cord is cut across low down in very young kittens or puppies, a great deal of compensation for this injury to the central nervous system can occur. With care and training, these animals can be taught to walk and stand, crouch, jump and even run. The reflexes needed for these skills can be developed in these infantile animals far more easily than in adult animals. The amount of change that can be developed in the built-in reflexes of the spinal cord has been recently demonstrated by Kozak and Westerman. They showed that by rubbing the skin for ten minutes daily or putting a hind limb in ice-cold or hot water daily, they could alter or suppress the built-in reflexes. This constituted one of the many examples of proof in the laboratory for what has been obvious to clinical observers for a long time: that patients with the spinal cord divided in the same way also show similar changes in reflexes. And doctors and physiotherapists who treat these patients see many examples of how they can alter, suppress and encourage various reflex postures and movements. They can train the bowels and the bladders of these patients to empty their contents reflexly in response to various forms of stimulation or to do so daily at a certain time.

Reflexes of the Lowest Levels of the Brain

In man, certain reflexes are built into the lowest levels of the brain, the parts immediately above the spinal cord. We have learned which are the most elementary of these reflex movements from studying those interesting deformities, anencephalics or babies born without most of the brain. Some of these babies have a spinal cord and only the very lowest parts of the brain; above this where the brain should be there is nothing but a bag of fluid. But these babies can breathe, suck and swallow. I do not know who the physician was who first examined and named the reflexes needed for these acts, but he seems to have been impressed with similarities between humans and pigs; for he named the reflexes sucking and rooting, pouting and snouting. When the skin around the corner of the baby's mouth is touched, the head is turned round towards the touching object, the mouth opens, and if it is touched with a nipple, a finger or a stick, this object will be sucked. Pouting and snouting are puckering and protrusion of the lips as a response to a light tap or pressure around the lips or just under the nose. A baby with only the most basal parts of the brain working can yawn, cough, sneeze, belch and vomit, as well as do the reflex movements arranged by the spinal cord. It can empty its bladder and bowels, like a normal and complete baby. It sleeps and can be woken up.

In humans, many basal movements organized by the spinal cord and the lowermost parts of the brain are present before birth, as every mother knows. Some mothers-to-be have had a tea-cup kicked out of their hands, the kick coming from within.

Human foetuses removed by operation can be kept alive for many minutes; and important researches on these specimens have been carried out in the United States. From these investigations, we now know that movements can be obtained from stimulating human embryos aged $7\frac{1}{2}$ weeks from conception. The first movement obtainable is a movement of the neck away from the stimulus when the mouth is touched. The $9\frac{1}{2}$ week old embryo opens the mouth when stimulated by a light hair around the mouth; at $10\frac{1}{2}$ weeks, this stimulus makes it carry out swallowing movements as well. At this time it bends its toes and its fingers when the sole or the palm is stimulated. A little later, stimulation around the anus makes the foetus contract the sphincter muscle, closing this orifice.

Reflexes developed when the baby is still in the womb are all ready to be used after birth. The sucking reflex evoked by touch on the baby's lips and the complicated swallowing reflexes evoked when anything touches the back of the throat are ready for immediate use. There are reflex movements evoked by light. During the first few days of life, the baby turns its eyes and head towards a light; but if a light is too bright, it will shut its eyes. Within fifteen days, the baby will follow objects moved horizontally in its field of vision, first with its eyes, and then by turning its head. Within a few moments of birth, the baby turns its eyes, both together, in the direction of a click made near its ears. Between three and five weeks, the baby smiles. By the second month reflexes develop allowing the baby to raise its heavy head when it is laid on its front. During the next few weeks the neck and back muscles develop and permit the baby to hold up its head when it is in any position. Gradually the baby learns to sit up, and then to move around on its buttocks and thighs, then to crawl, and finally to stand and walk. To attain these skills, the child is helped by its mother and others around it. This is not a feature of humans only. Chimpanzees teach their babies to do all the movements of which they are capable. Professor Yerkes, who spent many years studying chimpanzees and gorillas at Yale University, relates that the chimpanzee mother helps her baby 'to stand, first on all fours, then on its feet, and she lures it to walk toward her as she backs away'.

Standing

Standing is based on many reflexes. One of the fundamental reflexes starts in the skin of the sole and in the muscles and tendons of the foot. When the foot touches the ground, the receptors send impulses to the spinal cord; the response is that all the muscles of the limb contract, thus tending to make the limb into a rigid pillar capable of holding the body up. As soon as the pressure on the skin and the muscles and tendons of the foot is removed, the muscles relax again and the limb becomes loosened up.

When the animal is standing, gravity pulls on its body and limbs, tending to make it fall to the ground. But this pull on the muscles evokes their stretch reflexes; the muscles then contract and oppose the pull of gravity. Thus the very force that tends to make the animal fold up and fall is used to keep it standing upright.

Once we have mastered the skill of standing, only very few muscles are used. The muscles are contracted just enough to correct the tendency to sway and to keep the centre of gravity in the central line of the body. This economy of the use of muscles is an example of the effect of practice and training. The more used to carrying out a posture or a movement one becomes, the more relaxed one is and the less muscles one uses, the less work is done, the less tired one becomes.

Standing and sitting do not depend only on the spinal cord; the brain plays a part in such complicated acts. As we know, they both have to be learned and a lot of trial and error and practice goes into their achievement. The co-ordination of all muscles to maintain the upright posture depends too on the utricles within the inner ears, which are sensitive to the pull of gravity and to acceleration and deceleration imparted to the head. In man the eyes are more important than the utricles in keeping us the right way up. The human baby starts to sit only when these reflexes depending on these structures have developed. They are not present at birth, when the baby cannot support its weight and can only lie down.

There are some essential differences between a statue of a man made of metal or stone and a man of flesh and blood. The real man can balance, and if he is pushed off balance, he corrects the tendency to fall. All animals which walk on two legs, such as penguins, bears and men, must control the centre of gravity all the time, for it changes with every step and every movement of the trunk and upper limbs. If we raise an arm in front of us, muscles of the trunk and both lower limbs must be brought into activity to compensate for the change in the centre of gravity. One of the most impressive sights is that of an ostrich or a crane firmly planted on its stilt legs with its head bent right over and its beak touching the ground. But the less beautiful sight of a human being in the same position is really more astounding. For whereas nearly all the weight of the bird remains above its legs and feet and only a very small proportion is bent over in front, with human beings this is not so. If one bends forward with the upper limbs also hanging down, probably a half of one's total weight is hanging well forward of the legs and feet. Many receptors contribute to this achievement. The final co-ordination is organized by a part of the fore-brain called the basal ganglia. When the body or any part of it is tilted or when the ground is uneven, the nuclei of the basal ganglia organize the muscles to compensate. They receive a constant input from the labyrinths. If the labyrinths are destroyed or the basal ganglia are damaged, the eyes can compensate to a great extent. But if these two structures are damaged and the patient closes his eyes, his head falls forwards. When the basal ganglia are damaged, the patient cannot compensate for any pushes tending to upset his balance.

In Parkinsonism, there is degeneration of the basal ganglia. Patients with this disorder have much difficulty in starting and stopping movements and in changing from one movement to the next one. It seems likely that the correct balance between the two ways of working the motoneurons no longer occurs. When the patient walks, he has much difficulty in stopping, tending to walk faster and faster so that he may finally fall. He is unstable on his feet, and if he trips, he cannot right himself.

The Contribution of the Cerebellum

For he can jump over a stick which is patience upon proof positive.

There is a very large part of the brain filling the back of the skull, looking somewhat like a miniature version of the cerebral hemispheres; it is therefore called the cerebellum. It is shown in Plates 8, 9 and 10. The cerebellum co-ordinates all our movements; it smooths them out and is essential for accuracy.

The cerebellum developed out of the basal part of the brain, near the labyrinths. This region is near the upper part of the spinal cord, where all nerve fibres coming in from the entire musculature and skin of the body are gathered together.

During the course of evolution, the cerebellum first became large in birds. This is perhaps what might be expected; for the rapid movements of birds in three dimensions of space need the most perfect timing and control of balance. In man, the cerebellum does not look very big, as it is neatly tucked away into a small space. But if all its folds are spread out so that it looks like an ironed-out sheet, it would be 1·4 metres long; its area is almost as large as that of the cerebral hemispheres.

All inputs to the body send some of this input to the cerebellum. It thus receives an input from the skin, the muscles and tendons, from all specialized receptors, such as eyes and ears; and it receives a great deal of input from the labyrinths, the organs of balance. The cerebellum is essential for controlling the precision of movements so that we stop at the end of carrying out a movement exactly at the right time and place. It does not design movements but it stabilizes all the movements we perform. When it is damaged by injury or disease, all movements become jerky and irregular, the normal flow and grace of movement is replaced by jerky tremors, the hands and fingers overshooting their mark, while the movements of speech show the same disorders. Speech is broken up into jerky components, the breathing being improperly coordinated for the smooth flow of words.

The Contribution of the Cerebral Hemispheres

For he can jump from an eminence into his master's bosom.
For he can catch the cork and toss it again.

Many parts of the brain higher than the cerebellum organize total acts of movement. 'Higher' does not only mean anatomically higher, that is higher up in the head than the parts of the nervous system just above the spinal cord; it means higher in the sense that these parts have been developed later and are less automatic and more capable of modification in their behaviour. When certain whole sequences of movement are needed, these higher parts of the brain send down orders for these totalities. These higher parts know nothing of flexor and extensor muscles, of the organization of reciprocal innervation, of arranging the muscles and the parts in the right order, of seeing that the centre of gravity is maintained while the trunk is moved forward. The spinal cord can organize the movements of running; the cerebellum and related parts of the brain can arrange these movements so that the animal keeps its balance when running. The totality of running is organized at higher levels of the brain.

As structures are formed, so their functions develop. Life does not start when the baby takes its first breath. Human behaviour is present continually from $7\frac{1}{2}$ weeks after conception until death. The movements and functions built into the nervous system are not all present at birth. They appear at different times during the child's development, and they need the correct circumstances to allow them to develop. The stimulus to their development may come from the environment without or from the internal environment.

In higher vertebrates, many kinds of movements are innate, though they become manifest only at certain times after birth. Walking, running, jumping are all innate in man; normally they are learned with encouragement from others, but doubtless infants left to their own devices would acquire these movements on their own. Swimming, curiously enough, is not innate; for although all races develop it, human beings who have not learned it drown in deep water. Man's cousin, the chimpanzee, cannot swim and is frightened of water; he also dislikes rain. The orang-outang cannot swim either. It is not known for certain whether the gorilla, who is most like man of all animals, swims or not; there are reports that they cross rivers. Professor Yerkes considered that there was no evidence about the gibbon's ability to swim. Certainly a male and female gibbon I knew in Bangkok were not afraid of the rapidly flowing water of a river by which they lived, and they would spend a lot of time fishing floating debris out of the river.

We know from the various animals with which we are familiar that their young are born with every degree of prowess in movement. The newborn goat can stand at birth and in a few hours it jumps around and gambols. It is the same with the deer and the gnu, which immediately after birth get up and follow close to their mothers. Foals too can stand almost immediately and they very soon walk. The newborn dolphin can swim, it can remain under water and 'knows' to come up to the surface to breathe. The seal, however, cannot swim and needs to be enticed into the water.

Agile animals like deer which can run and jump at birth are taught to become more proficient and better at manoeuvring by their mothers, who teach them to play follow-my-leader. There are other games played by human children that are also played by some other animals. 'I'm king of the castle' is played by deer and by chimpanzees; and the game called 'tag' or 'touch-last' is played by chimpanzees.

So necessary is the stimulation from the environment in some cases that the movements never develop without it. A striking example of this occurred a few years ago in America. For certain work, it was necessary to breed white mice quite free from any bacteria. This meant that immediately after birth the newborn mice had to be taken away from their mothers and placed under bacteriologically sterile conditions. All these mice died. When they were dissected after death, it was found their bladders were full to bursting. Their attendants then realized that none of them had passed urine during their short lives. On observing the behaviour of other mice and their babies, they saw that the mothers licked the babies all over. When the mothers licked their babies' genital organs, the babies emptied their bladders. It was apparent that this external stimulation had to be added to the internal stimulation of a full bladder before the built-in mechanism of bladder emptying could work; without it, the animal could not pass urine and died. Once this was known, they could breed the mice satisfactorily by brushing their genitals with soft paint-brushes. Incidentally, they were surprisingly ignorant about the habits of the animals they kept. Anyone who has kept a bitch which has given birth knows that she noses around and licks the underside of her offspring and that this sets off eliminatory reflexes.

The difference between acquiring a skill and developing an inborn movement is a matter of degree. There is nothing essentially different in the baby's learning to sit up and the child's learning to sit down on a chair without looking, the older child's learning to run downstairs, and the still older child's learning to play the violin. All these skills start with simple reflexes. Then more complicated, co-ordinated control is added by higher levels of the central nervous system. With frequent use, the skill becomes more automatic.

Certain integrated movements rely on stimulation from within, from the action of hormones on the neurons concerned. Birds under the action of prolactin manifest all the movements necessary for constructing nests, although they may never have seen a nest or known what the finished product will be like. In species less developed than primates, the movements of copulation are inborn and do not have to be observed or learned; but they become more efficient with practice. They are inborn but they do not develop till puberty, when certain neurons react to the influences of hormones secreted by the ovaries and testes. No doubt those pretty movements of mother cats as they gently pick up their kittens in their teeth by the loose skin at the back of their necks are not learned but are inborn, though needing the secretion of hormones to come to fruition. And incidentally the kitten shows an inborn reflex, present at or shortly after birth, when it is picked up in this way; its whole back is flexed, as are its hindlimbs; the forelimbs remain moderately extended. Thus its hindlimbs are lifted from the ground, it tucks itself into a small space and when it is dropped back into its basket, its forelimbs are already extended to stop its head hitting the ground.

How we learn the skills of series of movements is not known. Presumably information has to be sent to many parts of the cerebral cortex; and presumably practice is somehow connected with using certain neuronal pathways and avoiding others. But even the effect of use and disuse on neural pathways is, as we shall see later, a field of inquiry where there are few known facts and many hypotheses. Certainly practice is

153

needed to acquire any simple motor skill, such as walking or swimming. Moreover, using the limbs and practising must be done at the right time. Experiments done in the United States have shown that monkeys brought up with their limbs encased in cardboard cylinders never learn to use them properly, remain abnormally clumsy, and cannot acquire all the deft movements characteristic of their race. In such an experiment, repeated and essential information has been withheld from many levels of the nervous system at a time when it is essential; if this information comes later, it is too late.

When we practise a skill, such as playing a musical instrument, information is repeatedly sent to the spinal cord, to the cerebellum, to the mechanisms coping with equilibrium, and to most parts of the cerebral hemispheres. Information regarding distances moved by the parts and rates of moving has to be sent to the cortex of the hemispheres and integrated and stored. In playing the piano, for instance, when we have to hit a certain note without looking, we must know just how far to move the upper limb, how to put the finger or thumb in the correct position, how high to keep the hand above the keys. As this movement is repeated and practised, it becomes easier and easier; it becomes more automatic, and the aid originally lent by conscious thought becomes a hindrance rather than a help. We take all of this for granted, but how remarkable it is; and still how little we know about how it is done.

In Chapter 12 it will be pointed out how many movements develop only under the influence of various hormones. Nest-building, sitting on eggs, copulating, all these activities of parental behaviour occur only when the correct hormones affect the centres in the brain and spinal cord. This influence can be seen in such an everyday occurrence as a dog passing urine. As we must have all noticed, male puppies do not cock a leg when they pass urine; they crouch a little, round their backs and lower the pelvis. The adult male dog's way of urinating is a secondary sexual characteristic; and it can be induced before the onset of puberty by the injection of testosterone proprionate. Bitches also acquire it if they are given this male hormone. If male puppies are castrated soon after birth, they do not develop the adult male posture for micturition; but they acquire it if they are given this hormone. It does seem curious that the position taken when passing urine should be a secondary sexual characteristic. Doubtless this is associated with the male dog's way of marking out its territory by means of urinary signposts. How the hormone affects certain neurons within the central nervous system to make them work in such a way as to produce a certain posture of the body, we do not know.

We take for granted all the skills we acquired before we knew what we were doing. For instance, we have to learn to work our two hands together and, perhaps more difficult, to work one without the other, and to do different things with the two hands. The ability to touch with our fingers the things we can see is a skill we learn during the first year of life. It takes weeks for the child to learn to know the feel of a cube or of a ball in the hand; and this knowledge is not automatically transferred from one hand to the other. All such cognitive skills are normally acquired as the child plays. For children's play is not just a diversion like the golf or tennis of adults. It is an important and essential part of neural learning. All higher mammals play and use this play to train both the sensory and motor parts of their nervous systems. One can see this occurring with otters, dogs, cats and foxes.

In man, the two cerebral hemispheres are not equal contributors in learning movement. In right-handed people the left hemisphere is in command of most learned movements. When this hemisphere is damaged or when the pathway by which it controls the right hemisphere is cut through, the movements organized by the right hemisphere, that is to say, movements of the left limbs, become curiously abnormal. The left limbs are not paralysed, but they may be unable to do those movements their owner intends them to do. The left upper limb may stop in the middle of a task and wander away. If the patient is asked to make the sign of a cross in mid-air, the left hand will not do it although the patient knows what he is trying to do. Or if such a patient is told to lick his lips, he may open his mouth and then rapidly shoot his tongue in and out, but he will not achieve the correct movement. Yet this very movement can still be carried out automatically. Immediately after a patient has failed to lick his lips when told to do so, he unconsciously licks a crumb off his lips if one happens to be sticking there.

Movements organized at lower levels tend to remain intact when disease strikes the nervous system. A common kind of paralysis in man is hemiplegia. The movements controlled by the opposite damaged hemisphere no longer occur, though a few reflex movements organized lower in the brain remain. The patient automatically moves the paralysed arm when he yawns or sneezes though he cannot do so when he wants to pick up a book.

It is no mere figure of speech to say that we are weak with laughing; laughter brings the flexor muscles of our lower limbs into activity. Fear can also bring us to our knees. With these emotions, the body tends to crumple up, bending at the hips and the knees, the trunk flexes, the head and neck bend forward a little. Such movements occurring without our intending to do them show us that the higher levels of the brain, those we use when we intend to do something, are not necessary for all movements.

There is a rather rare neurological disorder called cataplexy, in which the pathway from parts of the brain particularly concerned with the movements associated with emotion becomes abnormally easily available. Patients with this trouble crumple up and fall to the ground when they experience a strong emotion. Laughing may weaken them so that they fall; you can fell them with a joke. If a patient with cataplexy gets so furious that he wants to hit you, as soon as his emotion gets the better of him, he will fall limp to the ground. I once saw a mother of some young children who had this disorder. When she got so annoyed with them that she wanted to hit them, she just flopped down, unable to move.

Chapter 12

Needs, Desires and Emotions

> For he will not do destruction, if he is well-fed, neither will
> he spit without provocation.

During the last quarter of a century, a new science has been
evolved: ethology, the study of animal behaviour. This is
mainly the child of Konrad Lorenz. It is related to the anatomy
and physiology of the nervous system, as any science of
psychology has to be.

Just as fifty years before, Freud had uncovered his ears and
listened to his patients, so Lorenz opened his eyes and looked
at the animals around him. What he saw was animals imbued
with energy, inquisitive, active, always busy, and each one
preoccupied with the others of its group. That is all obvious to
anyone who looks at animals without having had any training
in a psychological laboratory. But at the time Lorenz began
observing the animals among whom he lived, psychologists
regarded animal behaviour as consisting of chains of reflexes
or as being responses to stimulation. In reality, motivation
comes from within. The brain leads the animal to seek from its
environment the things that are necessary for its survival. The
brain gives the animal its appetites and makes it carry out acts
of behaviour designed to satisfy them. It translates needs into
desires. People think of the brain as the organ of the mind, as
the source of the intellect, of thinking, of ideas. It is all that,
and it is much else besides. It is mainly the organ of motivation, the part of ourselves that makes us do everything we do.

Lorenz thinks of animal motivation in the following way.
There are certain basic instincts, each with energy at its disposal. The energy mounts up until it is discharged; after it has

been discharged in the consummatory act, it gradually builds up again. And this cycle of damming and discharging of instinctive energy makes animals spend their time seeking the stimulation that will discharge the energy. The necessity for discharging instinctive energy is what makes animals active and inquisitive, so that they move around the world exposing themselves to danger. Among most animals, there are cues that serve to make them discharge this instinctive energy in an act, named 'releasers'. As the fulfilment of desires is pleasant and the inability to fulfil them is unpleasant, animals learn to try and fulfil desires and thus to satisfy their needs. They thus learn by a natural system of rewards and punishments.

What the psychologists call instincts are fictional conceptions considered to be the basis of drives. To a physiologist, drives are recurring needs and the behaviour designed to satisfy them.

The animal's desire or need to perform certain acts of behaviour differs at various times. One factor causing the difference is the amount of hormones circulating in its body and affecting its tissues, including its brain. Depending on the presence of hormones, features of the environment may stimulate the animal or they may evoke no interest. From the animal's point of view, the stimulus is not the same on every occasion; it depends on the animal's internal state. If we present a male trap-door spider to the female, we might imagine that this stimulus is always the same, being the male of the species. However, the response of the female spider to this constant stimulus varies a great deal. She may live contentedly with him for several months, she may live with him for only a day or two, or she may eat him straight away, rather than await the inevitable tedium of married life. The male never knows what sort of reception he is going to get; he may be invited to the marriage bed or he may be invited to a supper, not to eat but to be eaten. The same stimulus – male trap-door spider – releases different behaviour in the female, depending on factors within, such as whether she is ready to mate or whether she has recently mated.

The more important the stimulus from the world without,

the less motivation there need be from within; and vice versa. When there is much motivation, an otherwise inadequate stimulus from the environment will suffice. Or if any kind of releasing mechanism fails to be found in the outside world, the total innate reaction can be manifested spontaneously without being triggered off by stimulation. This behaviour, reaction to a stimulus which is absent, is called vacuum activity or reaction to deprivation. Such vacuum activities have often been observed in birds and other animals reared apart from their fellows, and so there is no question of them having been learned. The existence of vacuum activities shows us that such acts of behaviour are innate and inherited.

Lorenz has reported instances of whole episodes of behaviour being manifested in the absence of the essential stimulus. He had a starling brought up in captivity and accustomed to receiving its food from a dish. This bird would fly up and carry out the complete motions of catching a non-existent fly; it would focus on it, swoop on it, apparently catch it and swallow it. It had never seen another bird catch an insect. Similar inborn behaviour has been seen in humming-birds. They fasten non-existent materials for nest-building to non-existing twigs. Whether the birds are actually experiencing hallucinations of the missing objects, we do not know. We do know, however, that humans under conditions of maximal deprivation often do have hallucinations; these are a sort of mirage, supplied by the imagination, driven by the need. It may be that dreams should be considered as such hallucinations. Hallucinations satisfy to some extent, and that perhaps is their purpose and the reason for their existence.

When a drive has recently been adequately satisfied, the stimulus must be ideal in every respect to serve as a releaser of behaviour. Even then, only a token reaction may be produced. A correct stimulus no longer works when the need for it is absent. Once the need has been satisfied, the animal will not respond to the very stimulus that previously evoked the response. For instance, a stimulus that gives rise to certain behaviour during the breeding season is meaningless and causes no response when it occurs at other times. This is common observation. When we have just finished eating a meal, another excellent meal placed in front of us evokes different behaviour from what it had previously done when we were hungry. Sexual stimulation that would evoke the behaviour of copulation in the male when he has not copulated for a long time does not do so when it occurs shortly after several copulations.

Among human beings, consciousness is used in the continuous seeking to satisfy needs. How far it is used in other animals, we do not know. Obviously it is used by the animals we know best, dogs and cats, tigers, lions and elephants. Because we use consciousness, we tend to overvalue conscious awareness, thought and planning; and we find it difficult to imagine how an animal acts effectively without this conscious thinking.

Clear examples of animals choosing the correct way of behaving can be shown by a technique worked out by Richter of Philadelphia. He has deprived the small animals that can be kept in laboratories of an essential ingredient of their diets, for instance, calcium or Vitamin B1. The animals are then put in a kind of help-yourself cafeteria and he observes what foods they choose. From a great deal of experimental investigation of this type, he has come to the conclusion that animals choose those foods that supply the elements in which their bodies are deficient. If they are deprived of a certain vitamin, they will choose foods rich in that vitamin. They seem to have a desire for these foods rather than for others.

The body's store of certain essential elements can be depleted in other ways than by leaving them out of the diet. The normal metabolism can be disturbed by removal of some endocrine glands. When the parathyroid glands are cut out, the body loses its calcium and retains too much phosphorus. Richter has shown that rats in which the gland has been cut out have a craving for calcium and a diminished appetite for phosphorus. He has also shown that pregnant rats choose a particular diet; they take an increased amount of calcium, phosphorus, protein and fat, all of which they need to build the foetus and to produce milk.

In these examples, we are observing the animal's needs giving it its desires. We do not know how this comes about; but we do know that it works through its taste receptors. If the nerves coming to the brain from these receptors are divided, the rat no longer makes these life-saving choices in its diet.

A similar mechanism, whatever it is, operates in humans; or rather, it tends to, before it is altered by social and psychological influences. That untrammelled human infants act like this is known from a few cases reported in medical literature. A particularly striking case was reported by Richter and Wilkins from Baltimore. A little boy, aged three and a half, had been born with a great deficiency of the adrenal glands. This had the effect of upsetting the body's control of its salts so that the child was constantly deficient in sodium, the most important element of all. The boy had a natural craving for sodium chloride, common salt. From the age of one, he had always taken large amounts of salt. At this age, the little boy started licking the salt off pretzels. He would chew salt biscuits and bacon; after he had got the salt out of them, he would spit the rest out. He eventually discovered the salt in the salt shaker, and then showed a great appetite for it. His mother reported to the doctor what had happened when the child was eighteen months old. 'When I would feed him his dinner at noon, he would keep crying for something that wasn't on the table and always pointed to the cupboard. I didn't think of the salt, so I held him up in front of the cupboard to see what he wanted. He picked out the salt at once; and in order to see what he would do with it, I let him have it. He poured some out and ate it by dipping his finger in it. After this he wouldn't eat any food without having the salt too. I would purposely let it off the table and even hide it from him until I could ask the doctor about it. For it seemed to us like he ate a terrible lot of plain salt. . . . After we gave it to him all the time he usually didn't ask for it with his dinner; but he wouldn't eat his breakfast or supper without it. He really cried for it and acted like he had to have it.' All the foods the boy liked were salty ones. And, interestingly enough, the first word he learned to say was salt. He took a lot of water too, which he also needed. The sad end to this tale is that when the little boy was taken into hospital, he was given an ordinary diet, with no extra salt; and he died.

The behaviour of this little boy, not only so sensible but so necessary, will doubtless be a surprise to us all. We think of the brain as being able to plan the future, making use of its experience of the past. But that the brain should possess this kind of intuitive or instinctive knowledge comes to us as a surprise. We always overestimate consciousness. For really it is unnecessary for animals to know the purpose of their activities. All that is needed is that they should carry out the right behaviour.

How the animal's needs come to cause its appetite is a large subject which is still being actively investigated. The physiological mechanisms differ for the different needs and among the various species. In the higher mammal, hunger, for instance, is caused both by the amount of glucose in the blood and by the activity of receptors in the stomach. Animals go on eating until they have a sensation of repletion. This sensation depends on the receptors in the stomach and also on a rewarding centre in the brain. When the glucose concentration in the blood is correct and when the receptors in the stomach have been quietened by the presence of food, the rewarding centre is excited, and the animal experiences a feeling of satiety and content.

An animal's needs are not only the obvious ones, eating, drinking, and avoiding enemies who prey upon it. Depending on the species, the baby animal may need to cling to its mother, to push its behind up against the side of the nest, as does the baby cuckoo, it may need to skip and jump, to strengthen its legs and learn to use them. In species akin to ourselves, such as the anthropoid apes, we can see the distress of the young animal if it is prevented from satisfying its basic needs.

As the young animal gets older, the needs and the consequent desires become more complicated. Again, depending on the species, it has general social needs. It may need companionship; without it, the animal cannot develop normally and will never function as a proper member of its social group. Yerkes, who knew chimpanzees better than anyone did at that time, has written of them:

The need for social stimulation, such as is provided by companions, becomes so strong during late infancy and early childhood that isolation causes varied symptoms of deprivation. In addition to overt behavioral expressions of distress, there is general physiological dysfunction. Taken forcibly from companion or group and left alone, the ape cries, screams, rages, struggles desperately to escape and return to its fellows. Such behavior may last for hours. All the bodily functions may be more or less upset. Food may be persistently refused, and depression may follow the emotional orgy.

Chimpanzees are very ready to accept other animals as companions, human beings, orang-outangs, gorillas, dogs or cats. It is the same with the young gorilla. Hediger has related how a child gorilla in a zoo succeeded in tricking its young lady keeper into its cage one evening; the latch of the lock clicked shut; and so she had to spend the whole night being hugged and loved by the poor lonely young gorilla. The social needs of animals in zoos are not considered; and in the arguments for and against having zoos, this inevitable deprivation is one of the reasons against imprisoning animals.

After puberty, reproduction demands that the animal should mate and found a family. After mating, the animal experiences the needs and emotions associated with preparing a home for the young. This brings about nest-building in birds, rodents and sticklebacks. After birth of the babies, there follow the emotions associated with the succouring and protection of the young, retrieving them and bringing them back to the nest in the case of rodents, teaching the fledgelings to fly in the case of birds, and for man all those thousand things from changing the nappies to earning enough money to send them to school. For the species must not only continue to exist; the new generation must be firmly established in life and taught the knowledge acquired by its forebears.

Emotions aid the satisfaction of desires. They seem to add to the energy provided by each basic need and drive. Although it is difficult to say what the various emotions have in common, we now know that they can be totally removed by cutting out certain parts of the brain. Without emotion the animal has no energy. In the case of man, he just sits or lies wherever he happens to be and does not bother to feed himself or get up and drink.

Behaviour is accompanied by emotions; and emotion itself generates behaviour. The exciting emotion of aggression is needed to make the animal establish its territory, to provide enough food for itself, its mate and its young brood-to-be. The painful emotion of fear is needed to make wild animals flee from man, their enemy. Grief is inevitable when we are deprived of a mate, of a companion, of our children. Painful emotions result from being unadapted to the environment; their purpose is to make the animal adjust better.

If the environment provides no stimulation, most animals experience boredom. This is a negative emotional state, though its unpleasantness is different from that associated with an inability to satisfy a strong internal need, such as hunger or thirst. Boredom is commonly seen in animals kept captive in zoos and in animals under domestication. In the zoo, it is observed in members of the cat family, showing itself in their compulsive pacing up and down and ritualized turning movements, to a psychiatrist so reminiscent of the behaviour of some human compulsion neurotics. If boredom occurs in animals under natural conditions, it may act as a spur in the search for necessary stimulation. In man, we know from introspection that it can lead to satisfaction in imagination, to the wish-fulfilments of dreams and daydreams, and to many kinds of substitute gratifications.

Many emotions are not for ourselves alone; they are produced for their effect on others; and they are a basic way of communicating with others. Subtle emotions are understood by other members of the same species. More basic emotions, such as fear, readiness to fight, and emotions accompanying pain or pleasure are understood by other mammals or perhaps by all other vertebrates. We can tell when a dog or cat is in pain or is about to fight us; dogs can tell when the stag is frightened and about to flee and when it is about to attack them.

It may well be that some other mammals recognize the emotions we are experiencing and expressing better than we do. Possibly they detect our fear or our intended aggression towards them. I do not mean the obvious threatening behaviour, when we pick up a stone or a stick, or obvious fleeing, as we turn our backs and start running away. One has the impression that they understand the meaning of our scarcely expressed intentions before we would know those of another man. It may be that we give off smells which our poor olfactory systems cannot detect but which the sniffing dog and deer understand and which warn them of our attitudes.

Reactions to emotions are not the same in everyone; people have different constitutions. Some react to difficult situations by increasing the activity of the parasympathetic nerves to their stomachs and bowels; others cause changes in the blood-vessels of the coverings of their brains and get migraine; others induce spasms in muscles and get headaches, backache, pains in their chests. Others do not express states of emotion or stressful psychological conditions physically, their bodies are not used to play out the dramas of their lives. They deal with them in the outside world. They create emotional situations, they quarrel with all their friends, they become involved in traffic accidents; or they get depressed or neurotic in various ways.

Sometimes shocks of a psychological kind can affect the endocrine balance of the body. Horror and continual fear can cause overactivity of the thyroid gland. Some disorders result from the continual use, perhaps in an unbalanced or pathological way, of the parts of the autonomic nervous system.

Nervous children frequently empty their bladders; so do elephants. Bats and monkeys pass their urine on to their assailants, using their bladders as offensive weapons. Perhaps this frequency of passing urine in children and some adults is a relic of this manner of showing aggression. Some adults, when nervous, get diarrhoea, others get constipation. Elephants and camels too are very prone to diarrhoea when they are anxious or upset. Many kinds of monkeys use defaecation as an offensive weapon. Travellers in South America have reported how irritated troops of monkeys will defaecate on them from above, their ability to hit the target being excellent. In chimpanzees and gorillas, micturition and defaecation occur with strong emotional states. It is the same with ourselves. Chronic or sudden fear and anxiety may give rise to frequent emptying of the bladder, to constipation or to diarrhoea. There is no doubt that certain chronic disorders of the lower bowel, such as ulcerative colitis, are caused by psychological and emotional events. They have been produced experimentally by prolonged stimulation of the hypothalamus. Also when a certain region of the hypothalamus is stimulated several times a day in monkeys, the animals develop ulcers of the stomach and duodenum. In man, psychological factors can cause gastric and duodenal ulcers and they can equally cause them to heal or not to heal. It is commonly found that an ulcer suddenly becomes worse or it starts to bleed when an upsetting psychological event occurs. There are several mechanisms known which could bring this to pass. One of the effects of adrenocorticotrophic hormone is to make the stomach secrete acid. When electrodes implanted in the hypothalami of animals are constantly stimulated, too much of this hormone is secreted, and the animals eventually develop gastric or duodenal ulcers or ulcers in the colon.

There have been one or two famous patients who have had openings made between their stomachs and the belly-wall and who have been observed by doctors aware of the importance of psychological influences on the body. Instruments could be passed through this hole, the inside of the stomach could be looked at and samples of the gastric juices could be taken. Every American and British doctor remembers hearing about such a case when he was a student. For this was a patient whose case was published by his doctor, Dr Beaumont in 1833 and who rejoiced in the name of Alexis St Martin.

In our own time two doctors at the New York Hospital, H. G. Wolff and S. Wolf, studied another patient with a gastric fistula. They had the advantage of having the modern psychological and sociological outlook as well as quantitative methods of investigation and colour photography at their disposal. In order to study human gastric function, they employed their subject, Tom, as a laboratory worker; they also got to know him so well, that they knew how any of the stresses, upsets or pleasures of day-to-day life would affect him psychologically. Knowing how Tom would be feeling in various circumstances, they could correlate this knowledge with the state of his stomach.

Fear had the following effects on his stomach:

Sudden fright occurred one morning when an irate doctor, a member of the staff, suddenly entered the room, began hastily opening drawers, looking on shelves, and swearing to himself. He was looking for protocols to which he attached great importance. Our subject, who tidies up the laboratory, had mislaid them the previous afternoon, and he was fearful of detection and of losing his precious job. He remained silent and motionless and his face became pallid.

At the same time the mucous membrane of his stomach became pale and it secreted less than the normal amount of acid. These effects lasted for five minutes after the doctor had found what he was looking for and had left the room. The mucous membrane of the stomach also remained pale with diminished secretion of acid, when Tom was sad, discouraged or was reproaching himself about anything. This effect resulting from his mood or other psychological factors would override the physiological effects due to food. For instance, beef-broth would cause an increase in the bloodflow in the stomach and the secretion of acid. But these would not appear if Tom was feeling depressed. If he was feeling resentful, there would be an increased secretion of acid with dilatation of the blood-vessels, and a great increase in the movements of the stomach. Quite different reactions were shown by the stomach when Tom was feeling hostile and aggressive. On these occasions, the stomach was in the same state as it would be at the start of a big meal: the amount of acid secreted was three times the normal and the mucous membrane was 'turgid, engorged and much redder than usual'. On another occasion, the investigators found that when Tom's face was red with anger and resentment, so was his stomach. Anxiety also caused an increased secretion of acid, abnormal redness and increased blood supply of the stomach; and when the anxiety persisted for weeks, so did these changes in his stomach. In Tom's case, this readiness of the stomach to receive a meal was unassociated with his feeling hungry or having a good appetite; on the contrary, he had no appetite. But in some patients, anxiety and resentment cause hunger, and these patients may eat a lot at the times when they have these emotions.

A doctor living in Chicago has recorded his own case. He had the interesting habit of examining his own gastric juices every morning. One day thieves entered his house and killed his landlady. On that day, his gastric hydrochloric acid was double its normal strength. For the following ten days, he expected to be shot by the gangsters in revenge for helping the police track them down; during this time the concentration of his gastric acid remained very high. After he had moved to what he considered a safe place, his acidity returned to normal.

The actual feeling of emotion is a mixed mental and physical experience. Fear and anxiety are felt in the pit of the stomach. When certain parts of the cerebral hemispheres are stimulated in conscious patients, the patients experience this feeling, and they cannot say if the sensation they feel is a physical one in the centre of the abdomen or if it is a mental or psychological one. When the same parts of the cerebral hemispheres spontaneously discharge, as they do in epilepsy, patients experience before the actual fit this sensation of fear or anxiety in the pit of the stomach.

Emotion will suddenly send up the blood pressure and this may cause a cerebral haemorrhage and death. Aubrey has recorded that when the Earl of Dorset was Lord Treasurer, he was giving evidence at a trial:

The Lord Treasurer had in his bosome some writings, and which as he was pulling-out to give in evidence, sayed 'Here is that will strike you dead!' and as soon as he had spoken these words, fell downe starke dead in the place.

Aubrey comments:

An extraordinary perturbation of mind will bring an apoplexie: I know several instances of it.

Chapter 13

Communication by Chemical Substances

The nerves are not the only messengers of the body; there are also general chemical messengers. These are the hormones, chemical substances passed into the blood by the endocrine glands.

If the obvious analogy for nerve fibres is telephone or telegraph wires, then the analogy for hormones is radio. The control of broadcasting resides in the central authority of the brain. Just as there are many broadcasting stations, so there are many different hormones. The programme is broadcast far and wide, but it can be picked up only by those with sets tuned to receive it. So it is with hormones. They are poured into the bloodstream and sent all round the body; but they bring meaningful messages only to those cells tuned in to receive them.

Hormones might be thought of as drugs manufactured in the body. Nowadays the chemical constitution of most of them has been worked out, and they are also manufactured by the pharmaceutical industry. The practical result of this is that if our own bodies give up making them, we can take them artificially, by swallowing them or having them injected.

All glands are factories producing chemical substances which they make out of the various products brought to them in the bloodstream. Endocrine or ductless glands pass their products directly into the bloodstream; other glands, such as tear glands or salivary glands, have little pipes or ducts through which they pour their products into the special place designed to receive them.

The behaviour of animals is organized by the brain. But the brain is not to be thought of as loftily surveying all that is going on. It is itself a part of the body and subjected to all the influences coming from the body. It receives the same blood that circulates through the whole body and has passed through the liver, heart and lungs. The blood comes to it full of food, digested and broken down, from the intestines, full of oxygen from the lungs. The blood coming from the endocrine glands contains their products, the various hormones. All these products, oxygen, food, drink, and hormones affect the working of the brain.

Hormones have a great effect on behaviour. To all bird watchers the gorgeous changes in the cock-bird's plumage are no more striking than the changes in its behaviour. The bower bird of Northern Australia and New Guinea collects its favoured coloured objects, arranges them in its bower, and then dances before this back-cloth. The weaver-bird of Africa, obeying its inner compulsions, makes its hanging nest. In our own islands at the end of winter, birds such as the peewit and the bunting, which have lived contentedly together in flocks, go off on their own. Every male acquires a territory; and as he does so, he acquires a new personality and a new kind of behaviour towards his former friends. He becomes aggressive and eager to fight anyone entering his new domain. In the few species in which this subject has been investigated, it is the increasing length of daylight that starts off the new behaviour. This affects the hypothalamus, and the hypothalamus makes the pituitary send out the appropriate hormones.

The presence in the environment of what satisfies the animal's desires also stimulates the desire. Potential sexual objects generate desire. It is found in rats that maternal behaviour can be kept going for far longer than normal by the presence of the young. If, as fast as the rat's babies are being weaned, they are replaced by a new litter brought to the mother, the mother rat will continue to show maternal behaviour for several months instead of the normal period of a few weeks. She builds nests and retrieves the wandering young; and without being fanciful, one may presume she feels the emotions related to these maternal acts. It is the same for most kinds of mammals and birds. It has often been observed that a childless woman soon after adopting a child conceives and starts to produce children of her own. Whether this is really so or not has not been examined statistically, as far as I know. It may well be true. The presence of the baby acts as a constant stimulus to parts of the brain, altering the balance of secretion of hormones, and this may allow fertilization to take place.

Hormones are not the only instigators of total behaviour. Thoughts and imagination can bring about the secretion of hormones. Thoughts are the activity of cortical and hypo-thalamic neurons, and these neurons connect to others controlling the pituitary. Thus imagination can call forth the hormones that can then re-stimulate the very same neurons in the brain. This is a positive feed-back mechanism; it can cause an ever-increasing demand made by the animal on its fellows and its surroundings till this cycle is broken by the factors that satisfy the desires and bring the relief of satiety. Similarly, the secretion of hormones can be stopped by thought. Grief suppresses lust far more effectively than religion.

To such questions as do hormones form behaviour, or does behaviour produce the hormones, the answer is that both are true. Hormones produce needs and desires which do not occur until the hormone reaches the brain. Although it is more difficult to observe, behaviour in its turn affects the neurons of the brain, and they cause hormones to be secreted. We thus have a circuit; and we cannot say which comes first.

At present we know very little about how hormones act on the cells they affect or how they have effects on the neurons of the nervous system to cause changes in personality and behaviour. Research is just starting to open up this basic territory of biology.

It has recently been found that some hormones work by acting on the genes. As genes control and organize the structure and function of the cells within which they are situated, any substance affecting the genes affects the whole tissue. But all hormones do not act in this way; for sometimes the action of a hormone is far too quick for this to be the mechanism. One example of rapid action comes from the world of insects. The singing of the male grasshopper attracts the female who, hearing it, arrives post-haste and ready for copulation. But when the act is finished, the very same song no longer attracts her. It has been found that the reason for the female's changing her mind is that during copulation the male has injected a hormone with its sperm; and this hormone suppresses the activity of certain neurons in her brain. When these particular neurons are active, the female longs to hear the music of the serenade; but when they are inactive, either this music is not heard or noticed or it means nothing to her.

Hormones can influence both the structure and the resulting function of many organs of the body. When the thyroid gland grows, for instance, more thyroxin is secreted into the bloodstream, and all tissues of the body speed up their activities. When the gonads start secreting a hormone at puberty, most of the tissues of the body are altered in structure; and this change demands new and different functions. At this time, male hormone enlarges the muscles, the penis, the larynx, the face, and it thickens the skin; female hormone enlarges the vagina, uterus and the breasts. In primates, this female hormone changes the character of the cells covering some of these tissues. Without this hormone, these cells produce a hard substance, keratin, and so the covering membrane is stiff and dry. Supplied with the hormone, the character of the cells is changed, and, instead of keratin, the cells produce mucin, a slippery substance, making the membrane wet and slimy. In this case the hormone has changed the entire character of the cells. This hormone must be presumed to act on the chemicals within the nucleus of the cell, as the character of cells depends on their nuclei.

With examples such as this before us, we suppose that hormones may act similarly on the central nervous system. It could be that certain hormones make neurons enlarge and send out new dendrites, perhaps with new spines on them, and thus provide more synaptic junctions. This would enable nerve impulses to pass along different routes within the central nervous system, routes that had not been available before.

Hormones which affect neural tissue do not act on all neurons; they affect certain groups and not others. Although we do not yet know how hormones affect the neurons on which they act, we can see that a selective action is necessary. A single hormone can have an effect on various parts of the central nervous system and it can give rise to many different acts. But it must not act on groups of neurons which organize opposing sorts of behaviour. Oestradiol, the hormone which induces oestrous behaviour in female mammals, acts on those parts of the female's brain that make the animal receive the male; it does not act on the neurons that organize fleeing or fighting behaviour; or it may act on them by inhibiting them. For when female cats are not on heat, they usually respond to the tom-cat's advances by spitting, scratching and biting.

While considering the action of hormones on various neurons, we should remember that any substances in the blood-stream may affect neurons in the central nervous system. From this point of view, there is not much difference between food, drink, hormones and drugs. The public with their newspapers seem to use the word 'drug' to mean only drugs which can cause addiction. Perhaps this is why patients often ask the doctor if the medicine they are being given is a drug. It always is, just as aspirin, alcohol or penicillin are. Drugs, as everything else we swallow, are passed into the bloodstream. The hormones secreted by endocrine glands are also passed into it directly. Anything circulating in the bloodstream can affect the neurons of the nervous system when they reach them and can have effects on the animal's behaviour. We can easily observe in ourselves how quickly this happens. All we have to do is to take some alcohol, say sherry or brandy, on an empty stomach. Within a few moments we will experience the effect the alcohol has on the neurons of the brain. Everything we eat or drink as well as the products of the hormones of our bodies have effects on our brains and on all the organs of our bodies, and so one may assume that everything the pregnant mother eats, drinks and experiences, will affect the foetus within her womb. This is a territory which is only just coming under experimental investigation.

Research has been carried on for many years on the effects of hormones on the behaviour of the small mammals that can be kept in laboratories. Most of this work has been on their sexual and reproductive activities. And so our knowledge of the effect of hormones on the brain and on the animal's behaviour has been influenced by the convenience of keeping and observing these small animals. This has left us rather ignorant about larger aspects of the behaviour of many species more difficult to observe. We do not yet know for certain, but it appears that the migration of birds is probably due to secretion of hormones.

One of the surprising general facts learned from many thousands of experiments on rats is that the pattern of behaviour of each sex is built into both sexes; and yet under the normal circumstances of their lives each one manifests only its own sexual pattern. That each sex has in its brain neurons capable of organizing the sexual activities of the opposite sex is shown by the results of the injection of male hormones into females and female hormones into males. In rats each sex then shows the behaviour of the opposite sex so successfully that it is treated by other rats as if it were of the sex belonging to the hormone injected; for instance, castrated males injected with female hormones are treated by other males as females. These injected males build nests, an activity normally carried out only by females after puberty; they retrieve the young and bring them back to the nest, behaviour normally shown only by females after the birth of their young. It is remarkable enough that a female rat, raised in isolation, knows how to build a nest. It is extraordinary that male rats, who are never normally called upon to do such a thing, also know how to do it, once they have been injected with the female sex hormone, progesterone.

Bird watchers also have seen evidence that the behaviour of each sex may be built into the nervous system of both sexes. Sometimes among those birds in which the male normally feeds the female in courtship, the opposite has been witnessed: the female will feed a male or other females. Aristotle recorded in his book on the generation of animals that two female doves will form a pair if there is no male available; this has frequently been corroborated for many other birds.

It may be that as each sex is capable of carrying out maternal behaviour and also the sexual behaviour of the other sex, the actual behaviour carried out by any individual depends on the hormones secreted. The hormones secreted depend on the brain and on constitution, which is inherited. The presence or absence of a hormone or combination of hormones during early life, or possibly in the womb, may influence the whole development and shape of the body. Hormones may make the male's body effeminate and the female's body masculine; and it may be that hormones acting on neurons of the brain make a person homosexual or heterosexual, though this would be only one of hundreds of causes of the choice of sexual object.

The most important part of the brain for influencing and controlling the making and supplying of hormones is a region in the centre, called the hypothalamus; it will be considered further in Chapter 14. The hypothalamus is related to large masses of the cerebral hemispheres above. It controls the economy of the hormones by its control of the main endocrine gland, the pituitary gland. The pituitary, in terms of our broadcasting analogy, is the actual transmitting station.

The pituitary gland is connected to and just underneath the front part of the brain. It is deep inside the head, behind the nose and between the eyes. The front part, called the anterior pituitary, secretes the following hormones in mammals: adrenocorticotrophic, somatotrophic, lactogenic, thyrotrophic, and two gonadotrophic hormones. Adrenocorticotrophic and thyrotrophic hormones stimulate the endocrine glands indicated by their names. Somatotrophic hormone organizes protein metabolism, and it is also known as the growth hormone. The gonadotrophic and lactogenic hormones are concerned with reproduction. There are also two hormones made by the hypothalamus itself, which are passed into the bloodstream from the posterior pituitary. These hormones are shown in the diagram below.

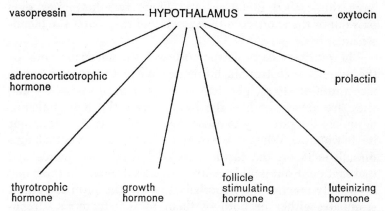

The hypothalamic-pituitary control of the endocrine glands is a self-adjusting system, the amount of hormone secreted being controlled by the amount already present in the body. In the hypothalamus, there are chemoreceptors sensitive to some of the circulating hormones. It is not yet known for certain whether these neurons are the ones that give rise to the secretion of the hormones or whether the neighbouring ones are. The pituitary, too, is sensitive to the amounts of hormones reaching it in the bloodstream. When very small amounts of the hormone secreted by the thyroid gland are injected into the pituitary gland of rats and rabbits, the pituitary reacts as if there is too much thyroxin in the body. It cuts down the amount of thyrotrophic hormone it secretes. Similarly, the pituitary is sensitive to the hormones secreted by the cortex of the adrenal glands, to oestrogens and progesterone, secreted by the gonads. By its ability to sample the amount of these hormones in the passing blood, the pituitary controls their production; for it secretes the trophic hormones, on which their production depends.

Some of the neurons of the part of the hypothalamus related to the pituitary are neurons that have become specialized for secretion. They produce two hormones, vasopressin and oxytocin, which pass along their short axons. These axons pass down the stalk of the pituitary gland, where they lie among large thin-walled blood-vessels. These two hormones then pass out of the axons into the vessels and thus enter the bloodstream.

The pituitary controls the cortex of the adrenal glands by the adrenocorticotrophic hormone. When the animal has to face times of stress, physical or psychological or both – and they are always both – the brain makes the hypothalamus stimulate the pituitary to cause the adrenal cortex to pour out its hormones. When the stress is acute, the hypothalamus directly acts on the inside part of the adrenal glands and makes it pour out noradrenalin. The noradrenalin in the blood eventually reaches the hypothalamus and the pituitary and it stimulates either or both of them to secrete more adrenocorticotrophic hormone. This is not the only way animals have of coping with a stressful situation. The total situation is put together, interpreted and understood by the cerebral hemispheres; they then stimulate the hypothalamus, and the hypothalamus makes the pituitary secrete the adrenocorticotrophic hormone.

The pituitary is the most important link in the chain causing the animal to pass through the various phases of growth, such as puberty, the period of reproduction, and the menopause. At puberty, the pituitary secretes gonadotrophic hormones and passes them into the bloodstream. It is driven to do this by the hypothalamus, and the hypothalamus may well be influenced by the rest of the brain to start off this new phase of development. At the menopause, the pituitary stops secreting these hormones; again, this is done under the influence of the hypothalamus, which may well be influenced by the rest of the brain.

The total growth of the animal is influenced by the hypothalamus. Experiments on small mammals have shown that when certain neurons in the middle of the hypothalamus are destroyed, the production of somatotrophic or growth hormone by the pituitary ceases, and so the animal remains stunted. If these neurons are artificially stimulated, more than the normal amount of growth hormone is produced, and the animal grows excessively. The same thing is found with the hypothalamic neurons that control the production of adrenocorticotrophic and thyrotrophic hormones. Damaging these neurons stops the pituitary making the hormones, and stimulating them causes the secretion of an excessive amount. In man and other animals, it seems that certain of the abnormalities of growth which produce dwarfs are due to a lack of secretion of growth hormone; they can be cured by giving this hormone. It increases the growth of all tissues of the body, except the brain and the eyeball. Although it is not yet known how this hormone makes cells grow, it works in a test-tube. If the hormone is added to amino-acids in a test-tube, proteins are synthesized. In the living animal, the hormone also increases the size of the bones and aids the production of blood. Such a universal effect as growth does not depend only on the secretion of one hormone. Other factors play a part. Heredity is important; and no matter how much growth hormone is secreted, if the proteins are not supplied in the animal's or child's diet, growth will not take place. Among humans the inadequacy of protein in the diet is the most important factor in whole populations not attaining the height and size which they could potentially reach.

The opposite of dwarfism is gigantism. It is not yet known how far the various forms of gigantism are due to disorders of the secretion of growth hormone. Giants are formed before puberty, when the bones and whole skeletons can still grow; after puberty the ends of the bones become permanently fixed to the shafts, and no further increase in their length can take place.

After puberty, there is a disorder of growth due to abnormalities in pituitary control, called acromegaly. The skin and all tissues become coarse and thick and the sinuses in the face and head enlarge; this makes the voice deeper. This is the result of an unbalanced secretion of growth hormone. As in some cases of acromegaly in men, milk has been secreted, so prolactin is probably circulating in excessive amounts. Cases have been recorded showing us that with this secretion of milk, these men have had maternal instincts and a longing to have children.

Occasionally the hypothalamic organization of pituitary hormones goes wrong, and puberty arrives abnormally early. Girls of three years old may develop breasts and start menstruating. In boys the changes that occur produce such well-developed muscles that the condition has been called Infant Hercules, where boys of four years old have big muscles, and their voices break; their genital organs enlarge and they can successfully perform sexual intercourse.

The pituitary secretes two gonadal hormones, of which the main action is on the ovaries in the female and the testes in the male. One is called gonadotrophin I or follicle-stimulating hormone, on account of its effect on a part of the ovaries called the follicles. The follicles produce the female hormone, oestradiol. In the male it works on the tubules which make spermatozoa. The other is called gonadotrophin II or luteinizing hormone or interstitial cell stimulating hormone. It causes the expulsion of the ovum from the ovary. In the male it activates the interstitial cells of the testes, which are the cells producing the male hormone, androgen. In both sexes, luteinizing hormone changes the gonads from their infantile to their adult forms at puberty. If the pituitary fails to produce these two gonadotrophic hormones, puberty and the physical aspects of adult life never arrive. The boy is a eunuch. The growth of the skeleton usually continues for longer than normal so that the patient has long limbs; his voice does not break; he does not have to shave and his hair is soft and fine. There must be quite a number of such eunuchs occurring in the enormous populations of all countries. It might be a good idea to train these naturally occurring eunuchs as alto singers. Instead of castrating infants for the

Pope's choir as used to be done for the greater glorification of God, we could obtain singers in a natural way. The female counterpart of a eunuch is rare; such cases do not seem to have been studied or to have aroused as much interest as the males.

Secondary sexual characteristics are caused by the hormones secreted by the testicles and by the ovaries; the male hormone is named testosterone and the two female hormones, oestradiol and progesterone. In both sexes these changes are enlargement of the genital organs and growth of hair on the body. In the boy, there is enlargement of the larynx and the sinuses of the face and of the body muscles. In both sexes at puberty there are important psychological changes, which must ultimately be caused by the effect of these hormones on the nervous system. These tend to cause difficulties for the young in those cultures that try to stop all sexual activities before marriage. In male birds testosterone makes the bird sing, take possession of a territory and makes it ready to fight other males of its own species. If this hormone is injected into male birds before the onset of puberty, these changes in its behaviour are induced before they would normally appear. It is surprising that some millionaires have not had this done to birds in mid-winter, so as to have the pleasure of hearing the sounds of spring out of season.

The importance of the central nervous system in organizing the output of lactogenic hormone or prolactin is made clear when cases are seen of virgins or men producing milk, in response to vigorous sucking of the nipples. Virgin heifers and virgin goats occasionally produce milk if they are repeatedly suckled. The stimulus of the sucking on the nipples sends impulses along nerves which eventually end up in the hypothalamus. The hypothalamus stimulates the pituitary, and prolactin is produced, making the breasts form milk. For adequate supplies of milk following birth, the pituitary has to produce also adrenocorticotrophic hormone and to pass oxytocin into the bloodstream; the oxytocin is needed to eject the milk. During birth, prolactin aids the contraction of the muscles of the uterus.

Prolactin also acts on certain neurons of the brain affecting behaviour. Its main effect is to make mothers feel maternal. Curiously enough, it does not seem yet to have been used for women who adopt babies; and it might also be tried in men who are bad fathers.

When prolactin is injected into virgin female rats or castrated male rats, it makes them retrieve the young and bring them back to the nest. Without this hormone, both of them are indifferent or even antagonistic to the young of their species. When it is injected into cocks, it makes them behave towards chicks in the way hens do, instead of showing the usual superior male attitude of indifference. In virgin hens, it causes broodiness; in the virgins of certain fish, it causes nest-building.

The activity of the thyroid gland is controlled by the pituitary gland, which itself is controlled by the hypothalamus. The amount of thyroid secretion or thyroxin needed by the animal varies with its activity, with the temperature of the environment and other environmental influences. When hamsters and rabbits are put in a cold environment, the amount of thyrotrophic hormone secreted by the pituitary is increased and the thyroid becomes more active.

There are two hormones made in the hypothalamus itself, vasopressin or the anti-diuretic hormone, and oxytocin, a hormone used in reproduction. They are passed down the stalk of the pituitary and thence into the bloodstream. Vasopressin constricts blood-vessels and reduces the amount of urine produced by the kidneys. It works by becoming attached to the outer part of the membrane of the cells that it affects. Its production is brought about by an increase in the osmotic pressure or a diminution in the volume of the extracellular fluid, and also by emotional and psychological states. The secretion of oxytocin is directly influenced by combined physical and psychological factors, such as stimulation of the genital organs of the female. This hormone affects the muscle fibres of the uterus, making them perform rhythmical contractions; these movements help the spermatozoa reach the ovum. The violent movements of the uterus during labour also make the hypothalamus secrete large amounts of the hormone; this again helps the uterus make rhythmical contractions, thus helping the expulsion of the baby. After the baby is born, sucking the breast stimulates the same neurons of the hypothalamus and more of the hormone is produced. In this phase, it aids the expulsion of the milk. Thus it is seen that each subsequent step in reproduction is induced by the previous step.

In some very rare cases, the pituitary ceases to work before the age of twenty; this causes a condition called progeria or premature senility. A person of twenty is then like one of eighty. He may become bald or white-haired, with a wrinkled skin, a feeble voice, arthritis of the joints, and his brain may show the characteristic changes of old age. In women, the pituitary can be destroyed immediately after the birth of a child. If the woman loses a great deal of blood during the birth, the blood pressure may fall greatly and the artery supplying the front part of the pituitary becomes blocked, owing to clotting of the blood. These patients then become prematurely old, all sexual life ceases, they always feel cold, they are anaemic, their skins are dry and full of fine creases; they become listless and apathetic.

There are other hormones besides those secreted by the pituitary which have effects on the central nervous system. The secretions of the thyroid gland act on all cells, including those of the nervous system. If a child is born without the thyroid gland working, it will be a cretin. Thyroxin is necessary for all parts of the nervous system to work properly. Without it, all reflexes are slow, and intellectual capacities never develop. An excessive amount of the hormone makes people excitable, restless, agitated and incapable of repose.

The control of the animal's temperature depends to a great extent on the secretion of thyroxin. This control is organized not only by mechanisms within the body; it relies equally on behaviour. The animal is expected to take steps to get warm or to keep cool. Even more complicated behaviour, such as making a suitable nest in some species, is related to its body temperature. When the thyroid is removed from rats, they build larger and thicker nests than normal, presumably to cover themselves effectively and keep warm. It is the same with man. Patients with an excess of thyroid hormone wear thin clothes in winter as they are always hot, and those with atrophied thyroid glands are always cold, they wear thick clothes and sit by fires in summer.

The hormones made by the adrenal glands, adrenalin and noradrenalin, stimulate neurons of the hypothalamus and of the reticular formation. If you have ever had an injection of this hormone, adrenalin, you will have felt its psychological effect. You feel strangely excited; but this is a somewhat apprehensive, anxious and restless excitement. As this is one of the hormones poured into the bloodstream during times of emergency, a part of the feeling of agitation comes from its effects produced on certain neurons of the brain.

The effect of sexual hormones on the nervous system of animals and thus on their behaviour is something man has known about for several thousand years. For he has understood that the removal of the testes alters the behaviour of male animals. More than two thousand years ago Aristotle reported that when the ovaries of sows are removed, their sexual desires are also removed. How man discovered the effects of these operations and how this knowledge became so general, we do not know.

Hormones secreted by the testes in males and the ovaries in females have the expected influence on the animal's behaviour: nearly all animals deprived of their gonads have no sexual interests and show no sexual behaviour. Among human beings, however, women may continue to have sexual desire after their ovaries have been removed at operation or after they have atrophied at the menopause. Cats, as we can all observe, are different. Feline sexual smells have no interest for castrated tom-cats. The gonads gone, many aspects of the feline world lose their interest. Female cats who have had their ovaries removed respond to the propositions made to them by tom-cats with hate and not with love. But if a minute pellet of oestrogen is injected into the correct part of the hypothalamus, their behaviour changes and they accept the proposals. In many species of mammals this reversal of behaviour occurs naturally. The presence and absence of sexual hormones in the bloodstream occurs in alternating cycles; it is not necessary to remove the ovaries to observe their effects on behaviour. Those hormones that have mainly sexual effects have effects on the aggression-submission aspects of behaviour in some animals. Whether they act on the parts of the hypothalamus that organize attack and flight behaviour is not yet known. The female of the American martin normally lives contentedly with the male, but when she is on heat she turns on him and fights him. On the other hand, the female short-tailed shrew chases the male away unless she is on heat, and can be so aggressive that she may kill and eat him.

When the ovaries of a female are transferred to a male and the testicles of a male to a female, the animal's behaviour changes in the expected direction: the male behaves like a female and the female like a male. Although in the act of copulation, different postures and different patterns of movement are needed from the two sexes, yet the muscles are used correctly and in the correct order by the animals injected with the hormone of the opposite sex. Here again, the males are treated as females and the females as males by the other animals. When injections of hormones are carried out in the correct sex before the onset of puberty, the changes in structure and behaviour normally occurring at puberty take place within a few days. Testosterone proprionate injected into immature or castrated males induces male copulatory behaviour. When it is injected into male chicks, they start, fifteen days after being hatched, to crow like cocks and to make propositions to females. As has been related, virgin female rats can be made both to build nests and retrieve the young when they receive prolactin. The neurons organizing these aspects of female behaviour do not do this unless they are acted upon by ovarian hormones. If the ovaries are removed before puberty, these females do not manifest the appropriate behaviour towards the male for copulation to take place. But after being injected with female hormone, they will crouch in the appropriate position. However, such experiments do not always lead to the expected result. It has been found that testosterone injected into the hypothalamus of male rats induces strong maternal behaviour.

Among the anthropoids, sexual hormones have different effects in the different species; the higher species are less under the control of hormones than lower species. Interestingly enough, the male macaque monkey is more sensitive to the hormones of the female macaque than she is herself. Although the female macaque with ovaries removed may still present herself for sexual intercourse, the male will not touch her. Moreover, male macaques do not groom females without ovaries, grooming being partly a sexual activity in monkeys. It has been found experimentally that the amount of grooming the male gives the female macaque is related to the amount of oestradiol injected into the female spayed macaque. We do not know what features of the female make her attractive to the male. Certainly the male's frequency of copulation is related to the female's menstrual cycle; but her behaviour is less influenced by this cycle than his is, for she will present herself for copulation at any time.

The effect of androgens on aggressive behaviour has been studied in many varieties of vertebrates. When testosterone is injected into farmyard hens, they become aggressive and move up in the pecking order. Androgens injected into both sexes of the following animals increase aggression: American lizards, turtles, valley quails, rats, cocks, hens, fish. The domestic hen calls other hens to food just as the cock usually does. Presumably these hormones act on certain neighbouring neurons in the hypothalamus, as will be explained in the next chapter.

Castration has less effect on man than on any other mammal. As Shakespeare tells us in *Antony and Cleopatra*, eunuchs may retain the desire though they lack the performance. But it is more complicated than that. Castrated men, that is, men who have had their testes removed by injury or disease, have erections but no ejaculations; but eunuchoids, men who have never had puberty, have neither erections nor ejaculations. Injections of testosterone will give them both. Some women continue to have sexual intercourse after operative removal of the ovaries and after the menopause. It is surprising that little is known about this interesting subject; no doubt this is due to gynaecologists and other doctors being shy about asking their women patients about these matters.

The effect of male hormones on those nuclei of the hypo-thalamus that organize aggressive behaviour is more compli-cated in primates than in species lower in the evolutionary scale. Among chimpanzees, the male is usually dominant; but when the female is on heat, she becomes the dominant one and the male accepts this dominance without question.

In the case of man, apart from direct physiological factors, behaviour is affected by all he has learned and experienced, including the immense influence of other people in the present and, more important, in the past. In man, the organiza-tion of behaviour in accordance with cultural factors has become overweeningly important. This means in anatomical and physiological terms that the fore-brain is very important and that the influence of hormones is correspondingly less important. This is why man is more intellectual and less emotional than other animals.

We have little evidence whether male hormones act on the parts of the hypothalamus organizing aggressive behaviour in man. Most doctors who have treated boys with lesions in the hypothalamus causing delayed puberty have had the impres-sion that testosterone made the boys more active and that it developed their muscles; they also thought that the boys became less timid and conciliatory and more combative.

In the West, we are no longer familiar with eunuchs. In the East, eunuchs have often been the real rulers of empires, and have held power in such autocracies as those of the Ottoman Empire and China. Indeed in the Celestial Empire, the palace eunuchs were the actual rulers of the state for more than a thousand years; until recently there still survived one or two from the retinue of the last Empress. They have also been directors of the armed forces and one or two have been generals as famous as any of ours in Europe. But it may be held that a general is an organizer who does not need to be brave and aggressive; bravery is expected only from the others.

Chapter 14

The Centre of the Brain: The Hypothalamus

The first physiologist to conceive of the idea of investigating the anatomical basis of animal behaviour was W. R. Hess of Zurich; and he has spent most of his life doing this. Before Hess, physiologists studying the nervous system investigated only reflexes, the basic components, the bricks and mortar, from which behaviour is made. Even the over-publicized Pavlov spent most of his life investigating one reflex, and imagined that he could build up the whole of behaviour on the basis of conditioned reflexes.

Hess brought an altogether fresh way of thinking about physiology and anatomy; he has provided all research workers too with one of their most useful ways of investigating the nervous system. This technique consists of introducing very fine electrodes into the brain, the leads of which come out through the skull; they are left in place for ever. After the operation of placing the electrodes, the animal recovers rapidly and goes on living its normal life, unaware of the electrodes in its brain. We know this, as the identical procedure has been carried out in human patients. When the animal is living its usual life, the electrodes can be stimulated; this excites the neurons among which the electrodes are placed. The effect on behaviour of stimulation of these neurons can then be observed; and thus one can learn about their function. Stimulation may be repeated whenever observations need to be made. When enough data have been collected, a destructive current is passed through the electrodes, which destroys the little block of brain tissue lying between the two electrodes. This is painless too; the animal feels nothing. Then the effect on the animal's behaviour of life without these neurons can be observed. When the animal is finally killed, microscopic examination of the brain is carried out to find out exactly which neurons were destroyed. In these, as in all experiments on animals, the way of killing is absolutely painless. The animal is given a large dose of a barbiturate drug, which sends it to sleep, and it never wakes again.

One of the most important conclusions drawn from Hess's work is that certain whole acts of behaviour are organized within the hypothalamus.

The essential acts of life are organized by the medulla oblongata. These acts are amplified, refined and improved upon by the mid-brain and by the hypothalamus. The hypothalamus organizes the metabolism of the body, seeing to it that the animal takes in the right amounts of fluid and food. It is essential for making the animal feel hunger and thirst, fear, lust and rage. It activates the two parts of the autonomic nervous system, sympathetic and parasympathetic, and adjusts their balance for every situation. It is apparently the main part of the brain for controlling the growth and the various phases of growth of the animal. It brings about hibernation among those who hibernate, and sleep for those who sleep. It is the essential part of the brain for controlling the temperature in warm-blooded animals.

None of these activities depends only on the hypothalamus. Most of these functions can be carried out by neurons situated at lower levels of the nervous system. But in this case, they are not organized properly to serve the ends of the animal as a whole. The more basic and important a function is, the more completely it can be organized by lower neural levels. The hypothalamus organizes whole entities which in most cases we see as acts of behaviour. Lower neural levels control various components of an act of behaviour; each higher level then adds its contribution, in accordance with what it has received from all the neurons connected to it. For example, the rhythmical movements of breathing are arranged at the level of the spinal cord and of the basal part of the brain. The hypothalamus alters the basic rhythm, the rate and the depth of breathing, when it is organizing acts of behaviour, such as running away, fighting, sleeping or waking up. Breathing has to be altered in accordance with various states of emotion; and when bosoms heaved, as they did in Victorian novels, it was presumably the hypothalamus that took over control.

Normally the hypothalamus controls the body's temperature. When this part of the hypothalamus is destroyed by injury or illness, the animal is at the mercy of the temperature of its environment. It cannot shiver or control the width of the skin blood-vessels. And it cannot raise its fur in anger, as many animals do to frighten their enemies. The control of temperature is achieved by the hypothalamic control of the sympathetic nerves. The nerves of this system can still work when the hypothalamus has been destroyed, but having lost their central control they work in response to local conditions and not as a system to serve the total requirements of the body.

Other instances of the general neural pattern of organization are the acts of micturition and defaecation. When these acts are ordered by the hypothalamus, it is not merely a matter of emptying the bladder and rectum. The animal performs these acts according to the way of its species, the whole skeleton and musculature being organized, the adult male dog micturating on three legs while cocking the fourth. Although these acts are performed in a normal manner, they are not fitted into the programme and circumstances of the animal's life unless the cerebral hemispheres are in control; for these highest levels of the brain are necessary to take stock of a total situation and to organize behaviour accordingly. One can observe the hierarchical organization of the brain from comparing the behaviour of an anencephalic baby with a normal baby. Whereas the deformed baby with only a medulla oblongata is able to suck and swallow when something touches its lips, a baby with a hypothalamus can demand food from its parent. By opening and shutting its mouth and making sucking sounds and movements, it makes its needs clear to the parent.

If it is a primate, it can smile and cry, showing its parents when it is satisfied and when it is in need. The basic elements of noise-making when the baby is in need or in pain are organized by the lowest parts of the brain. This simple cry is developed by the hypothalamus into the troubling cry of the normal baby.

The hypothalamus is in the middle of the brain. Its position is shown in Figure 16. It is above the pituitary gland, below the thalamus, and surrounded by the cerebral hemispheres. It is not directly in touch with the world. The later developed cerebral hemispheres are more directly related to the world; they can assess sensory evidence, they know what is happening. When they know what is going on, they can excite the hypothalamus into organizing certain of the basic patterns of behaviour.

Reward and Punishment

> For he purrs in thankfulness, when God tells him he's a good Cat.

Many instinctive acts of behaviour are accompanied by pleasure, and the inability to fulfil instinctive needs is accompanied by displeasure, discontent or agitation. The steps on the way to fulfilment of instinctive needs are also rewarded by pleasure. And so the animal learns to repeat these steps and finally to achieve a total purposeful act, without having to know what the point in each step is, or even the purpose of the whole act. Thus the brain rewards and punishes its owner according to the necessities of survival of the individual and the species. Payment in the coinage of pleasure and discontent teaches the animal to seek the stimulus that starts off the sequence of activities leading finally to the fulfilment of the need. Once an animal has some experience of being alive, it will remember from previous occasions that the discharge of energy in the instinctive act is associated with relief and pleasure; or it will remember that a certain conjunction of circumstances was accompanied by unhappiness or pain. In the nature of things, the animal is forced to avoid pain and discomfort; and so it is taught to avoid the state associated with these emotions and feelings and to seek the opposite state.

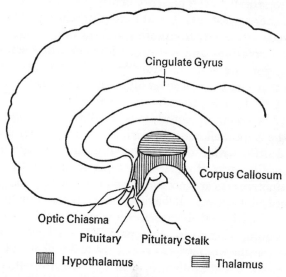

16. The position of the hypothalamus

There are certain parts of the brain that provide these rewards for behaviour, and there may be parts that provide displeasure. The parts called pleasure or rewarding centres are many. They are scattered through the hypothalamus, in the parts of the cerebral hemispheres connected to the hypothalamus, and in lower parts of the brain. These pleasure centres were discovered in 1953 by Olds of McGill University in Montreal. Olds used Hess's technique of implanting electrodes in the reward centres. He then connected these electrodes to a circuit incorporating a lever which the rat itself could press with its forepaws. When it did this, it excited its own pleasure centre in the brain. The rats found they got such pleasure from doing this that they would keep on pressing the lever till they fell asleep or dropped from exhaustion. Olds also put very hungry rats in cages with stacks of food; these hungry rats preferred pressing the lever to eating. Rats would run mazes and solve puzzles or put up with having a painful electric shock to a paw, all for the reward of just one press on the lever to stimulate the pleasure centre.

In rats, there are at least two different pleasure centres: one is associated with satiety from eating and the other is associated with sexual emotions and feelings. Monkeys will keep awake for forty-eight hours stimulating the sexual pleasure centre, whereas otherwise they sleep as often as man does.

It seems likely that pleasure accompanies eating and sexual activity on account of connexions established between the parts of the hypothalamus organizing these activities and the pleasure centres within the hypothalamus and the septal area. But the mechanisms of experiencing pleasure with these and other instinctive acts are more involved than merely suggesting an anatomical pathway. Behaviour must be modifiable; the behaviour that has just caused pleasure should eventually cause boredom, discomfort, even pain. For instance, maternal solicitude for the young has eventually to be changed to indifference, so that the offspring learn to stand on their own feet. Female behaviour of acceptance of the male may have to change to antagonism; at first the female may need to accept the male, and then later she may have to drive him off, so that he does not harm the offspring. If pleasure centres are activated in the first sort of instinctive behaviour, then this must be changed; and they must later be activated only by the subsequent kind of behaviour.

Apart from such long-term changes in behaviour, there are many examples of a reversal of pleasure to discomfort in short-term acts of behaviour. Eating is an obvious example. Pleasure is caused by eating when one needs food and is hungry. If one were forced as a kind of torture to eat more and more, eating would then evoke nausea, disgust and probably vomiting.

Olds also discovered regions in the mid-brain and in a part

of the hypothalamus that the animals avoided stimulating. These may be true punishment centres, which are now called aversive centres. Or else it might be that the electrodes had been placed among nerve fibres or neurons that are normally concerned with conveying sensations of pain or other unpleasant sensations.

Fighting and Fleeing

For when he takes his prey he plays with it to give it chance.
For one mouse in seven escapes by his dallying.

When Hess explored the hypothalamus of the cat, he found that when he stimulated certain regions, the animals would either show aggression and attack or flight and submission. Hess included these two opposite sorts of behaviour under the heading of the defence reaction, as both are used to preserve the animal's life. All animals use both elements of the defence reaction, though some favour the one rather than the other on most occasions.

Which sort of behaviour will be manifested, according to another Zurich investigator of animal behaviour, Hediger, depends on the critical distance between the animal and its enemy. When this distance is considerable, the animal will go off, either by walking away or by fleeing; when the distance is small, the animal will attack. The actual distance differs from species to species, and in the same animal from time to time. Hediger's concept covers the general observation that an animal when cornered will fight; and naturalists know that this applies also to timid animals, such as small antelopes, rabbits and mice. Before attacking, all or nearly all vertebrates threaten; they prefer to scare an enemy rather than fight. The defence reaction, including running away, threatening and fighting, is used only when an animal meets a potentially threatening animal.

Hess found that when he stimulated certain neurons with a

minimal current, the animal would show a state of vigilance. As the current was increased, the reaction would become more intense, finally becoming an actual attack with all the manifestations of fury. The usual bodily changes which are a part of fight or flight occurred. The cat would look for someone on whom to vent its rage; it usually found the experimenter, one is pleased to note. Its fur would stand on end, its ears would be laid back on its head, it would arch its back or crouch ready to spring and then jump at the experimenter, biting and scratching him. If another cat were placed in the cage, the stimulated cat would attack it, even though it was normally friendly or perhaps even afraid of the other cat. When the current was switched off, the animal quickly calmed down and went on doing what it had been doing before. When other nearby regions of the hypothalamus are stimulated, the cat shows the typical signs of fear and it tries to run away.

The behaviour induced by stimulating electrodes in the hypothalamus differs from similar behaviour arising naturally. Under normal living conditions, the defence reaction is integrated into the animal's total behaviour. Aggression or flight is preceded by preparatory behaviour and is followed by a slow cooling off. Before attacking, the cat threatens. When it attacks, it directs its attack well, aiming at the face or the eyes of its enemy. The aggressive behaviour of a cat being stimulated artificially by means of electrodes in the hypothalamus is directed at any living creature near it. The behaviour is carried on somewhat like that of an automaton.

One of the problems of such experiments in which a part of the brain is stimulated or destroyed is this. Although one can observe the results of stimulating or destroying the structure, one does not learn what part it plays in the normal organization of behaviour and how the part normally fits into the total physiology of the brain. In the case of the defence reaction, how are these neurons of the hypothalamus activated in the normal? How is their activity modified, so that the behaviour they can produce is properly related to the animal's circumstances?

The answers to these questions will eventually come from physiological experiments; but meanwhile we can make conjectures on the basis of the anatomical connexions of the parts of the brain involved in the behaviour. The hypothalamus controls the sympathetic and parasympathetic systems, which, in turn, control the viscera, the sexual organs, the blood-vessels of the entire body and the little muscles that make the hair stand on end. Above the hypothalamus there is a large mass of neurons in the front part of the temporal lobes, called the amygdala, as it resembled an almond in the eyes of earlier anatomists. This part of the cerebral hemispheres facilitates the neurons of the rage reaction and brings the animal into a rage, and it can also inhibit the hypothalamic neurons and stop the rage reaction. Probably the crude display of the rage reaction is organized by the hypothalamus. The amygdala brings subtlety into the reaction, modifying it according to the rapidly changing circumstances resulting from the aggressive behaviour. The highest levels of the brain provide the animal with consciousness and memory, enabling it to organize these acts of behaviour in accordance with its previous experience.

Hess's work has been extended by investigators in Munich to the domestic fowl. When the implanted electrodes are placed very accurately in the hypothalamus, different parts of the region giving rise to the defence reaction can be stimulated, and different sorts of flight behaviour and different sorts of attack are obtained. When the stimulating current is slight and is then slowly increased, successive parts of a total act of behaviour appear. At first the hen becomes alert, then she gets up, walks about, and finally jumps off the platform on which she is placed, at this stage showing the complete flight reaction. A whole territory of investigation of the brain and behaviour is being opened up by using a combination of two or more electric stimulations, by altering their timing, and by combining electric stimulation with natural stimulation and relating these to the needs the animal has at the time of the experiment.

Mating

For having consider'd God and himself he will consider his neighbour.

For if he meets another cat he will kiss her in kindness.

The total act of copulation is organized in the hypothalamus and the neighbouring parts of the fore-brain. When the cerebral hemispheres are removed from female cats, these animals still manifest the usual oestrous behaviour of cats. They still excite the male cat by calling and rolling and they assume the usual crouched position. After coitus, they show the usual behaviour of their species, rubbing, licking, rolling and squirming. It is essentially the same with the male; though most male animals need some help in carrying out coitus after removal of the hemispheres.

The parts of the hypothalamus organizing sexual behaviour are not the same as those organizing the defence reaction. In fact, these two functions are opposed. For a sexual act to take place, fight and flight have to be prevented. Females have to give up aggression and become receptive.

Human patients with lesions in the region between the fore-brain and the hypothalamus may get an increase in libido or sexual appetite. This region is either near to the region or it is the region of the sexual pleasure-rewarding centre of the rat, rabbit, cat and monkey. One patient I saw, aged forty-eight, had this part of the brain disturbed by a clot of blood. When she was in hospital waiting for an operation she would ask any man who was visiting to come to bed with her, then and there, in the ward. After the operation to remove the clot had been performed and the lady was again behaving normally, she was most embarrassed when questioned about this unusual behaviour. In some male patients, particularly after a great number of head injuries such as are inflicted on second-class boxers, there is an atrophy of this part of the brain. These men may lose all interest in sex, and some of them eventually become impotent.

When electrodes are implanted in the hypothalamus of the rabbit and the activity of the neurons is recorded electrically, it has been found that sexual intercourse creates a great deal of activity among the neurons concerned with sexual behaviour. When these neurons are excited into activity, they stimulate the pituitary gland to secrete the luteotrophic hormone that causes ovulation. Once the amount of this hormone in the circulation reaches a certain level, chemoreceptors in the hypothalamus stop the hypothalamic neurons stimulating the pituitary gland. In this example of the sexual activity of the female rabbit, we can see how one act follows another. A certain activity, in this case copulation, is caused by the actions of hormones on neurons in the hypothalamus. This activity in turn excites related neurons in the hypothalamus, and they act upon the pituitary to cause ovulation. Once this has been achieved, the balance of hormone secretion is again altered, so that no more ova are discharged, and the next stage in reproduction can be prepared with the implantation of the ovum in the uterus.

Although grooming and care of the fur are not sexual activities, they may be mentioned here. When cats were stimulated by Hess in the front part of the hypothalamus and in the septal region, they stopped doing whatever they happened to be doing, and groomed themselves in that thorough manner typical of cats. They would usually go on till they had finished, although the stimulation had ceased.

Eating and Drinking

For tenthly he goes in quest of food.

All parts of the central nervous system make a contribution to such important activities as eating and drinking; yet the hypothalamus is apparently the main centre organizing these acts. It controls the intake and output of water and the metabolism of fat and carbohydrates. It makes the animal aware of the need to eat and drink and it is essential in making it feel replete when it has had enough. What an animal chooses to eat is the concern of the cerebral hemispheres. They retain the knowledge of what is edible, they remember where it is to be found, and they direct their possessor's steps in search of it. When they are experimentally cut out, the animal will chew and swallow anything put into its mouth.

There are certain groups of neurons in the hypothalamus that when stimulated make the animal go round sniffing everything to find out if it is edible or not. The animal eats voraciously. When a strong current is used, the animal will eat anything, even chewing wooden sticks. In certain experiments, male rats with electrodes implanted in this region were put in cages containing both a lot of food and some females on heat. The males immediately showed interest in the females. When the current was turned on to stimulate the neurons organizing eating, the rats all left the females alone and started eating. When the current was turned off, they would stop eating and again take an interest in the females. Thus the desire to eat could be induced and made pre-eminent by stimulating these neurons. If the electrodes are left in permanently and are frequently stimulated, the animal goes on eating and eating, eventually becoming exceedingly fat. Two research workers in Warsaw have proved that the animal actually feels hunger. They trained a goat by means of the conditioned reflex technique to raise its foot whenever it felt hungry and wanted to eat. They then implanted electrodes into this animal's hypothalamus. Whenever they stimulated these neurons, the animal raised its foot.

Under normal conditions an animal must stop eating when it has taken enough. This is arranged by neurons in the region of the hypothalamus that inhibit eating. Artificial stimulation of this centre makes the animal stop eating; destruction of the centre makes the animal eat enormously. Thus we see that destruction of the eating excitatory neurons or stimulation of the eating inhibitory neurons stop the animal eating or drinking. Such an animal dies of starvation in the midst of plenty.

The pleasure-rewarding neurons are near the eating excitatory neurons. Rats with electrodes permanently implanted among these neurons will go on stimulating their own brains, according to the technique described earlier. They appear to be equally happy whether stimulating these neurons or eating; either activity satisfies them. It is probable that these are the neurons that under normal circumstances give us pleasure when we eat.

When certain neurons in this region of the brain of the rat are stimulated by implanted electrodes, the animal will hoard food. These cannot be the same neurons that make it eat, for when these neurons are stimulated, the animal will stop eating when it has taken enough, but it still goes on hoarding.

The hypothalamic neurons causing the animal to feel thirst are under the control of osmoreceptors, receptors sensitive to the osmotic pressure of the blood. They are also sensitive to temperature. And so the animal becomes thirsty both when the salt content of its blood starts to rise and when its blood temperature starts to go up. The amount of water the animal swallows is also noted by receptors in its oesophagus and stomach.

Andersson, working in Sweden, showed that if a dilute salt solution is injected into a small region in the centre of the hypothalamus of goats, the animals immediately start drinking large amounts of water. If the neurons of this region are stimulated electrically with implanted electrodes, the animal will do the same. Conversely when these neurons are experimentally destroyed, the animal stops drinking, even though the needs of its body demand water.

The neurons in the hypothalamus making the animal drink and those making it eat seem to be intermingled or at least very near each other. But the neurons related to the two functions differ in the way they work; those related to eating are noradrenergic, working by secreting noradrenalin at their endings, and those related to drinking are cholinergic, working by secreting acetylcholine.

These nuclei of the hypothalamus concerned with eating and

drinking, hunger and thirst, are also under the influence of the cerebral hemispheres. It is probable that when we think of food and drink and our mouths water, the pathways used are those from the temporal lobes running through to these nuclei. Patients with damage to the water balance mechanism of the anterior hypothalamus get a disorder known as diabetes insipidus. They lose an enormous amount of water in the urine and have to keep on drinking to make up for this loss. It can be controlled by the taking of the antidiuretic hormone, vaso-pressin.

Sleeping and Waking

For there is nothing sweeter than his peace when at rest.

Nearly all animals sleep – and no one knows why. Fish go through periods of inactivity, akin to sleep. The porpoise or bottle-nosed dolphin submerges when it sleeps but it comes up for air twice a minute, waking at each breath. When it is asleep, it keeps one eye open, scanning its environment. Snakes and lizards sleep with their eyes open, having no movable eyelids.

Domestic animals that chew the cud, such as cows, sheep and goats sleep very little, apart from when they are young or very old. Antelopes have even shorter periods of sleep, but when they are asleep, they are deeply unconscious and can be touched without being woken. It appears to be that the animals that feed on vegetation and are much preyed upon sleep very deeply but for only a short time, they copulate very quickly, and they produce offspring that can stand and walk within a few hours of birth.

Many muscles are contracting actively during sleep. Fish keep their tails gently moving so as to maintain their position constant in the flowing water. Sleeping ducks make continual paddling movements with one foot and so they describe circles in the water. Horses can sleep standing up. The European swift can sleep while flying. Apparently soldiers can sleep while they are marching. This means that the neurons working innumerable muscles are active, as well as the neurons of the labyrinths, and the neurons co-ordinating these activities.

Hess and his colleagues have found that there are certain neurons which when stimulated make the animal go to sleep and other neurons which wake it up. Sleep is not an inactivity of all neurons; there are active sleeping and waking centres in the brain. The neurons of these centres are scattered in many regions of the brain. They are in the most primitive parts of the cerebral hemispheres, that is in the front parts of the temporal lobes, in many parts of the hypothalamus, in the thalamus and in the reticular substance throughout the central core of the brain. Those of the lowest level of the brain are at the level of the pons (see Figure 18). When the sleeping centre in the front part of the hypothalamus is destroyed, the animal no longer sleeps. In the opposite kind of experiment, when this centre is stimulated, the animal becomes sleepy. It looks around for somewhere cosy, becomes quiet and relaxed, curls up and goes to sleep. It remains asleep for hours without these neurons being stimulated again. When the waking centre is active, it activates the cerebral cortex. The animal becomes lively and ready to face the world.

A Russian surgeon reported a case of a soldier on whom he operated during the war against the Germans. A metal fragment had entered the patient's skull and had lodged in the hypothalamus. When the surgeon, operating under local anaesthesia, tried to pull the piece of metal out, the patient immediately fell asleep. The surgeon then stopped as he thought the patient had gone into a state of shock. After a few minutes the patient woke up, and when questioned said he had had an irresistible desire to sleep. The surgeon finally removed the metal fragment on the third attempt; on each occasion when his forceps moved the piece of metal in the hypothalamus, the patient went to sleep.

Waking and sleeping still occur after the entire cerebral hemispheres have been removed or are not working; and they occur too in babies born without hemispheres and in patients in whom the hemispheres have been destroyed.

The state of the brain in waking and sleeping can be monitored by means of the electroencephalograph. Using this technique, investigators of sleep have found that sometimes when we think we are awake, and particularly when we are tired or bored, we are in fact occasionally asleep; these periods of sleep last a second or two. Sleep tends to come on us when the cerebral cortex is becoming inactive; and this occurs when its input is cut down or when it is not required to work on its contents. Only parts of the brain sleep; or, to be more accurate, only parts of the brain are inactive during sleep. And further, some parts are inactive during some stages of sleeping and other parts at other stages.

Man spends a fifth of the night's sleep dreaming. Now that we know this, we realize that we remember only the merest fragments of our dreams. Probably when we are dreaming only a very small part of the brain is inactive, perhaps only the parts concerned with vigilance, awareness and the continuous recording of events. It used to be believed that when children (or adults for that matter) walk in their sleep, they are dreaming actively and living out their dreams. It now appears that this is not so; sleep-walking takes place during the parts of sleep when dreaming does not occur. During dreaming-sleep, a large part of the cortex of the hemispheres is active. Obviously the parts which record and store experience are active, for if they were not we would not remember our dreams. It has been found in experiments in animals that when the lowest part of the sleep centre, the part in the pons, is destroyed, sleep with dreaming no longer occurs, but deeper sleep is unaffected.

Recording the electric potentials of the brain, the so-called brain waves, and the movements of the eyes during sleep, investigators have found that certain periods of sleep are accompanied by rapid to-fro movements of the eyes. This part of sleep has now come to be called 'rapid eye movement sleep'. Experiments carried out on the subject of sleep during the last few years have shown that not only is sleep as a whole necessary for health and life but that this phase of sleep is necessary. If a man or another animal is deprived of rapid eye movement sleep by being woken up whenever he is in that phase, he will make up for this loss on the following night, by spending more of his sleeping time in this rapid eye movement phase; but this phase never reaches more than 60 per cent of the time spent sleeping. Rapid eye movement phase of sleep is always scattered throughout the total duration of sleep; it never occurs altogether at one period. Breathing is more rapid and shallow during this phase, the heart rate is irregular, and most muscles are relaxed.

People who are born blind or who have been blind for many years do not show these rapid eye movements during sleep and their dreams are not visual. Those born blind have tactile, auditory and olfactory dreams. Those born with sight and who become blind early in life usually retain visual imagery in their dreams and their eyes then show the typical rapid movements. When people dream they are moving, they do in fact make slight movements of their hands and faces. Deaf-mutes make small hand and finger movements when they dream they are talking. Curiously enough, talking in one's sleep mostly occurs in the non-dreaming phases of sleep; and what the person says is unrelated to the dreams he remembers having had when he wakes up.

Animals other than man dream. One may safely draw this conclusion from their rapid eye movements during sleep and from the form of the electroencephalogram. Before the use of the electroencephalograph to investigate sleep, many experiments had been carried out on animals' dreaming. For example, sausages were placed in front of sleeping dogs; the animals would, without waking, make chewing movements and wrinkle the skin around their mouths. Records have been kept of the movements sleeping puppies make from the moment of birth. At about the end of the first week, they make lip-smacking and sucking noises; later they snarl and make a sort of barking noise; and later still, they carry out running movements.

Human babies move about in their sleep, make sucking movements and suck their fists or thumbs. From doing electro-encephalograms on them, we now know that they spend a lot of time during the rapid eye movement phase of sleep, a far greater amount than children or adults; and premature babies spend from 50 to 80 per cent of sleeping time in this phase, as against 20 per cent of the average adult.

Which parts of our brains act as our internal alarm clocks, we do not yet know. Most of us wake every morning at about the same time. At this time sleep is light, and it may be that the daily visual and auditory stimuli help to wake us. But this is not the whole matter; for these stimuli have all the insignificance of familiarity. In winter it may be dark, in summer light. More remarkable is our ability to wake ourselves automatically at some unusually early hour, say five o'clock. This is not a perfect mechanism; for usually we wake before this set time and keep waking ourselves up several times before five; and then the final waking may occur after five. It is likely that the parts of our brains concerned in the waking are the cerebral cortex and part of the reticular substance concerned with alerting the brain. But how one sets this mechanism going, no one knows.

The Autonomic Nervous System

The sorts of behaviour we have been discussing make use of the entire nervous system. If an animal is fleeing for its life, it is using all its muscles, its nerves, its balance organs, everything it has. In addition, fleeing and fighting, copulating, digesting, sleeping and waking make use of the autonomic nervous system.

This system has two parts, the sympathetic system, which is a mainly monoaminergic transmitter system, and the parasympathetic, which is a mainly cholinergic transmitter system. Both parts of the autonomic system are controlled by the hypothalamus. The sympathetic nerves act by liberating nor-adrenalin into the space between their endings and the structures on which they end; parasympathetic nerves liberate acetylcholine from their endings. In addition to this, the sympathetic system has a large depot of noradrenalin and adrenalin in the central part of the adrenal glands. These hormones are poured into the bloodstream when exertion or stress demands.

The behaviour of flight or fight, rage or fear, activates the entire sympathetic system. Even a part of these reactions alerts this system. A sudden noise or a sudden pinprick constricts the blood-vessels of the skin within one or two seconds, speeds up the heart rate and makes it beat more forcefully. If the stimulus is startling enough, the pupils dilate, the eyelids are retracted, the hair stands on end, the bronchi dilate; glucose is released from the liver and enters the circulation to be available to the muscles, should they need to be active.

Obviously the same behaviour is not manifested under different circumstances. Behaviour is different whether the animal is fleeing or attacking; it also differs in accordance with the kind of aggression being manifested. The pattern is different for enemies swooping from the skies and those approaching on land, for enemies of one's own species and of other species. A good picture of sympathetic and parasympathetic activity associated with aggression and fleeing is given by Professor Yerkes, who spent many years of his life with chimpanzees.

When a cow approached, the apes would retreat in alarm; but when the potential threat to safety chanced to walk away it was boldly chased and threatened. There were corresponding sudden changes of bodily attitude and appearance in the apes and indications of secretory and excretory processes. When it is aggressive the chimpanzee is likely to march or run forward erect, swinging its arms and seeming to swell in size, partly because its hair rises. It stamps or beats the ground and bangs anything near that will resound. Often it screams, barks, or shouts, with its mouth wide open and the lips drawn back to expose the teeth. A chimpanzee retreating is an entirely different creature.

Its hair lies flat, its body seems to shrink as if to escape attention, and it runs away quietly. Unless, indeed, every hair stands on end with terror and the challenger becomes a capering ball of fur. In all these cases and apparently correlated with the strength of the stimulus, frequent defaecation may occur, or, less commonly, urination and vomiting.

All sorts of sudden events and chronic stresses alter the balance of the two parts of the autonomic system. Both parts are continuously played upon by the emotions. Anxiety or contentment express themselves via both parts of the autonomous system. In man, anger causes the secretion of noradrenalin, anxiety causes the secretion of adrenalin. Although these two hormones are both secreted by the adrenal glands, the secretion of each is controlled by different neurons of the hypothalamus.

The hypothalamus has four principal ways of using these two parts of the autonomic nervous system; it can diminish or increase the activity of the sympathetic system and diminish or increase the activity of the parasympathetic system. Only in extreme circumstances does it both decrease the one system and increase the other. Normally both systems are active all the time, their activities being harmoniously balanced according to the needs of the moment.

As an example one may take the rate at which the heart beats. This rate depends on an intrinsic rhythm of the heart muscle, and on the sympathetic and parasympathetic nerves. The actual rate is always kept slow by the parasympathetic nerves. When the rate needs to be increased, as when we run or climb, the brake of the parasympathetic nerves is taken off. If the rate is still not enough, then it is speeded up further by the action of the sympathetic nerves.

The sympathetic system has two ways of acting. At first it acts by stimulating many organs into activity. Then, if more sympathetic activity is needed, the depot of noradrenalin and adrenalin in the adrenal glands is made to pour out its secretion into the bloodstream; this acts as a booster.

In the case of the alimentary canal, the sympathetic and

parasympathetic nervous systems have opposite effects. As the sympathetic system is used to make the animal active and ready to face the world, its action on the alimentary canal is to quieten it and make it inactive. If in the middle of running away or an important interview, you had a great increase in the activity of your colon and rectum, this might lead to personal disaster; and so the movements of the alimentary canal are inhibited by sympathetic nerves. The parasympathetic system is active when the animal is withdrawn from the demands of the world and ensconced in security. It eats, chews the cud, digests, defaecates and micturates at leisure. Throughout the alimentary canal, parasympathetic nerves excite all the glands into activity so that they secrete their enzymes and lubricants to digest the food. In many carnivores, the smell of blood activates the parasympathetic nervous system so that their mouths water and enzymes are secreted throughout the alimentary canal.

The parts of the brain in which the parasympathetic centres are located are the same parts that contain the rewarding or pleasure centres; these are the regions that the animal will endlessly stimulate in itself by pressing the lever. The parts where the sympathetic centres are located are parts that the animals do not stimulate if the permanent electrodes are implanted in them. It appears then that the parasympathetic centres give a feeling of contentment and pleasure whereas the excitement or agitation of sympathetic activity is not welcomed.

Over and Above the Hypothalamus

We now need to think about how the various aspects of behaviour organized by the hypothalamus are normally fitted into the animal's life. One of the problems about investigating how nervous systems work comes from the way in which we learn about them. We investigate the anatomy and physiology of the nervous system by stimulating different parts electrically.

From this method, we obtain knowledge of what certain parts can do. Stimulation of the lower part of the spinal cord produces running movements of the hind-limbs. Stimulation of a region within the hypothalamus produces a certain total act. It may be running away, which is associated with all manifestations of fright; it may be attack, the attack being well aimed at some living animal nearby. Stimulation in the human of a region of the occipital lobe produces visual sensation: the patient sees white light or squiggles and diagonals in his visual field. Such are the facts. The problem comes when we try and put these separate pieces of information together. There we leave the realm of fact and enter the hazy land of conjecture. Yet obviously we must take this step, even if we do so apologetically. In considering how the functions organized mainly within the hypothalamus are used in the total life of the animal, we are deep in this land of conjecture.

There are certain regions of the cerebral hemispheres that have remained in close relation to the hypothalamus throughout evolution. The first part of the cerebral hemispheres to develop was a part connected with the olfactory input: the cerebral hemispheres evolved to deal with the world of smells and to store that which had been smelt within the olfactory memory. And smell remains the sense most intimately connected to the parts of the cerebral hemispheres that are both concerned with remembering and connected to the hypothalamus.

These parts of the hemispheres are shown in Figure 17. To understand this figure, one has to imagine that the brain has been cut through from ear to ear. In the middle is the hypothalamus. The parts of the hemispheres particularly related to the hypothalamus are the insula, the cingulate gyrus, the hippocampal gyrus, the uncus, and the amygdala. The insula is a part of the cerebral hemisphere concerned with the whole alimentary canal; it controls the movements and the secretions of the stomach and the rest of the gut. Briefly, these other old parts of the hemispheres, which will be discussed below, are concerned with the affective life of the animal, with its memory of all that it has lived through, the recognition of what it already knows and what is strange so that it can produce the appropriate reactions to its situation.

These parts of the hemispheres work together with the hypothalamus to call forth the behaviour centred in this small structure. A most suitable analogy of the relation between the hemispheres and the hypothalamus is once again a funnel. The wide part of the funnel, its mouth, consists of the two

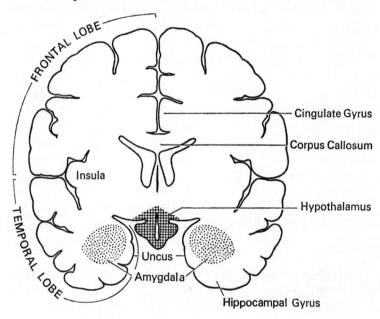

17. Section through the human brain

cerebral hemispheres. The walls coming down to its neck are the amygdaloid neurons and the two hippocampi, the older parts of the hemisphere still most intimately related to the hypothalamus; the stem is the hypothalamus itself, the narrow part of the brain able to produce a few stereotyped reactions; the narrow end of the funnel consists of orders to the lower centres of the brain and the spinal cord to carry out the relatively simple, final movements involved in behaviour. It includes the organization of the pituitary control of hormones and the activation of both parts of the autonomic system. And, as always, it includes a return of information back to the cerebral hemispheres to let them know how the behaviour they are helping to organize is getting on.

Within the hypothalamus we have centres for three activities: sex, eating, and defence, with its two components, flight and aggression. The first two, sex and eating, could be seen as being opposed to the third, the defence reaction. Probably the neurons organizing the defence reaction inhibit those concerned with eating and sex, and vice versa.

When the amygdala and hippocampus are removed experimentally, there is an increase in sex and eating and a decrease in defence. It appears that a system of braking has been removed from the activities of sex and eating and that a brake has been put on the defence reaction. As these activities may work reciprocally, merely one mechanism may have been removed when these parts of the temporal lobes are cut out, for the removal of one brake might suffice to obtain the whole result. Eventually, however, these animals do show rage, but the provocation has to be very high. Evidently what had changed was the threshold for aggressive reactions; as would have been expected, the animal was still capable of manifesting them.

Further experiments have shown that if these operations are carried out on animals in which the gonads had previously been removed, or if they are removed after the operation, then the sexual components of the behaviour did not appear. This supports other evidence that the hypothalamic nuclei organizing sexual behaviour function only when supplied by hormones secreted by the gonads.

What the hypothalamus receives has already passed through the cerebral hemispheres. The animal behaves by responding to the situation in which it finds itself. This means that before it can respond to this situation, all the inputs have been integrated and assessed. To do this is the function of the cerebral hemispheres. Here what is occurring is related to past experience and in the higher vertebrates it may also be related to a probable future. Only when the situation has been interpreted and judged is a line of behaviour ordered and the hypothalamus called upon to organize this behaviour.

It works similarly with regard to more simple aspects of behaviour too, such as defaecating, eating and drinking. It appears that when we imagine a delicious meal or see, smell or start tasting food, we are activating the insula, and, as we have seen, this part of the cerebral hemisphere is closely connected with the hypothalamus. And so, the smell or taste or just the thought of food activates the hypothalamus and the parasympathetic system. This makes our mouths water; and farther along the alimentary canal, other digestive juices are similarly secreted, and the movements of the stomach and duodenum are increased, all ready to receive the meal.

It is possible that the cerebral hemisphere-hypothalamus circuit can be short-circuited at every level. For instance, the foot is pulled off the thorn of the cactus before the cerebral cortex knows what is happening. Something sudden and potentially dangerous alarms the animal before it knows what it is. The alarm reaction is set off by certain regions of the reticular substance in the mid-brain. The whole nervous system is alerted, and the cortex is made vigilant to find out what has happened. The cortex does not need to find out and then spread the alarm throughout the central nervous system; though things can also happen in this order.

There is one other situation in which it may be that hypothalamic behaviour is in control, the cerebral hemispheres being short-circuited: fleeing in panic before an unknown horror. Many people in a panic-stricken crowd have no idea why they are fleeing. They are wholly taken up in terror and the urge to flee, and that organizes their behaviour. The contributions of the cerebral hemispheres, reasoning, memories of past experience, planning, play no role.

It is likely that the same occurs in boxing or other fighting when one loses one's temper; and the skilful boxer may try to make his opponent do so if he can. For the man who has lost his temper may be wilder and may be able to punch with greater strength; but he has lost his cunning. All that he has learned and remembers, all his strategy and his planning has gone. These are the contributions of the cerebral hemispheres. It may be that when one loses one's temper, one short-circuits the cerebral hemispheres and acts with the hypothalamus alone.

The relationship between the cerebral hemispheres and the hypothalamus is not merely one of inhibition. In normal life, it could be that the hemispheres call upon the hypothalamus to produce the patterns of behaviour organized in this structure when the total situation of the animal demands them. Now that the patterns of behaviour obtainable from experimental stimulation of the hypothalamus have been observed, it appears that such acts of violent behaviour are almost never seen in pure form in natural conditions. For what was seen in these experiments was somewhat different from what is seen in normal life. When the cerebral hemispheres are in control, the animal is capable at all times of reviewing the situation. It is not merely a wildly fighting object or a wildly fleeing animal. Its behaviour is related to the total situation. A bird will be aggressive when it is attacked within its own territory; it will be far less aggressive when it is on the border of its territory; it will flee when it is attacked in someone else's territory.

Hypothalamic behaviour is adjusted and graded by the hemispheres. Using its cerebral hemispheres, the animal can appreciate the whole situation and is able to choose. The cerebral hemispheres provide a means of delaying direct responses. Above all, they integrate the basic ways of behaving into the whole situation. When the animal is hungry, the cerebral hemispheres organize the finding of food. When it is thirsty, they are needed for finding water. They keep the record of previous experience, they know the landmarks in the country, the paths to the water pools, they remember the smell of approaching rain; they are the end-stations of all sensory inflows, so that they know the sight, the smell, the sound, the combined sensations of water.

Chapter 15

General Plan of the Human Brain

In the fifth century B.C., Hippocrates studied and taught medicine on the island of Cos in Greece. As far as we know, he was the first who taught the function of the brain correctly. The following has come down to us.

Some people think that the heart is the organ with which we think, and that it feels pain and anxiety. But it is not so. . . . From the brain and the brain alone, arise our pleasures, joys, laughter and jests, as well as our sorrows, pains, griefs and tears. Through it, in particular, we think, see, hear, and distinguish the ugly from the beautiful, the bad from the good, the pleasant from the unpleasant. . . . It is the same thing which makes us mad or delirious, inspires us with dread or fear, whether by night or by day. It brings sleeplessness, inopportune mistakes, aimless anxieties, absent-mindedness, and acts that are contrary to habit.

This essential knowledge was lost to Europe after the savages from the east overran the Roman Empire. When the influence of Greek civilization was lost, it was forgotten that the brain is the seat of the mind and of consciousness. Human behaviour ceased to be based on a real thing, the brain, and was believed to arise out of a wisp of nothingness, the soul. It is difficult for us to conceive how ignorant these forebears of ours were. At one time in Europe it was believed that the brain was nothing but a bag of mucus; and when one had a cold and one's nose filled with mucus, it was thought that this was part of the brain mucus coming down into the nose through little holes at the base of the skull.

The philosopher, as Nietzsche said, is the first cousin of the priest. And most philosophers have continued to speculate on what they call the mind–brain relationship without knowing how to do experiments to find the answers to their questions. Meanwhile scientists have gone ahead with their painstaking investigations, based on the belief that the nervous system and all its manifestations are subject to the usual laws of physics and chemistry. This approach, and no other one, has obtained results, so that we already know a lot about how the brain works. And the mysterious world of the unknowable, known only to the priests of all religions, shrinks year by year.

The brain, like the rest of the nervous system, consists essentially of neurons; there are about ten billion of them. All of them are present when the baby is born, though they are not then all functioning. These neurons, like all neurons, are irreplaceable; if we lose any on the journey to the grave, they are lost for ever. In this respect, neurons differ from all other cells of the body; for other cells divide, increasing their number to make up for losses to repair the damage done by accident and disease, and to increase the tissues for growth. By the time we come to die, owing to general wear and tear, injuries and pathological processes, and the narrowing of the blood-vessels, we will inevitably have lost many of the neurons we were born with.

Anatomists have various ways of dividing the brain up. A simple way is to divide it into two parts, the brain-stem and the cerebral hemispheres; this is shown diagrammatically in Figure 18. The brain-stem includes the hind-brain and the mid-brain. Above the spinal cord is the first part of the brain-stem – the medulla oblongata. Then comes the pons or bridge, so called as it takes masses of fibres from one side of the cerebellum to the other. The cerebellum is above the pons, over-lapping the medulla oblongata. These three structures, the medulla oblongata, the pons and the cerebellum constitute the hind-brain. Above the hind-brain is the mid-brain which consists mainly of passing nerve fibres, the main mass of fibres going up to the fore-brain and coming down to the medulla oblongata and the spinal cord. Above the mid-brain there is the

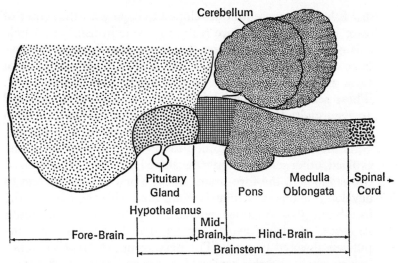

18. Diagram showing how anatomists usually sub-divide the brain

fore-brain. It is made up of the two cerebral hemispheres and the hypothalamus. The fore-brain is not essential for life. The deformed babies mentioned earlier can remain alive for a few months without this or any other parts of the fore-brain. But it is essential for any kind of normal life. Here are built in all the acts relating the animal to its environment. The hind-brain merely keeps the animal alive if food and drink are given to it. If the deformed baby has a functioning mid-brain, it can also cry and follow sounds with its eyes. With an intact hypothalamus, an animal can keep itself at the correct temperature. The animal's intake of food and drink is adjusted and the amount of urine formed is also adjusted by this part of the brain. The organization of sex is under the control of the hypothalamus; and when copulation has succeeded and the next generation appears the hypothalamus enforces maternal and paternal behaviour. It influences the structure as well as the functioning of the body to carry out these many acts.

The greater part of the fore-brain consists of the two cerebral hemispheres and the masses of nuclei within them. These parts of the brain started to develop in the ancestors of present-day fish. They were first developed to cope with the senses of taste and smell, which are really the same in fish. The whole existence of fish depends on this input. Smell was always related to the alimentary canal, and so the chemoreceptors of taste and smell developed in the mouth part of this canal. These senses are essential for the fish to find good food and to regurgitate bad and for it to find a sexual partner, and in some cases to avoid predators and to keep with its kith and kin.

As the vertebrates continued to develop and as their brains evolved, other sensory inputs developed, and they also acquired end-stations in the fore-brain. But the first sensory system to develop remains immediately connected with the parts of the fore-brain that organize emotion. By the time the South American mud-fish evolved, more than half the sensory input was devoted to smell. The next group, the reptiles, relies less on smell, and this sensory input occupies less of the fore-brain. In their brains, there develops the hippocampus, the part of the cerebral hemispheres related to the hypothalamus, as was seen in Chapter 14. Reptiles used their tongues as tactile organs to examine the world, and so they evolved a large sensory tactile region in the fore-brain. When birds developed as an offshoot from reptiles, smell lost its pre-eminence; the sensibility of the beak and the tongue became more important. Birds, however, are not the main trunk of evolutionary development; they are out on a limb. The main trunk continued with the first mammals, and they used smelling rather than seeing. Smell remains the most important sense for most mammals today. It was the few mammals who took to living in trees that developed sight and neglected smell; for life among the branches of trees demands good eyesight. And so man, returning to the earth from the trees, has good sight and a poor sense of smell.

Although the rest of this book will be concerned with the cerebral hemispheres, they are not essential for life. They are an added refinement, coming rather late in development and provided only for the later models. All essential functions had been built into the previous models for millions of years.

The cerebral hemispheres give the brains of mammals an astronomical number of neurons and junctions and inter-connexions. It has been calculated that the number of junctions between the neurons of the human cerebral cortex is $10^{2,783,000}$; this number is so enormous that to write it out in figures would fill several books. If this figure is too astronomical to think of, one may settle for remembering that any one neuron may be connected to 25,000 others and that there are 1,000,000,000 neurons in the cerebral hemispheres.

Within the members of a species, size of brain is not related to intelligence. Very intelligent men and women have had smaller and lighter brains than half-wits. But when we compare the sizes of brain of the various species of animals, then the difference in size seems to be related to the animal's ability to learn. With regard to size, man's brain is not the largest of any animal's; the porpoise's, the whale's and the elephant's are bigger. But in relation to the animal's total size, the whale has a small brain, indeed, one of the smallest of any mammal's. At the other end of the scale, we have the brain of the blowfly; it weighs 0·4 mg. and its maximum diameter is 1·5 mm. Although insects are more reflex-bound than mammals, many can learn, as every flea-trainer knows.

A large brain means large cerebral hemispheres with thick layers of neurons in the cortex; this means millions of neurons and inter-connexions. It may also mean that the cortical neurons have more and larger dendrites, more inter-connecting branches. This means that more inter-connexions are possible; and these may be necessary for learning.

It is true that the bee and the ant are astonishingly successful in dealing with life, and yet both have minute brains. But they both are almost incapable of learning. This way of evolving seems to be no longer available to them.

Apart from the overall size of the hemispheres, the brains of the different orders of animals differ according to which aspects of the environment particularly concern them. To the dog and the deer, the world is a place of smells, to man and the lemur, it is a place of sights. In accordance with these interests, the former species will have the olfactory parts of the brain well-developed and the latter the visual parts. From examining the brain of an animal we can thus tell whether the animal was orientated towards hearing or smelling, whether it had big eyes or a well-developed nose. For within the phylum of vertebrates, among the various classes and species, the same parts of the brain subserve essentially the same functions. As the development of the skull is necessarily related to the size and development of the brain within, we can deduce from examining the skulls of extinct animals what sort of life the owner of that skull once had. One can know whether it lived mainly visually or relied mainly on smell; just as from an examination of its teeth, we know whether it lived on meat or vegetables and fruit.

The cerebral hemispheres do so many things that one can hardly say in a few words what their functions are. From a distant viewpoint, we should consider them as the last intermediate neurons between the afferent and the efferent neurons. They add necessary complications to the never-ending task of adaptation to the environment. They add vast numbers of intermediate neurons between the input from the environment and the response of the animal to this input. They store the animal's own experience of life, all that the individual has learned. From earlier experience, from the pain of previous deprivation and the pleasure of previous satiety, the animal has learnt when to produce the copulating, sleeping, fighting, fleeing, eating, drinking, micturating and defaecating organized by the hypothalamus. These patterns of behaviour are integrated into the animal's life by the cerebral hemispheres. They choose the moment, the occasion and the place, for the right behaviour.

It was known to Greek medicine that an injury to one side of the brain causes paralysis of the limbs of the opposite side of the body; and from this it was deduced that movements of one side are organized by the opposite cerebral hemisphere. The rest of our knowledge of the fore-brain was acquired during the last century from the study of patients with neurological disorders during life and the careful investigation of their brains after death.

The easiest way to get an idea of the general shape and construction of the brain is to go to the butcher's and buy one. It is unlikely that he has a human one, but a sheep's or a bullock's is sufficiently like the human one to make no difference.

Four photographs of a human brain are shown as Plates 7, 8, 9 and 10. Plate 7 shows it from above, Plate 8 from the right side, Plate 9 from below, and Plate 10 shows the medial surface of the left hemisphere, the two hemispheres having been divided from each other.

The hemispheres are divided for convenience into lobes. The front half is the frontal lobe; it is separated by a fissure, called the central fissure, from the parietal lobe behind it. The part at the back of the skull is the occipital lobe. They are shown in Plate 7.

In Plate 8 all four lobes can be seen. The cerebellum is below the occipital lobe and the medulla oblongata is below that. Beneath the frontal lobe, the slight projection is the olfactory bulb, which receives the olfactory nerves coming through the skull from inside the nose.

Plate 9 shows the brain from below; this surface sits on the floor of the skull. The frontal, occipital and temporal lobes are seen; the parietal lobe does not reach the undersurface of the brain, and so it cannot be seen in this view. A great deal of the temporal lobe is seen in this photograph. Within this part of the temporal lobe is the hippocampus and amygdala. Behind the hemispheres is the cerebellum with its folds and furrows, narrower than those of the cerebral hemispheres. It is at the back of the brain, situated just above the neck. Between the two cerebellar hemispheres is the medulla oblongata, which continues below into the spinal cord and above into the pons. In front of the pons, in shadow, is the floor of the hypothalamus, and in its centre is the stalk of the pituitary gland cut through. Bordering the hypothalamus are the two optic nerves joined together. In front of them are the two olfactory stalks ending in front in the olfactory bulbs, which receive the olfactory nerves. On each side of the pons are the two afferent nerves from the face and head through which all sensation reaches the brain.

All four lobes of the right hemisphere can be seen in Plate 10. The cerebellum is also cut across and so its cut surface is seen. The medulla oblongata and the pons are cut through. In front of the cerebellum the pineal body can be seen. Here Descartes placed the seat of the soul. The large curved bridge of the corpus callosum has been cut through; this is the main structure connecting the two cerebral hemispheres. Another and more ancient bridge can be seen above the optic nerve; this is the anterior commissure. The hypothalamus is behind the optic nerve. A large mass of white nerve fibres can be seen descending into it; these fibres come from the temporal lobe of the other side.

Our bodies are bilaterally symmetrical, most structures being in pairs. We have two arms, two legs, two eyes, two kidneys, two gonads. The whole body is not built on this plan of course, for we have one heart, one liver, one pancreas. If we have two eyes, two ears, two limbs, the brain has to be built on the same bilateral plan. We must have two optic nerves from the eyes, two auditory nerves from the ears, and parts of the brain related to the opposite side of the body. A brain built on this double plan runs the danger of behaving as two incoordinated organs. This is overcome by building bridges between the two halves; in anatomy these bridges are called commissures. They are present throughout the spinal cord, the hind-brain and mid-brain. In the upper and later developed parts of the brain they are more obvious, as this part of the brain is more obviously constructed in two halves. The main one here connecting the two cerebral hemispheres is the corpus callosum.

The cerebral hemispheres, when cut, are seen to be made up of white matter and grey matter. The grey matter is along the outside of the hemispheres and so it is called the cortex (Latin: rind or bark; French: *écorce*, which also gives us cork, the rind or bark of the cork oak). The white matter consists mainly of nerve fibres, and the grey matter of nerve-cells. The surface of the cerebral hemispheres is thrown into ridges and furrows, so as to get a large sheet of cortex into the restricted space of the skull. On account of this folding, about two thirds of the cortex is hidden from view, being folded into the depths of the furrows.

The general plan of the working of the hemispheres will now be considered.

The main afferent pathways end up in the thalamus (shown in Figure 19). This is the highest part of the older brain; it is from the thalamus that the cerebral hemispheres developed. How the inputs to the cortex of the hemispheres from the thalamus are arranged can be seen in Figure. 19. The main sensory pathways cross the mid-line and go to the opposite thalamus and cerebral hemisphere. Within the thalamus and the hemisphere every sense has its own receiving area. The primary receptive area for the sense of smell is in the olfactory bulb, shown in Plate 10; this is a prolongation of the brain, situated above the nose. From the olfactory bulb bands

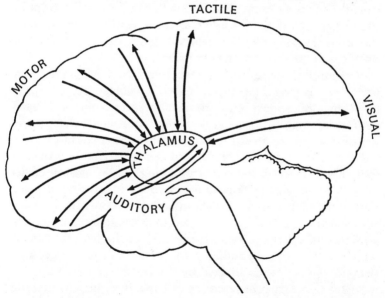

19. Some connexions between the thalamus and the cerebral cortex

of nerve fibres run back to the under-surface of the temporal lobe, where they reach the secondary olfactory area. The pathway for the visual input is from the optic nerves to the most posterior part of the hemispheres, to the back of the occipital lobes. In man, each half of the visual field goes to one hemisphere. Everything seen on the left goes to the right cerebral hemisphere and everything seen on the right to the left. The two occipital lobes are connected together by bands of nerve fibres passing over the bridge of the corpus callosum. Most of the visual area in man is on the medial surface of the brain. Above the ear and deep in the upper part of the temporal lobe is the primary receptive area for hearing. It receives from both ears but mainly from the opposite one. Between this region and the secondary region for smelling is the primary region for taste. There is a long and wide strip of cortex along the front of the parietal lobe, running from the vertex of the head to above the ear, which is the primary receptive area for all the varieties of touch, pressure and kinaesthetic sense; this is called the somaesthetic area. Below this region and in front of the visual area is the receptive area for vestibular sensations, the sense that one's body is where it is in space, with the feet on the ground and one's head upright.

Surrounding each primary receptive area is its parasensory or secondary area. The output from the primary area goes only to its own secondary area. Here it is spread out, with each neuron of the primary area being connected with many neurons widely scattered throughout the secondary area.

Each primary area is not devoted exclusively to its own sensory input; there is some intermingling of the sensory channels. This mixing of the various sensory inflows takes place first at the thalamus. Visual stimuli affect not only the primary visual area but also the primary auditory areas; and an auditory stimulus affects the primary tactile area of the parietal lobe as well as in the primary auditory area of the temporal lobe. The primary tactile area is affected by the vestibular inflow.

As well as each primary receptive area with its surrounding association or parasensory area, there are other receptive areas.

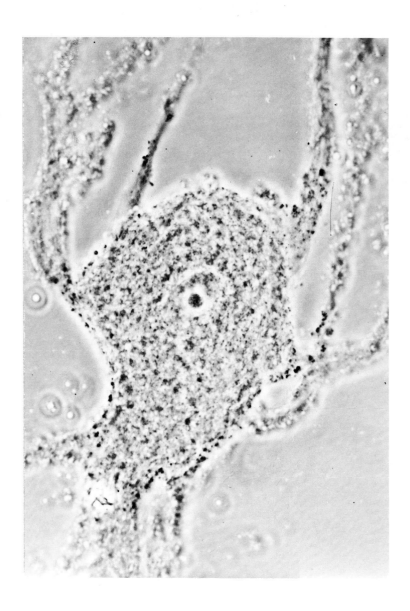

1. A living neuron dissected from the brain of a rabbit

2. (below) Section through the mid-line of a man

3. (top right) A nerve fibre in the skin of a man's finger

4. (bottom right) Several nerve fibres ending among disks in the skin of a man's finger

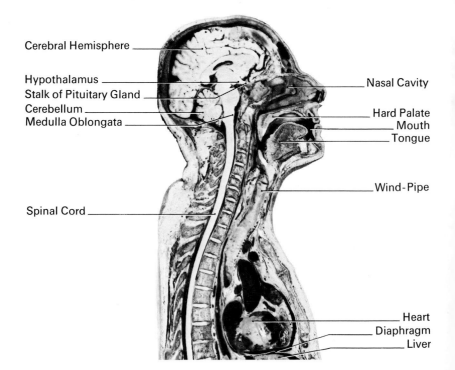

Cerebral Hemisphere

Hypothalamus

Stalk of Pituitary Gland

Cerebellum

Medulla Oblongata

Nasal Cavity

Hard Palate

Mouth

Tongue

Wind-Pipe

Spinal Cord

Heart

Diaphragm

Liver

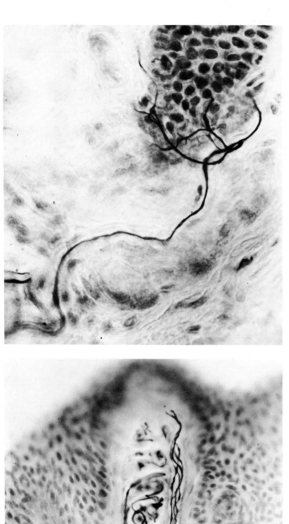
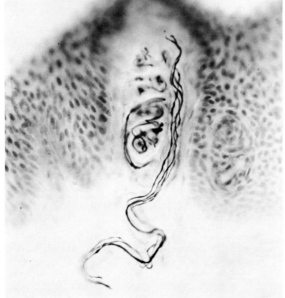

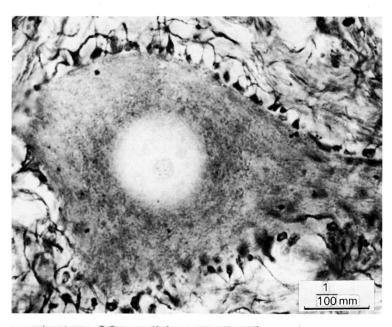

$$\frac{1}{100\,mm}$$

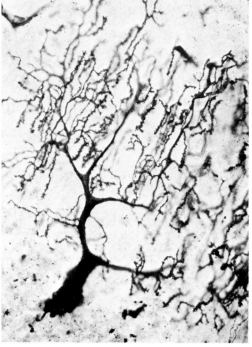

5. (top left) Photograph of a large neuron from the spinal cord. The nerve-endings on this neuron cover its edges; they do not cover the middle as the neuron has been cut through, to show the internal structure

6. (bottom left) A Purkinje cell from a human cerebellum

7. (below) The brain of a fifty-year-old man from above

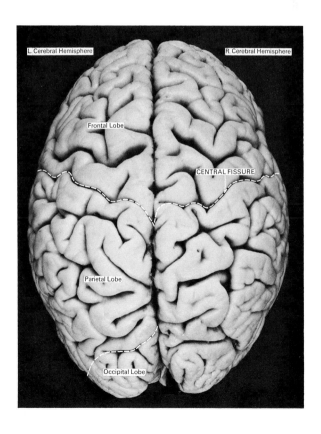

8. (below) The same brain taken from the right side

9. (top right) The same brain from beneath

10. (bottom right) The same brain cut through the middle in an antero-posterior direction

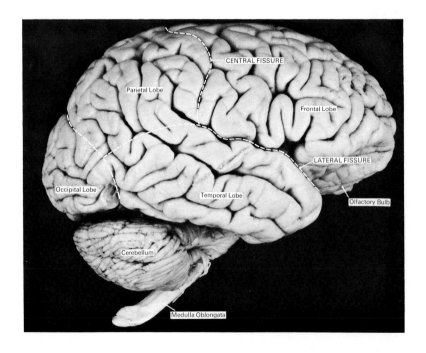

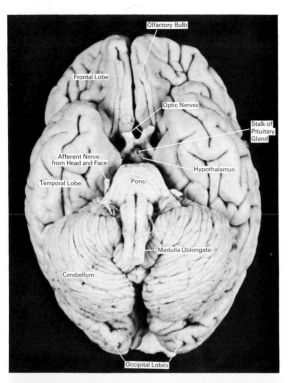

Olfactory Bulb

Frontal Lobe

Optic Nerves

Stalk of Pituitary Gland

Afferent Nerve from Head and Face

Hypothalamus

Temporal Lobe

Pons

Medulla Oblongata

Cerebellum

Occipital Lobes

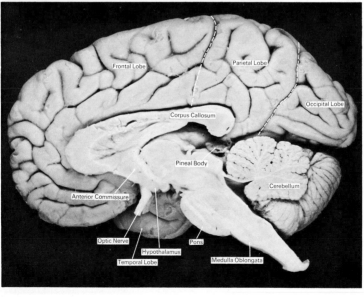

Frontal Lobe

Parietal Lobe

Occipital Lobe

Corpus Callosum

Pineal Body

Cerebellum

Anterior Commissure

Optic Nerve

Hypothalamus

Pons

Medulla Oblongata

Temporal Lobe

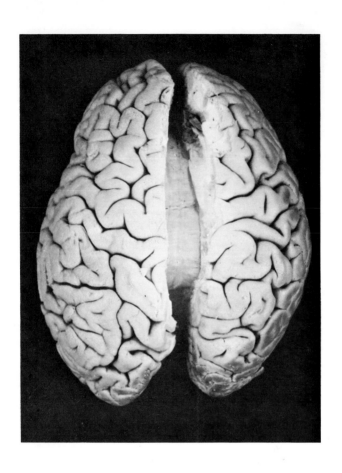

11. Dissection of a man's brain showing the corpus callosum

In the temporal lobe there is another receptive area for tactile and kinaesthetic sensations. Impulses from both sides of the body reach this region; whereas in the primary receptive area for these sensations, impulses come only from the opposite side of the body. In the more medial and lower parts of the temporal lobes there are also receptive areas for input from the auditory, visual and kinaesthetic channels.

Curiously enough, it is not known for certain whereabouts in the cerebral hemispheres the complex of sensations we call pain is located; in fact, there is probably no one part mainly concerned with pain, in the same way as there are parts concerned with vision and hearing.

We perceive sensation when the impulses reach the primary receptive areas. But some form of sensation may be experienced when impulses are in the thalamus. We know that when the primary receptive areas of the cortex are stimulated in conscious patients, sensation is experienced. When the nerve impulses are spread out into the secondary sensory areas, we get perception. And when these areas are stimulated, the patient perceives real things: he has hallucinations. He may hear a brass band playing 'Land of Hope and Glory' or he may see an old lady in a pointed green hat.

Each secondary or parasensory area is connected with the homologous area of the opposite hemisphere, the connecting fibres running through the corpus callosum. In addition to this, every secondary area of one hemisphere is connected to every other secondary area of the same hemisphere. Further, each secondary area is connected to certain other regions of the cortex, called association areas. As we ascend the evolutionary scale, the secondary areas become larger, and the association areas become far larger; both reach their peak in man.

The way in which the cerebral hemisphere is organized reminds one of the traditional government of Japan. The primary receptive area is like the emperor; he is the primary one, the acknowledged head of the government. The secondary or parasensory area is like the shogun; he is the minister and is therefore only secondary. Although the emperor was the most important man in Japan, he had no power to transact any business whatsoever. All business and all political affairs, all communication with ambassadors from other countries had to be performed by the shogun. In the brain, all communication is carried out by the secondary areas. Each primary receptive area merely receives. It then passes on messages to its secondary area; and the secondary areas pass messages among themselves and communicate with association areas.

The association areas are also connected with the motor areas. The main motor area, as far as we know, is situated in front of the primary receptive area for touch, for sensations and movement and knowledge of position of the parts of the body; there is a good deal of overlap between these two, some sensory nerve fibres ending in the mainly motor area, and motor fibres descending from the mainly sensory area. The strip immediately in front of the sensory area makes few connexions with the rest of the cortex, its outflow being to the spinal cord and to the neurons working the muscles of the eyes, face and throat. The motor area in front of this strip is somewhat like a secondary sensory area. Its input is from very many parts of the cortex as well as from the similar area on the other side of the brain; its output is both to the motor strip behind it and to lower parts of the brain concerned with the organization of posture and movement.

There are many association areas, and there are more in man than in any other species. After an input has gone to many secondary sensory areas, some of it is sent to the hippocampus of both hemispheres, as far as we know. By this time it has acquired meaning. It is not a spark on the left or a large mass of blue colour; it is Mr Jones shouting or a table in a restaurant implying food. In the hippocampus this integrated input is somehow compared with and related to past experience. It is related to other tables in other restaurants, with other occasions of eating; and behaviour can then be organized accordingly.

The plan of the hemispheres might be thought of as being two funnels, mouth to mouth. The various inflows come up a narrow stem to their primary receiving areas; from here they are spread out, each minute region of a primary receiving point sending the impulses to scattered regions within its surrounding parasensory area. This is only the beginning of the sides of the funnel. For the rest of the funnel consists of the further spreading of the input: to the similar region of the opposite hemisphere, to other association areas of both hemispheres and to association areas of other association areas. That is the wide open mouth of the one hemisphere. Now, the input is collected in the opposite direction. It is collected into the secondary motor areas, and these converge down to simpler and more basic primary motor areas. From here, impulses are finally sent down the neck of the motor funnel to all lower motor centres of the nervous system, to the hypothalamus, the reticular substance, to the spinal cord, and finally to the efferent nerve fibres that control the muscles.

It has been realized now for a hundred years that the two cerebral hemispheres are not equal and equivalent, that the one is not the mirror image of the other. What first upset the assumption of equivalence was the realization that speech and thinking relying on internal speech is organized by the left hemisphere. Now that we know that a large region of the left parietal, temporal and occipital lobes is given up to the activities of speech and the thinking behind speech, we might ask what is occupying the same region of the right hemisphere. But actually this question is not the right one. We inevitably ask it because speech is so important to us. The right question is – what was there on the left side of the brain before our new acquisition, speech, was developed there? The essential answer to this question is, I think, that before speech was developed, this region had not evolved. In animals lower in the scale of evolution than ourselves, most of this part of the hemisphere is absent; and of the parts that are present, we are not sure which are the homologous ones.

Behind the speech area within the left hemisphere and in the homologous region of the right hemisphere, there is a region for organizing a function more basic than speech and one well-developed in all mammals: it is the region organizing visuo-spatial perception. In man, this function is organized mainly by the right hemisphere. This region provides us with topographical knowledge and topographical memory; here reside the learned perceptions allowing us to find our way about the world. The more posterior part of this region is concerned with visuo-spatial elements of perception. The part nearer the temporal lobe is concerned more with auditory-spatial aspects of the environment and is close to the region where vestibular sensations are elaborated. Vestibular components are essential for our perception of space and of our own bodies in space. For our conception of space is intimately related to the position of our own bodies and the parts of our bodies to one another. When this perception is disturbed, the patient may not realize that parts of his own body are parts of himself and he may also neglect part of his environment, such as half the clock face or everything on his left. Both hemispheres contribute to the ability to judge distances in three dimensions and to make constructions in space, an ability relying on the cognizance of the three dimensions.

When we say that an ability depends on only one hemisphere, this does not mean that the hemisphere needs no contribution from the other. At first the inflow comes to one hemisphere and then it is passed to the secondary receptive area of both hemispheres; from here it is sent to the association areas. Some of the higher association areas are concerned with one kind of basic function. Although such an area of one hemisphere carries out a function related to that performed by the homologous association area of the other hemisphere, the function may be sufficiently different for us to recognize one function as being performed by one hemisphere and another function by the similar region of the other hemisphere. It is only the higher association areas that have become so specialized.

Whether people who are not good at things – clumsy in constructing clay models, bad at drawing maps, bad at finding their way about – are born with these parts of the brain poorly developed or incapable of being fully developed, we do not know.

Chapter 16

Exploring Man's Living Brain

It is about a hundred years since we began to learn about the functions of the different parts of the cerebral hemispheres. Before this higher level of neurology could be studied it was necessary to conceive the idea that various parts of the hemispheres might carry out various functions. It was taken for granted over a hundred years ago that each hemisphere works as a whole, the one reduplicating the functions of the other. The first investigator who denied this was Franz Josef Gall, an anatomist and neurologist working at the end of the eighteenth century. Gall is now remembered chiefly as the founder of phrenology, a subject which is usually considered to be nonsense. In fact, phrenology was not only an original conception of how the brain is organized; in many ways it was the right one. In the first place, Gall took it for granted that the physical organ of the brain engenders the mind. For this heresy in the so-called enlightened eighteenth century he was expelled from Roman Catholic Austria. Secondly, Gall put forward his belief that higher neural functions are localized to certain regions of the cerebral hemispheres. The orthodox view at that time was that the brain works as a whole and that there are no separate parts having different functions. Again, Gall's view is the correct one. The mistake the phrenologists made was in their choice of functions to localize in the cerebral hemispheres. This remains a very difficult problem for psychologists and neurologists. For instance, the ability to knit is not an ability organized by one part of the brain. It is made up of skilful use of the fingers, of an ability to measure, an ability to plan, to think in three dimensions and other more basic functions of the brain. But the ability to pronounce words is carried out by certain regions of the brain. The phrenologists thought they could localize within the cerebral hemispheres such functions as language, calculation, hope and philoprogenitiveness. They were right about language. They were wrong about calculation; but until a few years ago most neurologists regarded an ability to calculate as a basic cerebral function. They were wrong about hope; perhaps they should have sought it in the human breast. As for philoprogenitiveness, they were not very far wrong, for there are certain parts of the brain which organize sexual activity. The most serious mistake the phrenologists made was to think that the indentations, bumps and dips on the surface of the skull resulted from the underlying parts of the cerebral hemisphere. Another mistake was to imagine that if a faculty is particularly developed in someone, then the part of the cerebral hemisphere in which that faculty is located will also be large and well-developed. Gall's method of locating faculties within the brain was absurd. For instance, looking back at his schooldays, he remembered that two of his schoolmates had had good verbal memories and large eyes, and so he connected verbal memory with protuberant eyes; he concluded that the faculty of verbal memory is in the frontal lobes just behind the eyes.

Phrenology soon became the craze of fashionable society and those who practised it ceased to concern themselves with acquiring knowledge. Serious anatomists came to regard the whole subject as quackery and the phrenologists as charlatans, which indeed they had become; and the contributions of phrenology to science have been overlooked for a hundred and fifty years. Their contributions to the antique business remain in those charming china heads, on the bald surfaces of which are written such attributes as 'wisdom', 'ambition' and 'will-power'.

Knowledge of the function of the parts of the cerebral hemispheres has been acquired in three main ways. One is the electrical stimulation of the brain in living animals, including man; this is the subject of this chapter. Another has been by the removal of parts of the cerebral hemispheres or the division of connexions between parts; this again has been done in animals and man. The third way has been the correlation of naturally occurring disorders studied during life with the lesions found in the brain after death. We first learn how things go wrong, and then deduce how they work when they go right. We learn from the abnormal; we deduce physiology from pathology.

Lesions within the cerebral hemispheres can destroy the end-stations or the connecting links or both. Destruction of the end-station is just like destroying a railway terminus. Both sorts of termini, railway and cerebral, have afferent and efferent functions. One receives and sends off trains; the other receives and sends off nerve impulses. Destruction of the links between stations disconnects the two stations; it is the same whether the connexions are railway lines or nerve fibres.

The most important neural disorder that has contributed to our knowledge of the brain is epilepsy; and the first worker to make use of this material was the founder of British neurology in the nineteenth century, Hughlings Jackson. A hundred years ago, he concluded that epilepsy is due to the spontaneous firing of groups of neurons. When fits start with visual, auditory, olfactory or gustatory hallucinations they do so because the neurons normally occupied with vision, hearing, smelling and tasting are spontaneously active. If, after the patient's death, the lesion causing the fits is found, it will show which parts of the brain are normally concerned with those functions. When, for instance, a fit starts with a tingling numb sensation in the right foot, and a lesion is found in a certain region of the left hemisphere of the brain, it may be concluded that this region is where sensation of the right foot is organized. If neurons of the primary receptive area for smelling spontaneously discharge in a fit, the patient will be aware of a strange smell.

The preliminary features of the fit which the patient experiences are called the aura. An aura may be a sensation of vertigo, tingling spreading up a limb, butterflies in the stomach, an overpowering fear, or the vision of a scene from the past. When the features of the aura are correlated with post-mortem evidence of the location of the lesion causing the fit, we learn where in the cortex the neurons subserving that function are located.

Using this method, Hughlings Jackson showed that certain parts of the hemispheres are mainly concerned with movements and neighbouring parts are concerned with the sensations associated with movement. He also showed that when a part of the front of the temporal lobe is stimulated by the epileptic discharge, hallucinatory states appear, with strange disturbances of the awareness of reality and of oneself as a part of reality. He described this state by saying that the patients show 'dreams mixing up with present thoughts', and he called it 'double consciousness'. Now that we know more about psychopathology and about normal psychological mechanisms, we realize that sometimes repressed psychological material accompanied by strong emotion comes to the patient's consciousness during this early part of a fit.

It is interesting to find that Dostoyevsky in describing his own fits described the kinds of epilepsy starting in the temporal lobe twenty years before Jackson did. As his kind of fits were not recognized as being a part of epilepsy at that time, both Dostoyevsky and his doctors believed his attacks were partly or entirely hysterical. Dostoyevsky's accounts of his fits, given in his letters, his diaries and his novels, are so well described that one can say without doubt that they began in the left temporal lobe of his brain.

The method that has been most useful in investigating the function of the brain, electrical stimulation, was first used in 1804. A physiologist called Aldini stimulated the brains of animals in the slaughter-house immediately after they had been killed; he observed that the muscles of the opposite side of the body showed movements. He then took his investigations a step farther by stimulating the brain of a freshly decapitated man; and he observed movements of the opposite side of the face (it is unknown whether the head felt this or not). The cerebral hemispheres of living human beings were first stimulated electrically in 1874 by Robert Bartholow, professor of medicine in Cincinnati. He was able to pass the electrodes through the skulls of two patients as the bone had become softened and rotted away by abscesses. As he expected, he produced movements of the limbs of the opposite side.

A great step forward in the study of the brain was made in 1870 by Fritsch and Hitzig. As no facilities were provided by the Physiological Institute of Berlin for this work, they started their investigations in Hitzig's wife's bedroom. They explored the surface of the hemispheres of lightly-anaesthetized dogs. From such stimulation they worked out in detail what parts of the cerebral cortex control what movements. They showed, among other facts, that Gall's main idea was right – that the brain does not work as one single organ, but that different parts of it perform different functions. Stimulation of certain parts of the cerebral hemispheres caused movements, whereas stimulation elsewhere caused nothing observable. Obviously, parts of the brain concerned with sensation, with thought, emotion or remembering, could not show up in dogs with this stimulation technique.

The next step forward was made by Foerster in Germany and Cushing in the United States, both of whom stimulated the brains of conscious patients. By the first decade of the twentieth century, neurosurgery had been developed and local anaesthetics were used routinely. It became possible not only to map out the motor regions of the cerebral hemispheres in man, but also to stimulate other parts of the cortex and find out what the patient experienced during stimulation. The patient did not know when the electrode was placed on the brain or when the current was turned on or off.

It might be thought that stimulation of the living brain in conscious patients is painful and injurious. It is neither. As has been mentioned above, the brain can be touched or cut or stimulated without the subject feeling any pain or anything he can localize to the brain itself. When a part of the cerebral cortex is to be cut out because it causes fits, this part must be

233

located accurately. From investigations by various x-radiological methods, one knows roughly what part of the cerebral hemisphere has to be cut out; but the exact region can be found best by stimulating the region electrically.

The technique of stimulation, localization and excision was brought to a point where it became a routine neurosurgical procedure by Penfield of Montreal. He also applied Cushing's and Foerster's techniques to a systematic exploration of the cerebral cortex of man. The operations were performed for the removal of tumours, or scars, or for the cure of certain kinds of epilepsy. The brain was stimulated to enable the surgeon to reproduce the features of the patient's fits. When the patient reported having the same aura as he usually experienced with his fits, the abnormal region of the brain had been found. The surgeon then cut out this part; and this often stopped the fits.

This has been a useful method of treating certain unusual cases of epilepsy as well as a very rewarding method of exploring the human brain. It is rather surprising that such a crude intervention as the application of an electric current through an electrode should produce normal phenomena, normal movements, visual hallucinations, the recall of scenes from the past. One might have expected that it would produce some sort of chaos or caricature of normal phenomena. But in fact it imitates normal functioning of the brain to a surprising degree. One notes too that all the phenomena caused by electrical stimulation in these patients also occur spontaneously as a part of their epilepsy, and they can also be induced by certain drugs. It is apparent that the stimulation of the cortex and the discharge of neurons occurring during epileptic attacks can both teach us the functions of certain parts of the cortex of the hemispheres.

The regions of the hemispheres that give responses when stimulated are shown in Figure 20a and b. Visual hallucinations are obtained from the back of the occipital lobe and auditory hallucinations from deep in the temporal lobe. Movements are obtained from stimulating the motor strip, and bodily sensations from equivalent regions just behind the deep central fissure. The various experiences to be described later, which may all be called psychical experiences, are obtained from stimulation of the temporal lobe.

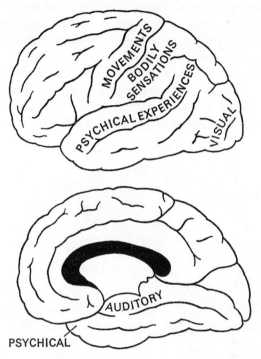

20a and *b*. Parts of the human cerebral hemispheres which produce observable phenomena when stimulated in conscious patients

Movement and Sensation

Just as one brave man flies across the Atlantic to be followed within twenty years by a regular passenger service, so the first experiments of Foerster, Cushing and Penfield are now repeated daily in many neurosurgical centres. The best way for the neurosurgeon to find out exactly what part of the cerebral hemisphere he is examining is for him to stimulate it electrically and note what movements this causes or ask the conscious patient what he feels. When a part of the motor region

235

of the hemispheres is stimulated, a part of the body is moved. The patient is astonished to find his arm or his leg moving of its own accord; for he does not have the feeling that he is doing the movement himself. Sometimes no movement occurs but the patient feels a strong desire to move. If a part of his body is already moving when the surgeon stimulates the motor area, the movement may be stopped and the patient is amazed to find he cannot move. The regions of the hemisphere from which movements can be obtained on electrical stimulation are shown in Figure 21a and b. Figure 21a shows the cerebral hemisphere seen from the left and Figure 21b from the medial side,

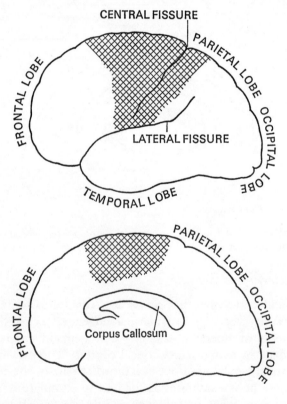

21a and b. Parts of the human brain which produce movements of the body when stimulated

which abuts against the other hemisphere. Figure 22 shows the same view of the left side of the brain as Figure 21*a*. In front of the central fissure is the motor strip. Movements of the right side of the body are most easily obtained from stimulating this part. On the figure, the points at which stimulation causes movement of the various parts of the body are marked. It will be seen that these points on the cortex are upside down: the foot is at the top and the face and mouth are at the bottom of the strip.

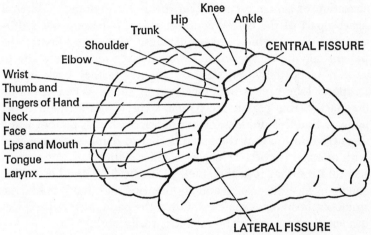

22. Human brain showing the regions of the motor strip giving rise to movements of the opposite limbs

The size of the cortical regions related to a certain part of the body is related to the importance of that part in that species. In man for instance, the cortical region related to the mouth and tongue is very large. This is because man is a great talker. Also the region related to the hands, fingers and thumb is large – again on account of the importance of these parts in man. In the pig, the largest motor region is related to the snout, which for the pig is hands, fingers and thumbs, as well as the organ of smell and a general instrument for the exploration of the environment. The horse has an equally large region for its muzzle.

237

Stimulation of the cortex also causes movements or the stopping of movements of the internal organs. The insula and surrounding regions organize the movements of the alimentary canal. When this region is stimulated, the patient may move his tongue and lips or he may keep swallowing. Violent contractions of the stomach and intestines may be induced; or the patient may feel visceral sensations without there being any change in the movements of his bowels. He may feel gas and fluid rumbling through his bowels or he may have a strange sensation of things turning over inside his abdomen. When a nearby part of the cortex is stimulated, the patient has hallucinatory tastes, which are unpleasant. With these tastes, the patient may be compelled to make chewing movements and to swallow repeatedly. Stimulation slightly farther back in the temporal lobe causes hallucinations of smell. When epileptic fits start in this region the patient experiences a smell. Most patients find this unpleasant and indescribable. A patient I saw recently told me that the smell is that of damp rocks covered with moss and lichens. He is a gardener. More than one patient has told me that it is the smell of musty hay, another said it smells like a chicken-run and another one said that it is like the smell of phosphorus matches. Often the patient cannot tell if it is a smell or a taste, or he says it is really both.

Stimulation of the primary receptive areas of the cortex gives the patient crude sensations related to each primary area. As the stimulating electrode is moved away from the primary area to the surrounding parasensory area, the patient reports a sudden change from the crude sensation to a more meaningful sensation. In the case of auditory sensation, when the primary area is stimulated, the patient hears clicks, buzzing, ringing, chiming, chirping, rumbling, knocking or rushing sounds. He does not hear words or music. Stimulation of the surrounding parasensory area gives him more elaborated auditory sensations, as well as buzzing and clicks. The difference in the sensation experienced was often shown by Penfield when he moved his stimulating electrode from the primary to the surrounding parasensory area. One patient heard a buzzing when the primary auditory area was stimulated; when the electrode was moved to the surrounding association region, the patient exclaimed, 'Someone is calling'. Stimulation of this parasensory area may make the patient hear music, and he may hum what he is hearing. More than one patient has heard an orchestra playing. As long as the electrode stimulates, the orchestra continues playing. In one of Penfield's patients, whenever that particular spot on the cortex was stimulated, the patient heard the orchestra playing a certain popular song. This music was so real to her that she was convinced that a gramophone was being turned on in the operating theatre and still believed this when she spoke about the operation several days later. A boy who was being operated upon heard his mother talking on the telephone when this region of the right temporal lobe was being stimulated. Each time the current was turned on, he heard the same conversation. He said, 'My mother is telling my brother he has got his coat on backwards. I can just hear them.'

Very near the primary auditory receptive area is the primary area for vestibular sensations. Penfield found that stimulation of this area makes the patient feel dizzy; or he may get a sinking feeling or have the feeling that everything is swinging round him.

When the electrical stimulus was moved from the primary to the secondary visual area, one Canadian patient of Penfield's said suddenly 'Oh, gee, gosh, robbers are coming at me with guns!' They were on his left and coming from behind him. Similar scenes were seen when the stimulating electrode was put in many places in front of the primary visual area. Stimulation in one place made the patient exclaim, 'Oh, gosh. There they are, my brother is there. He is aiming an air rifle at me.' He said his brother was walking towards him, and the gun was loaded. When he was asked where he was, he said he was at his house, in the yard.

Emotions

Electrical stimulation of certain parts of the temporal lobes in conscious patients makes the patient experience emotion. The emotion is in a pure form, a terrible fear, an intense feeling of loneliness, disgust, sorrow or intense depression. The emotions may be strong, stronger than when felt in real life. When this part of the brain spontaneously discharges in epilepsy, these emotions may occur as the first part of the epileptic fit, or they may follow the fit. The patient finds this emotional experience very difficult to explain; it is a sort of hallucination of emotion. Hughlings Jackson first showed that strong emotions could be an epileptic attack and also that they could precede an attack; and from a correlation of the clinical manifestations of the epilepsy and the examination of the brain after the patient's death, he showed that this form of epilepsy starts in the temporal lobe. The intense fear preceding some of these attacks Jackson described as 'a fear that comes of itself'. There may be nothing the patient is frightened of; he just has fear. One patient in whom the amygdaloid nuclei were being stimulated at operation said that it was the same feeling as we would have if we looked up and found a bus just about to run us down. Another patient who was terrified as something was going to attack her would say to the doctor standing by, 'Stop them, doctor; don't let them do it'. Such a patient is still in touch with reality enough to know she is in hospital and talking to the doctor whom she knows; yet at the same time she is quite convinced that her hallucinations are real. Within one second this patient would regain a little more normal conscious awareness and then she would tell you that her hallucinations were not real but only seemed real to her when they happened, and hardly had she got these words out than the attack would return and she would say: 'There they are again', once more under the spell of her hallucinations.

In some patients, the feeling is rather one of dread than of fear; it is vague though intense, for there is no object or event that they dread. Some patients describe a transient feeling of intense anxiety, which may mount up to panic. Some have the feeling that everything is becoming dangerous. Sometimes, though this is rare, the emotional component of the fit is a strong feeling of guilt, of being guilty of having done something dreadful, though the patient has no idea what it is.

Dostoyevsky had this feeling of guilt, the feeling that he had committed some momentous crime, associated with his fits. But far more striking was a rare aura before his fits – a feeling of ecstasy or great joy. He has described it like this.

For a few moments before the fit, I experience a feeling of happiness such as it is quite impossible to imagine in a normal state and which other people have no idea of. I feel entirely in harmony with myself and the whole world, and this feeling is so strong and so delightful that for a few seconds of such bliss, one would gladly give up ten years of one's life, if not one's whole life.

The terrible depression or despair which a few patients have during temporal lobe attacks may well have been the cause of their suicide. The patients can never say why they feel depressed. The utter misery comes on them quite suddenly, without cause or reason; and it may pass off equally quickly, so that within a few minutes it has gone. Attacks of uncontrollable rage may also occur as preludes to epileptic attacks or as the manifestation of the epilepsy itself. These are particularly common in children whose epilepsy begins in the temporal lobes. During such attacks children or adults may smash up furniture, put their fists through glass windows or attack other people.

In those patients in whom the fit starts in the part of the temporal lobe where emotion is organized, the normal experiencing of emotion may bring on a fit. This occurs commonly in childhood; and epileptic children often get much benefit from psychotherapy. Dostoyevsky, doubtless relating his own experience, wrote, 'Fright alone will bring one on'.

Professor Heath of Tulane University in New Orleans has

made some important observations on the parts of the brain that make human beings feel emotion. He has implanted electrodes in the brains of certain patients with severe and uncontrollable epilepsy or with psychotic mental disorders, and left them in permanently, just as Hess originally did in small animals. Once the electrodes have been put in, either the patient can be encouraged to stimulate his own brain or the psychiatrist can stimulate the patient's brain without the patient knowing it. Good results from these procedures have been reported from Louisiana and Norway in certain psychotic patients.

It is found that in the brain of man, as in the brain of the monkey and the rat, the septal region, connected to the hypothalamus, is a pleasure-rewarding region. When this region is stimulated in man, the patient becomes more alert, active and generally brighter in mood and reactions. In one patient suffering from psychotic depression, Heath reported:

Expressions of anguish, self condemnation, and despair changed precipitously to expressions of optimism and elaborations of pleasant experiences, past and anticipated. Patients could calculate more rapidly than before stimulation. Memory and recall were enhanced. One patient on the verge of tears described his father's near-fatal illness and condemned himself as somehow responsible, but when the septal region was stimulated, he immediately terminated this conversation and within fifteen seconds exhibited a broad grin as he discussed plans to date and seduce a girl friend. When asked why he had changed the conversation so abruptly, he replied that the plans concerning the girl suddenly came to him. This phenomenon was repeated several times in the patient; stimulation was administered to the septal region when he was describing a depressive state, and almost instantly he would become gay.

Another patient, an epileptic, was one day agitated, violent and psychotic. The septal region was then stimulated without the patient knowing it. 'Almost instantly his behavioural state changed from one of disorganization, rage and persecution to one of happiness and mild euphoria. He described the beginning of a sexual motive state.'

Immediate relief from intense physical pain and anguish has been obtained with stimulation to the septal region in patients with advanced and painful forms of cancer. Stimulation of any region of the brain that causes pleasure stops physical and emotional pain. It appears then that these regions are more powerful than those parts of the brain where pain is felt.

Many of these patients have had the electrodes left permanently in their brains so that they can stimulate the various regions when they want to. In the New Orleans group of patients, three lots of electrodes were left in, connected to three levers so that these patients could have the experience of stimulating three different structures in the brain. One of these patients would have a most pleasant feeling when he stimulated the septal region. It 'made him feel as if he were building up to a sexual orgasm. He was unable to achieve the orgastic end point, however, and explained that his frequent, sometimes frantic, pushing of the septal button was an attempt to reach a "climax" although at times this was frustrating and produced a "nervous feeling".' Another patient also found that stimulation in this region made him 'feel wonderful'; it gave him sexual thoughts. Regardless of the subject under discussion at the time, this patient 'would introduce a sexual subject, usually accompanied by a broad grin. When asked about his response, he said "I don't know why that came to mind – I just happened to think of it".' When he stimulated a certain part of his thalamus, he got the partial recall of a memory, with anger and frustration. Sometimes the patients, like the rats and monkeys, have continued to stimulate their brains until they went into convulsions. Stimulation of a neighbouring region has made patients experience fear or rage; and stimulation of another region close by causes a strange, unreal, dream-like state. When the patients experienced rage, it was unmotivated and was not directed particularly at anyone. Stimulation of parts of the hypothalamus itself has given rise to terror, anxiety, rage, and also to 'a good feeling'.

Heath considers that this is a useful form of treatment for some cases of schizophrenia. Most of such patients are devoid of emotion, and stimulation of the pleasure-inducing regions has helped some of them experience emotions more normally.

Evocation of the Past

After Fritsch and Hitzig had opened the way for investigation of the cerebral cortex by means of electrical stimulation, other research workers repeated their results. A methodical mapping out of the surface of the hemispheres was undertaken in many different animals. Finally the method was found by Foerster to be useful for treating some cases of epilepsy. When the method was used in conscious patients the various sensory experiences described earlier in this chapter occurred.

The first observations of higher neural activities, of integrated cortical activities, aroused by electrical stimulation of the brain occurred when Penfield obtained what he called 'psychical experiences' from stimulation of the temporal lobes.

Hallucinations had been produced throughout the known history of mankind by drugs, by making use of starvation and sensory deprivation. Nevertheless it came as a surprise when Penfield found that higher level experiences could be obtained by stimulation of small points of the cerebral cortex.

Penfield classifies these psychical responses in two groups: experiential hallucinations and interpretative responses. Experiential hallucinations are an evocation of the past. Penfield describes this as follows: 'The record of the stream of consciousness may be activated as though it were a strip of cinematograph film, recording the sight and sound, the movement, and the meaning which belonged to each successive period of time.' The emotion of the original scene is there when the scene is re-lived. Patients called these experiences flashbacks of dreams, explaining that they were similar to the flashbacks used in cinematographic techniques of story-telling.

As an example, the following case is described in some detail.

This girl was operated upon by Penfield when she was aged fourteen. She suffered from terrifying epileptic fits which always started off with 'what seemed to be an hallucination. It was always the same; an experience came to her from childhood.' With this experience, she was frightened and often screamed.

The original experience was as follows. She was walking through a meadow where the grass was high. It was a lovely day, and her brothers had run on ahead of her. A man came up behind her and said that he had snakes in the bag he was carrying and how would she like to get into the bag with the snakes. She was very frightened and screamed to her brothers, and they ran home, where she told her mother about the event.

After that, she occasionally had nightmares in which the scene was re-enacted. At the age of eleven, it was recognized that she had attacks by day, in which she habitually saw the scene of her fright. She saw a little girl, whom she identified as herself, in the now familiar surroundings. She experienced the scene with such distinctness that she was filled with terror lest she should be struck or smothered from behind. . . . Sometimes this 'dream' constituted all there was of her epileptic attacks.

At operation, under local anaesthesia, I applied the stimulator to the temporal cortex. 'Wait a minute' she said, 'and I will tell you'. I removed the electrode from the cortex. After a pause, she said, 'I saw someone coming toward me, as though he was going to hit me'. It was obvious also that she was suddenly frightened. . . . In a moment she called 'Don't leave me'. Thus the stimulating electrode had recalled the familiar experience that ushered in each of her habitual attacks. But stimulation at other points had recalled to her other experiences of the past, and it had also produced the emotion of fear. Our astonishment was great, for we had produced phenomena that were neither motor nor sensory, and yet the responses seemed to be psychological, not epileptic.

By this, Penfield meant that he was observing phenomena of a normal kind and not the distorted fragments of acts and sensations that most epileptic phenomena are.

During the electrical stimulation, some of these patients no

longer knew where they were and lived entirely in their hallucinations whereas others did not lose their awareness of their
present situation. Patients explained after the current had been
turned off, 'I could see the desks, and I was there'. Or 'I had
a dream'. Or 'I was listening to music from "Guys and
Dolls"'. These experiences during stimulation had all the
freshness of a new experience: they were not memories of the
past. Other patients knew they were having a brain operation
while they experienced these hallucinations. Some of the more
intelligent patients were amazed by this sort of double consciousness, realizing that it was a peculiar phenomenon.

One of the conclusions we may draw from these observations of Penfield's is this. From this region of the brain, electrical stimulation draws out a total record of some previous
experience. This is the record of what the patient experienced
and not of the actual event. It is accompanied by the feelings
and emotions he had at the time, and also any estimation he
made of the event, of its significance to him. What he thought
of the situation is stored with the experience. The record is
stored in a particular place in the temporal lobes. This product
we know must at first have consisted of parts, each localized
in other parts of the brain; these parts are such things as
emotions, sense of familiarity, of strangeness, of unfamiliarity,
of sights, of names. They are already integrated, it seems, before they are stored in the temporal lobes as a whole experience. Moreover, as Penfield has said, 'There is stored away
in the ganglionic connection of the brain [i.e. the neurons and
their connections] a permanent record of the stream of consciousness; a record that is much more complete and detailed
than the memories that any man can recall by voluntary effort.'

Misinterpretations of the Present

From stimulation of the region of the temporal lobe that gives
rise to the flashbacks from the past, Penfield also found what

he called interpretative illusions of the present situation. Jackson called them 'a dreamy state', these being words used by one of his patients, a doctor with epilepsy. The same words were sometimes used by Penfield's patients when he stimulated the temporal lobe. One of his patients reported: 'I had a dream, I had a book under my arm. I was talking to a man. The man was trying to reassure me not to worry about the book.'

Sometimes in epilepsy and during stimulation of the temporal lobes of the brain, there may be an increased awareness of reality: the patient says that for a brief period everything seems to be more intense and more significant. One of Penfield's patients got this 'new awareness' both before his fits and when Penfield stimulated his right temporal lobe; on stimulation, he became unusually conscious of the weight of his coat and of the weight of his feet upon the floor.

A commoner feeling is that of being out of touch with reality. The patient watches everything and experiences everything, including himself, from outside, from a distance. He may say that he is behind himself watching everything that is going on; and he cannot shake this strange feeling off.

More rarely there are misinterpretations of time sense: everything seems to be slowed down, even the movements of themselves and others seem as if they are carried out in slow motion and very deliberately. Penfield has found that stimulation of the temporal lobes has often caused illusions of recognition or of comparison. This also occurs with fits starting in the same region. Everything may seem strange to the patient and unreal. The patient may say that everything is unlike ordinary life; suddenly the room in which the patient is sitting seems unfamiliar. Jackson reported some epileptics who described this as 'I feel in some strange place', 'A panorama of something familiar and yet strange'.

The opposite sort of feeling also occurs in epilepsy. Everything suddenly seems familiar, the patient has the feeling that it has all happened before and that he knows exactly what is going to happen next. This state is called by its French name, 'déjà vu'. Dickens mentions it in *David Copperfield*, like this:

We have all some experience of a feeling which comes over us occasionally, of what we are saying and doing having been said or done before, in a remote time – of our having been surrounded, dim ages ago, by the same faces, objects, and circumstances – of our knowing perfectly what will be said next, as if we suddenly remembered it.

That this feeling can be a part of epilepsy had already been recognized in the last century. Hughlings Jackson first reported it and rightly associated it with lesions of the front part of the temporal lobes. The feeling that time is unrolling abnormally slowly may also accompany the déjà vu phenomenon.

During stimulation of their temporal lobes, some of Penfield's patients experienced déjà vu. One patient had the feeling that the whole operation had happened before and that she knew what the surgeon was about to do. Another patient experienced a feeling of unnecessariness, 'a strange feeling like it is unnecessary – the craziest, doggone feeling'. In two patients Penfield obtained a pure feeling of familiarity, an unattached sensation. One patient whose brain was being stimulated told him that the feeling of familiarity had already commenced before he started speaking to her, 'as though the stage or background had been set to embrace in familiarity any concomitant perception'. One patient whose temporal lobe was stimulated had the feeling of falling over, 'something which, in fact, he had not previously experienced', and yet this sensation was accompanied by the sense of familiarity. This feeling seems to be, or is similar to, an emotion, like fear, dread or depression.

The feeling that an occurrence is either strange and new or else that it is familiar would seem to be an important accompaniment of experience. For the animal has to know if what is happening is the same as what usually happens or something different. If it is different and new, the situation produces surprise and an alerting of the whole brain, followed by behaviour of cautious investigation. Perhaps the comparison with what is already familiar takes place at many levels of the central nervous system. The highest neural level is the temporal lobe.

In actual epilepsy, misinterpretation of the present may come with intense emotion. The aura of elation may be like this: the patient may feel that he is lifted from the ground, suspended above it. The emotion so fills his consciousness that he does not take in the familiar room, the people talking to him. This lack of awareness of the present situation occurs particularly with the emotional aura of fear.

These curious disturbances of awareness can be restricted to one kind of sensation. They can be mainly auditory, when the patient may say that all sounds appear to come from a long way off and be very faint; or they may be the opposite, seeming to be very near, louder and clearer than normal. If they are mainly visual, things seen may appear to be very small or very large, blurred or seen more clearly than normally. If they are mainly visuo-vestibular, everything appears out of its true alignment and tilted to one side. The visual illusions were obtained by Penfield from stimulating in or near the parasensory visual cortex. The two temporal lobes were not equally likely to give rise to the same sorts of illusion.

Automatic Behaviour

The kind of fits in which the patient lies senseless on the floor, making strong jerking movements of his limbs, is not so common. There are all sorts of fits which are not usually recognized as epileptic phenomena. One of the most disturbing of these is the kind known as automatic attacks or automatic behaviour. These were first described and studied by Jackson when in 1875 he wrote about them under the name of 'epileptic somnambulism', somnambulism being fashionable at the time. During these attacks, the patient unconsciously performs organized acts of behaviour. He is unconscious in the sense that he is not conscious of what is happening or what he is doing; and after the attack has passed he has no memory of what has happened or where he has been. During the attack the parts of the temporal lobes needed for the recording of events as they occur are not working; for this reason the patient can recall nothing. In the attack the patient goes on carrying out the routine behaviour automatically; he is not open to new suggestions; but he may be quite capable of walking down a crowded street. This automatic behaviour occurs when the epileptic discharge or electric stimulation at operation affects the amygdaloid regions of the temporal lobes.

Automatic behaviour is always to some degree abnormal behaviour. The patient may seize the telephone, examine it and then put the receiver down on his desk, or he may start tearing his clothes. He may get up, murmur something incomprehensible, walk to the window and open it. If the automatic behaviour results from stimulating the brain at operation, the patient may no longer know he is being operated on. He loses touch with the surgeon and everyone else in the operating theatre, he may try to throw off the sterile towels, get up and go off.

Sometimes, though very rarely, total acts of behaviour may be performed, carried out quite normally in all details, although the whole act is not planned and is not consciously done. For instance, a man may appear confused, look around as if searching for something, go out to the garden-shed, seize a chopper and hack his wife to pieces. The patient in an epileptic automatic attack has no memory for all the events and all that he did during his attack. When he is told about it, it is just as if he was hearing about the exploits of somebody else; it is all news to him. Those whose job it is to deal with the legal aspects of such a situation have great difficulty in fitting it into their artificial categories. It certainly is difficult to sort out actions performed during unconsciousness, which is the state of automatic behaviour, from those acts that the patient might have wanted to perform anyway. This is made more difficult when the patient is intent on deceiving. For anyone, epileptic or not, is likely to plead that he performed his criminal act during an automatic attack, and that he knows nothing about it. Furthermore, epileptics can kill people and rob banks, just as anyone else can.

Chapter 17

Sensation Acquires a Meaning

The General Problem

I have stressed already that the input to the central nervous system and sensation are not the same. Sensation consists of what we feel, see, hear, taste or smell. It occurs only after the highest levels of the central nervous system have dealt with the mass of afferent impulses they receive. At lower levels of the central nervous system, the meaning of an input is of little importance. What matters is a correct response to stimulation. At the higher levels, it is different. Meaning must be given to sensation; the product is perception. To obtain perception from sensation and sensation from the input is one of the purposes in developing the higher levels of the nervous system. The cerebral hemispheres provide us with a mental representation of the environment within which we live.

As this level of neural functioning is the most recently developed during evolution, as it is the least automatic and the most complicated, it is not surprising to find that it is the most difficult to investigate and that we know less about it and we understand it less well than the input at lower levels of the central nervous system.

However, one of the questions neurology attempts to answer is, how do we know what a thing is, how do we collect all sensory impressions together and combine them to say: 'There is a white kitten lying curled up on that sofa'; how is it that the excitation of one lot of neurons gives us the sensation of something seen, of another lot that of something heard. The straight answer to the straight question is, we do not know.

We know quite a lot about the anatomy. The various kinds of

sensory inputs go to different parts of the cerebral hemispheres. But this fact alone seems to be insufficient to account for our different kinds of sensation. It may be that the different neurons of various sensory inputs differ from each other in ways which at present we do not know, possibly in some physical or chemical ways. Differences in sensation might reside in the fact that the neurons have different connexions to other groups of neurons. It could be that the different sensations may be the result of the experience of groups of sensory neurons having been different. All neurons may start off the same, yet it may be that, by the time the animal has lived a portion of its life, every neuron has become different from every other one.

Or, perhaps, after all, there is no problem. One can equally well ask the question 'How can it be that nerve impulses cause the movements of my hand?' To someone who does not know any of the answers, this looks like a similar and almost insoluble problem. But because we do know most of the answers, and because we understand most of the physical and chemical steps involved, this question seems to be of a different order from those concerning sensation and perception, questions involving our consciousness. We now know what physical changes occur when a message spreads along a nerve fibre, and how the message is passed from one nerve fibre to the next nerve cell, until finally it reaches the myoneural junction. We know the biochemical and electrochemical reactions involved in passing nerve impulses on to the muscle fibres and how this electrical stimulation makes the contractile proteins of muscle fibres contract. This makes the fingers move. If we know all the essential steps for making movements out of the activity of certain neurons, it is probable that one day we shall know those for making sensation from the activity of other neurons. This seems likely as sensation is a step on the way to movements. An animal does not ask what a thing is, it wants to know what to do with it. Life consists of responding, and the response is a movement.

Inborn Knowledge

For he knows that God is his Saviour

From the work and the conceptions of the ethologists we begin to have some idea of how the world appears to animals other than ourselves. One of the most important and unexpected facts we have learned is that certain species of vertebrates are born with the ability to recognize and respond to some total sensory patterns they are likely to meet. They are born with knowledge of a certain shape, a certain sequence of sounds; and when this occurs in their young lives, they react to it in a way suitable for self-preservation. Many birds already know on leaving the egg the shape and movements of the predator that may be looking for them. They know the essential outline of the hawk, planing overhead. Seeing that outline, they rush off to mother and nestle beneath her wing. The herring gull knows how to behave towards a red spot on a yellow rectangle as soon as it leaves the egg, for that is how its mother's beak will appear to it. When the little duckling breaks through the shell of the egg, it already knows the quack of a mother duck. It will follow that sound; no other sound has meaning for it. If the ducklings feel themselves deserted by her and – as Lorenz so sweetly says – peep their abandonment, then even if this is her first brood she knows the meaning of this sound. Born with this knowledge, a motor pattern of behaviour is set off by this and only this sound, and she returns to her brood. The North American chameleon reacts to its first sight of another chameleon by appropriate behaviour, either retreating, threatening or fighting. It does this immediately; it does not need to learn by experience that what it sees before it is another North American chameleon, the same as itself.

If we ask the question how does a newborn duckling know the sound of its mother's voice or how does it know that she is its mother, we put the question badly. If we ask how does it know what to do when it hears its mother's voice or when it sees her moving away, we are putting the question in a somewhat better way but still in a form that cannot be easily answered. When we observe a mother duck with her first brood, we see that she responds to the alarm call of her ducklings by an innate, unlearned, complex pattern of behaviour, that of defending the young. But if one of the young whose cry produced this reaction turns out when she examines it to have the wrong markings, she will attack it and drive it off. The correct markings produce mothering and sheltering response; the wrong markings make her drive off an intruder. Certain totalities of sensation automatically cause certain forms of behaviour. Whether it seems to the reacting animal that it has a free choice, that it chooses to react in that way and in no other way, we do not know. In fact there is no choice. The duckling inevitably follows the adult duck's quack. Once it has been subjected to imprinting, it follows the moving object that it saw at the critical period.

We come nearer the mark if we think of the animal as never asking for meanings, as not formulating such a question as 'What is it?' On experiencing anything in its environment, its only questions are: 'Do I eat it, do I drink it, do I copulate with it, do I fight it or flee from it, can I bathe in it or roll in it?' For its reaction is always some sort of movement, or rarely, a freezing of all movement.

As animals appear to know what to do with things rather than to know what they are, at times an animal may be said to recognize something, while at other times it does not do so; its ability to recognize depends on its needs at the time. Moreover, at different times it recognizes the same object as two different things. For the female, the male is something with which to copulate on one occasion, on another he is something to eat. To the female spider, the male is never the objectively seen male spider it is to us. What meaning an animal possesses for another of the same species depends on how it behaves, on its carrying out the right social behaviour. This is of course the same for human beings, though in our case it has to be learned. Depending on accent, on clothes, gestures, way of standing, sitting and picking the teeth, we behave to another one of our own kind in certain ways, and we do not see the other person objectively (not that there is such a thing as considering anyone objectively, anyway).

We do not know the first thing about the neural basis of these inborn perceptions and the behaviour fixed to them. We must avoid being astounded by the total phenomenon as we see it in its finished complexity. It is pleasant to stand transfixed with awe and wonder before the phenomena of nature. It is pleasant too, and more rewarding, to find out how it all works and to arrive at an understanding of what is going on around us. And this need not diminish our first feelings of wonder. When each example is finally broken down into its essential components, we may eventually find that the basic feature triggering a certain act of behaviour is quite simple. It may be that it depends on a diagonal line casting a shadow across the retina; perhaps it will be that the quacking of the mother duck will turn out to be the only frequency range of sound to which the auditory apparatus is sensitive at that stage of development.

We must avoid separating sensory from motor, the perception from the behaviour. This may be the traditional neurological and psychological way of investigation, but it may well make problems where none exist. In the examples we have been considering, what we have been noting is that certain patterns in one member of a mutually reacting pair constitute a sign; this sign-stimulus fires off an act of behaviour in the other member. Such sign-stimuli often occur in chains, each stimulus setting off an act of behaviour, constituting the new sign-stimulus to the other reacting animal. It has been found by the ethologists that many acts of behaviour are organized in this way: this is so for mating among sticklebacks and many kinds of birds, for feeding among birds, for fighting and avoiding fighting among territorial animals. This way of organizing behaviour takes us a long way from the question how we and other animals know what something is; or rather, it takes us a long way out of the psychological laboratory where such questions were investigated in traditional psychology.

The integration of many different sensory aspects of an object in the environment is unnecessary in unlearned or instinctive behaviour. A few sensory clues are enough; the rest is irrelevant. For instance, the male wasps mentioned in Chapter 2 needed only to have the smell of the secretion of the female's abdominal glands to make them carry out copulation; and they would copulate with the cut out glands and not with the female wasp deprived of these glands. If man does not interfere with the natural course of events, this economic way of determining behaviour usually suffices. The proper clues are few that make the male attack, or the female present for copulation. In the case of the female leopard frog, it suffices to put a rubber band round her chest; she will then lay her eggs. On the other hand, the sign-stimuli may be complicated and they must be correctly presented. The male may have to perform a complicated dance, each series of movements being presented in the correct order, for the female to accept him.

Work on human beings on sign-stimuli is now being done. The advertising industry knows quite a lot about this without realizing it. They can present human figures so that they cause reactions of tenderness and a desire to give or so that they cause repulsion and avoidance. They sell little furry objects which make children and women want to cuddle them and which have no use other than that. Psychologists are now carrying out research to find out what sign-stimuli are innate in the young human and what sorts of behaviour they induce.

If we look at the whole animal kingdom, we see that every sort of sensory channel is used for signalling: emitting odours, performing dances to be looked at, making sounds, drumming on trees to cause vibration. David Lack, from his study of the behaviour of robins, has shown that it is the red breast that makes the robin attack. Whether in this case the robin is aware of other stimuli from the oncoming robin or not, one does not know. But it is clearly of no importance in the situation; it is red breast alone that determines its behaviour.

257

The final evidence supporting this interpretation of the facts is that when the male robin sees himself in a mirror, he threatens and may attack his own reflection. Other sensory clues are not so definite. When a cock-robin hears the song of another cock-robin, he seeks further stimulation from the singer. His subsequent behaviour depends on many different factors. Some of these are the actual place where the other robin is seen. Is it within, on the boundary of, or well outside the territory of the first robin? He will respond differently in accordance with the reaction of the singing robin to his own display of threatening aggression. His behaviour is also related to the time of the year, for this affects the robin's brain; and the brain controls the robin's secretion of hormones; and lastly and most important, these hormones act on the brain itself and influence its behaviour.

The fact that an animal's response to the same object differs at different times indicates that our philosophical questions about perceiving the real nature of an object are the wrong questions. It seems that to many animals an object has no continuity. At one time blades of grass are something to eat, at another time, they are the wherewithal to make a nest. It would be an anthropomorphic assumption to believe that the bird knows that it is dealing with the same object on the two occasions. It is far more likely that when it eats grass, the bird sees this as pleasant tasting green stuff to be pulled out of the ground; and when it entwines it into the fabric of its nest, it sees it as green nest-building material that has to be pulled off the ground and intertwined and lined with feathers from the breast. The grass is always there; but only at times do rodents and birds see it as a suitable material for nest-building. Thus the meaning of sensation changes. When the season changes, the grass that was always there acquires a new meaning. When spring arrives, the cock bird acquires a new meaning for the hen. The meaning of sensation changes with the hormones circulating in the bloodstream. Hormones cause needs; needs breed desires, and desires recognize objects in the environment that are there to satisfy them.

The fact that the sensory clues constituting a sign-stimulus may be few, means that mistakes can be made. Birds can be deceived, as man has always known; for catching birds by decoy was known before man could shoot them with a gun. Alexander the Great thought that his sculptor was amazing because Bucephalus, his horse, recognized a bronze statue of itself as another horse. But we now know that this is nothing. A lifesize two-dimensional true-to-life painting is enough; a horse reacts to such a painting as though it is a real horse and is clearly puzzled when he walks round to the other side of the canvas and finds nothing there. Baby monkeys in India, shown paintings of the heads of tigers, are terrified; and this, incidentally, when they have never seen a tiger in their brief lives. This is not very different in the young human child. How often we have seen little children quickly turn over the page in the picture book because they are frightened of the picture of the wolf. To the child, it is all but real, it is almost a wolf.

Sensation and Perception

In man, it is apparent that most of our perceptions are complicated. They are based on many previous experiences, on the memory of these, and on the ability to evoke these memories – all this done in a trice. They also entail the making of symbols (which will be discussed in Chapter 19). For we immediately categorize what we see, put it into a class of objects or events. Returning to our first example of the white kitten curled up on the sofa, we realize that the word 'kitten' is a concept, entailing that a kitten is a young cat, that it will grow up to become an adult cat, that a kitten is an animal, that it is fond of playing, and that it brings out mothering and petting behaviour in ourselves.

Although this chapter is called 'Sensation Acquires a Meaning', in reality we hardly ever experience such a thing as pure sensation. Almost everything we hear, smell, see or feel has meaning. Sensation demands an innocent eye, but we left the age of innocence soon after birth. We make perceptions based on sensation; that is to say, we interpret what we feel as soon as we feel it. We do not think: 'There is such or such a form of green on a white background'; we say 'There is a leaf on the path'. We hear music not sound; we see objects, not light, reflected from edges and angles.

The image each eye receives is two-dimensional. The three-dimensional picture of the world to which we are accustomed is a perception not a sensation. It is an interpretation based on hours of learning throughout babyhood and childhood. This picture of the world has become so ingrained that when we lose the sight of one eye, we still see the world in three dimensions. Only when we then have to do something needing the careful judgement of distance, such as pouring tea out of a narrow spout into a cup at arm's length, do we find that we have lost our ability to judge distance. Stereoscopic vision does not depend only on having two eyes. There are many visual clues that tell us about relative distance. When things are moving, those moving faster appear to us to be nearer than those moving more slowly. All the rules of perspective show us the relative position of objects. The smaller of two objects appears to be farther away; the more brightly coloured of two objects appears nearer. Objects seen clearly with much detail appear to be nearer than those seen less distinctly. Also at the service of stereoscopic vision are other sensory channels such as hearing, touch and kinaesthesia.

For the higher animals, among whom man has placed himself, there is much difference between sensation and perception. Sensation is partly innate; perception has to be learned. Just as we need to go through a long period of practice to acquire the skills of walking, of running downstairs, so it is with perception. Whatever neural processes occur when we learn, learning is as necessary for perception as it is for motor skills. It is the same for emotional development and for the acquisition of the skill of living with other members of a group.

Some instructive experiments on the necessity for learning

for perception have been carried out in the United States. Chimpanzees were reared in total darkness from birth. When these animals are eventually brought out into the light, they behave as if they see nothing; they take no notice of their visual environment. They have certain innate visual reflexes, such as the feedback mechanism for adjusting the best amount of light to fall on to the retina; but apart from such reflexes, these young chimpanzees behave just as if they are still in complete darkness. Similarly, chimpanzees reared in an environment of universal diffuse bright light are equally blind. Some of these baby chimpanzees had their heads enclosed in a translucent plastic orb, so that all the light reaching their eyes was general diffuse light, devoid of patterns and definite colours. When these orbs were removed, these young animals behaved just like the chimpanzees reared in complete darkness. These experiments show that the animal needs to experience the varied patterns of light and the changing patterns of moving objects in order to learn to perceive.

Moreover, in order for learning to be permanent, it must come at the right time. If a baby chimpanzee is reared in a normal environment and then put into darkness for two years, it is just like a chimpanzee reared always in complete darkness. The early rearing in a normal environment did not help.

From these and other similar experiments, it becomes clear that an animal must have the proper early environment in order to develop its innate potentialities. If the right opportunities for spontaneous learning are not presented during the first two or three years of life, then the child will be unintelligent and will remain so. Freud and his successors realized that this is so for the normal development of sexuality and emotion. It is now clear that this is so for every aspect of intelligence and mental and psychological functioning. Further, the performance tests, wrongly known as intelligence tests, were designed on the premise that native or inborn intelligence is separable from what has been acquired or learned. The two are so intertwined that it is meaningless to try to separate them.

The question of how much our perception of the world depends on learning has always been one of much interest to philosophers. Locke has recorded in his 'Essay Concerning Human Understanding' that in 1690 he was asked the following question by his friend Molyneux, whose wife had gone blind:

Suppose a man born blind, and now adult, and taught by his touch to distinguish between a cube and a sphere of the same metal. Suppose then the cube and sphere were placed on a table, and the blind man made to see: query, whether by his sight, before he touched them, could he distinguish and tell which was the globe and which the cube? . . . The acute and judicious proposer answers: not. For though he has obtained the experience of how the globe, how the cube affects his touch, yet he has not yet attained the experience that what affects his touch so or so, must affect his sight, so or so.

And Locke commented:

I agree with this thinking gentleman, whom I am proud to call my friend, in his answer to this his problem; and am of the opinion that the blind man, at first, would not be able to tell with certainty which was the globe and which the cube.

Diderot, too, was much interested in perception; but unlike most philosophers, he got out of his chair, went out of his room, and made some observations on the matter. He recorded in his letter on the blind that one blind man with whom he talked said that if he were offered the gift of sight by some miracle, he would prefer to have enormously long arms instead. This most perceptive man said: 'If curiosity were not to dominate my wishes, I would like to have long arms; for it seems to me that my hands would instruct me better what is happening on the moon than your eyes or your telescopes. It would be better for me to bring to a state of perfection the organ that I have than to give me the one I am lacking.'

In our time Molyneux's conditions have come true. The very cases imagined by him and by Locke have occurred. We can answer the philosophers' questions not only because the surgery of the eye has advanced but also because all the known cases have been collected together and studied by von Senden and published in his absorbing book *Space and Sight*.

As Diderot's wise informer foresaw, the acquisition of sight by the congenitally blind has not been an unmixed blessing. The two conditions that can be cured by operation are the removal of cataracts and the removal of a scarred cornea with replacement of someone else's cornea by corneal grafting. Those patients who were born blind or who lost sight early in childhood and who have had sight restored to them many years later, have explained how they have had to learn to interpret the strange world of sight and how difficult it has been for them to acquire a visual picture of the world.

After their operations, most of these patients have been unable to see much. They cannot distinguish between shapes which appear quite different to us. They have to train for months before they have any useful vision, and some never succeed in acquiring it; they prefer to remain in a tactile world.

Those who were blind from birth till the operation have no true conception of height or distance. To those patients who are first able to see after their operations, colours are more important than shapes, and they have less difficulty in learning colours than shapes. One would probably have believed that it would have been exactly the opposite. Pictures or photographs – which are two-dimensional representations of three-dimensional objects – are at first meaningless. For a picture, like a map or a written word, is a learned symbol. In this case, the actual size of what is represented is symbolized by something much smaller (except in the opposite cases where an object is magnified in a photograph). Children, after these operations, when shown a picture or a photograph, notice the frame rather than the actual picture, for visually it is more prominent. The content of the picture is prominent only to people who know that there is one, that the picture represents someone or something. Von Senden has reported that one little girl aged eight, on being shown a photograph, first noticed the wooden frame, which she called a box lid, and then added that there was something painted on it. Even when she was told it represented a human face, she could not discover any of the parts, such as the eyes or the nose. Another patient asked, when she was handed paintings or photographs: 'Why do they put those dark marks all over them?' Her mother then told her that the dark marks were shadows and if the shadows were not put in, 'many things would look flat'. 'Well, that's how things do look,' the patient replied.

One recent case of restoration of vision has been studied by two psychologists. The first thing their patient saw when the bandages were removed from his eyes was the face of the surgeon who performed the operation. The patient said that he saw a blur and he knew it must be a face as a voice was coming out of it. He thought that had he not known that voices came out of faces, he would not have known that it was a face. As he got used to seeing, he continued to find facial expressions difficult to interpret, though he could tell someone's mood from the sound of their voice. The things that he could recognize were things he already knew from touching and feeling. He found distances very difficult to conceive. At first when he looked down from a window about 30 to 40 feet above the ground, he thought he could easily have climbed out of the window and lowered himself to the ground while hanging on to the window sill with his hands. He was amazed when he first saw the moon and thought it was a reflection of something in the window. Reflections continued to fascinate him for a year or more after the restoration of his sight.

In these patients some objects seemed to be surprisingly large and others equally small; some objects surprised them by being too close and others by being too far away. An American blind girl explained that to a blind person 'a skyscraper is not thought of as towering into the heavens, but as indefinitely higher than a blind man can reach'. All the patients have difficulty in distinguishing two-dimensional from three-dimensional things. One of these patients could not tell a ping-pong ball from a white disk. At first, these patients cannot identify colours and they have to learn to do this. They then do not see colour as we see it. The colour does not fill out the whole extent of the coloured object. According to Macdonald Critchley,

'In the environment there looms up a medley of colour patches, with differing tonal qualities and with properties of shininess or dullness.'

These rare patients who recover from blindness are quite different from children learning to look for the first time. For the patients already have tactile and motor experience of the world. Yet, from the difficulties experienced by these patients in learning to see and acquire the same perceptions and concepts of the visual world as the other people of their culture, we get some hints of how the child learns to put meaning into sensation, to turn sensation into perception.

Those who are born blind build up a kinaesthetic-tactile image of the world, whereas people who can see acquire a visual image. For someone born blind, perspective does not exist and congenitally blind people cannot grasp what it is. Their idea of distance is very different from that of people who see. For them, objects remain the same size wherever they are, within touch or out of it; to us, objects appear smaller when they are in the distance. They have never seen an object from different angles, from above, from the side; they know the object only from feeling, smelling or tasting it. Whereas for us, the different appearances of objects seen from various angles teach us about perspective, distance and space.

Much of perception is guesswork; we perceive a few clues and we guess the rest. This is quick and it is efficient. For we live in a familiar world. We are not likely to see cones walking down the street or to hear bats communicating ultrasonically. When we have no past experience on which to base our guesses, we get a glimpse of the gulf there is between the sensation and our perception of the world. Perception is sensation plus meaning, and sensation without meaning is a spur to further investigation.

How much of our vision is innate and how much has to be learned is a subject still being discovered. Although we have innate preferences (to be mentioned later), they need to be developed and amplified.

From various clues we deduce the presence of the objects

with which we are familiar. What we actually see is something quite different from what we think we see. We do not have visual sensations, we have visual perceptions – everything we see has meaning. This is the same for the whole realm of sensation. What we think we see is based on guesswork; it is an interpretation made from various sensory clues based on our previous experience and knowledge. We do not arrive in this world seeing the things we adults see: birds, clouds, perspectives of lines and angles, shadows and the reflections of things; this all has to be learned. When we see a certain black circular object, we say we are looking at a gramophone record. And we still say this whether we are looking at it from above, from the edge or if we see it at an angle. Yet in each case we are receiving a totally different sensory impression.

We are told that St Goar hung his cloak upon a sunbeam. Be that as it may, one can easily make mistakes in one's perceptions of the visual world. One sees what appears to be a mass of flowers in the distance; when one gets near, one finds it is paper and litter. What one sees is the same; the two interpretations of the same visual material differ. And how strange that this seen material then arouses two opposite emotional reactions. When we imagine that what we have seen is a mass of flowers we are delighted, and when we know that the same visual material is litter, we feel cheated.

If a baby has normal sight for the first two years of life and then loses it, it is just the same as if he had been born blind. Later restoration of sight by operation demonstrates that this early ability to see has had no permanent effects. But if the child does not become blind till the age of four, all that it has learned to see remains and gives it a picture of the world. Such children are quite unlike those congenitally blind. There is no doubt that the difference between the two groups – those blind by the age of three and blind by the age of five – depends on structural differences in the neurons and their connexions.

Professor Robert Fantz in the United States has begun to find out what young infants prefer to look at. They prefer patterned objects to plain ones and a stylized face, black on a pink background, to a face all muddled up or to a large black patch on a pink background. This preference occurs so early that it must be innate. Infants between the ages of one and six months prefer solid spheres to flat circles.

Next time we see a baby lying on its back with its beautiful big eyes wandering apparently purposelessly around, we will remember that it is fully occupied with one of its most important tasks, learning to see.

The Anatomy of Perception

In the beginning of this chapter, I stressed that some animals are born with knowledge of some of the things they are going to meet during their early days in the world. This is so surprising that it tends to stand out in our conception of how animals come to understand the world. But in actual fact this sort of knowledge constitutes only a very small part of an animal's knowledge of the world. Further, we know very little about this subject for most species. It is certain that the kinds of animals with which we are most familiar, such as dogs, cats and monkeys, have to learn to put meaning into sensation and to acquire conceptions, just as we do.

The anatomical basis of sensation was briefly described in Chapter 15. The inflow from the world is at first selected and controlled at the level of the receptors. It is then distributed to various parts of the spinal cord and the lower levels of the brain. It finally reaches the higher levels of the brain. When this inflow reaches the forebrain we become conscious of sensation. It is probable that at the level of the thalamus in the centre of the cerebral hemisphere, we are conscious of pain and of a crude sort of tactile sensation, of pressure, of being touched. It seems probable that affect is added to sensation in the thalamus. When this part of the brain is damaged by injuries or disease, every sort of sensation acquires an unpleasant quality. Severe pain can occur spontaneously. All sensation is felt excessively. Pleasant smells such as lavender become repulsive. Even a draught causes the patient pain. It is fortunate that this lesion occurs only rarely, since disease attacks the just and the unjust indiscriminately.

Each kind of sensory input runs from its relay in the thalamus to the primary receptive area of the cortex. Here it causes a crude amorphous form of sensation. From the primary receptive area it is spread out into the surrounding secondary or parasensory area. When the primary visual cortex is stimulated electrically in conscious patients, they see flickering lights, the jumbles of colours we see when we press on our eyeballs, streaks, twinkling light, and forms, moving or still. These images are visual sensations not visual perceptions. When the parasensory areas are stimulated, sensation becomes integrated into meaningful perceptions. In the visual parasensory area, stimulation causes pictures of the real world, things seen and known; in the auditory parasensory area, stimulation causes the patient to hear sound with meaning. Recent auditory memory is organized at first in the auditory parasensory area and recent visual memory in the visual parasensory area. In the secondary association areas – association areas of the parasensory areas – deduction occurs; we not only perceive that it is a male mallard duck, we deduce it is the mallard duck we saw flirting with a female on this pond yesterday.

These association areas of the hemisphere are larger in monkeys than in lower species and they are larger still in man. In fact they are one of the regions that has become greatly developed in man. One of these areas is in front of the occipital lobe, behind and above the temporal lobe, and occupies a large part of the parietal lobe. It is thus related to the visual area behind, the auditory and vestibular areas below, and the kinaesthetic and tactile and skin areas in front. This region on the left is where the conceptual part of speech is developed and on the right is where spatial thought or spatial orientation is developed.

In addition to the thalamus the temporal lobes and the

frontal lobes contribute mood and emotion. When parts of the temporal lobes are cut out, all emotion goes; and when the frontal lobes are cut out, there is a state of utter indifference. We have learned from the operations of leucotomy, in which bands of nerve fibres between the thalamus and the frontal lobes are cut, how these connexions are needed for the person to feel involved in his own life. When this operation has been performed in patients with terribly severe pain, the pain remains but the suffering and depression is removed. How misery, anguish, loneliness and even guilt can accompany chronic pain is shown by Tolstoy in his masterpiece *The Death of Ivan Ilyich.*

A sudden pain alerts the whole central nervous system, making the animal vigilant. The various sensations have various amounts of such accompaniments. Touch and hearing are also senses having a large tendency to alert the central nervous system. If one is lying dozing out of doors, the smallest of flies has merely to walk along one's forearm and one will immediately wake and sit up; and how much more alarming it is with the fly up one's nose or in one's ear. The alerting action of this sensory input is due to connexions made with the reticular formation in the centre of the brain.

The passage of impulses from the primary receptive areas to their secondary areas, from these across the corpus callosum to the homologous secondary area of the other hemisphere, and from these to the association areas, normally takes only a matter of a few thousandths of a second. But sometimes the mechanism does not work so well. It may be that we are tired or that we have had some drug which upsets cerebral mechanisms or that the brain is damaged by some pathological or degenerative process. It can be that the time taken for all this passage of impulses is much longer and needs more effort – whatever effort is from a neural point of view. Or it can be that we cannot remember the name of a thing or of a person. We know and remember all its other sensory attributes, its smell, its appearance, its texture: just the name will not come to mind. Freud showed that in many cases the inability to remember is motivated, or that the forgotten word is connected to a repressed complex. But it is very unlikely that psychological factors underlie all these defects of memory.

Sometimes it is visual memory that will not work. Someone telephones; one recognizes the voice, it is endowed with the feeling of familiarity; the feeling tone, the emotion is there – one knows this is someone one likes, or a slightly unpleasant tone accompanies the heard voice, it is someone one does not want to talk to. But one cannot think who it is or whom to picture in one's mind's eye.

When in man the visual parasensory area is disturbed or largely destroyed, as may happen with tumours, with missile injuries in wartime, or with strokes, visual memory may be lost, while other memory is intact. The patient in hospital cannot remember what his house or his bedroom looks like, he has forgotten the furniture and the other things in his home, he may not remember anyone's face. When this lesion is made experimentally in dogs and monkeys to both hemispheres, the animal cannot retain what visual material it has just learnt; and when the lesion is made in the secondary auditory area, it cannot remember auditory learned material.

The two cerebral hemispheres of the adult are not equal in their contribution to our vision; indeed the hemispheres are probably unequal with regard to all sensory, perceptive and motor functions. Tests carried out on patients with either one or the other occipital lobe damaged have shown that certain meaningful visual patterns are discerned by the left cerebral hemisphere whereas unrecognized patterns and visual impressions not yet endowed with meaning are discerned by the right. It is almost certain that such differences are acquired by learning during childhood. Before the child learns to perceive, both hemispheres are probably equal and untaught. When the child learns to read, the left hemisphere becomes trained, leaving the homologous region of the right one naïve and free to take in unknown visual forms. There are some other differences between the more anterior parts of the occipital lobes, the region merging into the temporal lobes.

Patients with lesions of this region on the right have difficulties with short-term remembering of things seen. They cannot retain and reproduce pictures they are shown and they cannot learn things presented visually. If something seen needs understanding and interpretation, they may be unable to do it. For instance, if one shows them pictures in which there are manifest absurdities in the contents, they either do not see them or it takes a long time. They also fail on visual tests which are meaningless, such as counting dots on a piece of paper. One draws the conclusion that in the posterior part of the temporal lobe on the right side, there is a visual association area, used in the elaboration and learning of unknown visual material.

Also the auditory functions of the two temporal lobes are different. Verbal material goes mainly to the left temporal lobe and sound and music go to a similar part of the right. The ability to localize the source of a sound is probably performed more by the right temporal lobe than the left. This function is related to the appreciation of space and one's position in space. As mentioned above, this ability depends on the right hemisphere.

The sensory input from our own bodies, coming in via all sensory channels, is integrated in the parietal lobes; this product gives us what is called the body schema. This is the basis of our feeling that our bodies are us, that they are placed in such or such a way in the environment, and that the parts of our bodies make up a whole. Neurologists obtained this concept of body schema from seeing the results of sudden damage to the cortex of the parietal lobe. With the kind of damage to the brain that occurs nowadays from wars, small circumscribed areas of the cortex of the hemispheres can be ruined without there being much damage to the rest of the brain. When a part of one parietal lobe is selectively damaged in this way, the patient no longer realizes that the limbs on the opposite side of his body to the damaged lobe are his own. He pays no attention to these parts of his body; when asked to move them, he does nothing. Often when he is told to clasp his two hands together, he merely clasps one. If one then holds up the neglected hand in front of the patient's eyes, he still does not recognize it as being a part of himself, and is unable to move it. It is in fact not paralysed, for it still moves adequately in automatic movements. When there is this inability to integrate one half of one's body, the patient usually neglects and cannot conceive the same side of the bodies of others. For example, one patient with a neglect of his own left limbs, when asked to lift my left hand, always lifted my right hand and took no notice of my left. Such a patient may show little intellectual deterioration, apart from this one sort of defect. During the last war, I saw a patient with a severe injury of the right parietal lobe. When I held up his left arm in front of his eyes, he would take no notice of it; and when I asked him whose limb it was, he answered 'Oh, that! That's the arm Sister puts the penicillin injections into'. In such cases, the patient may think that the arm on the opposite side to the brain lesion is someone else in his bed, and he may give it a name. Another of these patients I saw in the war used to say that the limbs were his brother. He strongly objected to their presence in bed with him and he would try and hurl them out of bed. Once or twice I have seen such patients throw themselves out of bed by mistake in their efforts to get rid of their right arm and leg, which they thought were somebody else in the bed.

When a patient neglects and cannot integrate half of his own body, he usually neglects the whole of surrounding space on that side of his body as well. He does not notice the half of the face of the clock, he may walk into objects in this side of space or he may even walk around in a circle, turning always to the neglected side of space. He cannot localize sounds coming from the affected side and he hears them as coming from the other side. These disturbances of perception perhaps suggest that normally our conception of the space in which we live may be arrived at as an extension of our conception of our own bodies.

The opposite kind of defect is the loss of a part of the body with retention of the part of the brain where past and present inputs are integrated. This gives rise to phantom limbs. Here the brain centres remain; the peripheral part has gone. The central integration region is intact and it tells us that the whole body is still there. One might have imagined that the loss of the part would be registered in the brain and that it would no longer be felt as being present. But this is not so. The reason probably is that there is no silence, no ceasing of impulses coming in. The nerves coming from the part that has been cut off, whether it is a limb, a breast, a finger or the penis, are still there, though their peripheral parts have been removed. They can still function at their cut ends, and they may send off nerve impulses from their ends. This can easily be observed in anyone who has had a part amputated. If one finds one of the nerves in his stump, and then squeezes or bangs it, the person will feel some sort of sensation in the phantom limb. He may get pins and needles running down the leg to the toes; or he may get a burning pain in the ankle. For one has stimulated the very nerves which previously went to those parts of his limb.

One of the difficulties in understanding the activities of the brain is that the words we use are often inappropriate, coming, as they do, from everyday speech, philosophy and even religion. Usually they cover very many different activities and tend to make an impression that a complicated matter is simple. For instance, let us take the example of the cerebral organization of the perception of music. Much of the appreciation of music is carried out in the temporal lobes; here the different frequencies of the sounds go to different parts of the primary receptive area. The region of the right temporal lobe adjacent to the primary auditory area is the region essential for the appreciation of music. Analysis of the loss of this ability in patients with lesions restricted to this region shows that they cannot tell how long a note is held, they cannot tell which is the louder of two notes played successively and they have lost the ability of appreciating the timbre of a tone; they cannot reproduce or learn a pattern of tones. This is an example of the contribution of the highest levels of the brain to the basic material of sensation. Fine discrimination and the ability to make music out of musical sound is lost. It is factors such as these that are necessary to turn a crude sensation into a perception.

The ability to read and write music depends on the left temporal lobe. When there is damage to this part of the cortex the patient may lose his ability to read music entirely or he may only lose the music he learned last. Wertheim and Botez of Bucharest have taken a particular interest in the effects of strokes in musicians. They reported the case of one patient, a violinist, who could still use the treble clef after his stroke, but could no longer read or understand the C or viola clef; this was the last clef he had learned and he had used it only when he played the viola, which was not his usual instrument. This patient could read separate notes but he could not put them together and make them into a meaningful whole, such as a melody.

We can recognize the nature of sounds we are used to, even when many of the essential components are removed. The use of the telephone depends on this fact. It is unnecessary to reproduce all the frequencies of the voice for us to have clear and complete understanding. Experiments have shown that the sound of the piano is recognized if all frequencies below 55 and above 7,000 cycles a second are cut out. Some hi-fi engineers do not seem to know this. They make great efforts to reproduce the highest cycles and yet the listeners remain unaware of them.

When we hear music, probably something like the following occurs. The selected incoming mass of sound passes from the primary auditory receptive areas to its parasensory areas. It acquires musical meaning in the right parasensory area or neighbouring region. Nerve impulses are also sent to a part of the left temporal lobe, a part essential for thought, for making concepts; without this, perhaps the music would just be a mass of sound, without form and without musical meaning. Nerve impulses also go to the parts of the temporal lobes where emotions are experienced. For music which does not arouse emotion would be just a meaningless sound. It is not known for certain where the intellectual aspects of listening to music are performed; it is probably also in the temporal lobes. Different parts of the cerebral hemispheres are used by different sorts of musicians. Much of the activity of singing is organized by the right side of the brain. This is unexpected, for speech is organized by the left side of the brain. The appreciation of heard musical sounds depends on the right temporal lobe and the organization of singing movements and control of the breath depends probably on the right frontal lobe, on the part that organizes movements of the throat, tongue and lips. There have been some rare cases in which disturbances of this region or of the connexions between the right frontal and right temporal region have occurred in singers. This has prevented them from singing properly and they can hear how wrongly they sing. Oboists and horn-players need perfect control of the movements of their lips. To them this control of the lips on their mouthpieces is a part of the music. All musicians need constant, accurate, auditory feedback; as soon as they have begun to produce a sound, they must hear it, compare it with the desired sound, and modify it in accordance with this imagined and perfect sound; and this must be done not only continuously but also so quickly that the audience does not notice it. Indeed what makes a great singer or a great performer may be a good ear as much as a good voice or the ability to control the fingers, lips or tongue.

Sensation for us humans is largely a visual matter, with tactile and auditory perceptions coming second. But one must be aware that the world presents other faces to other animals and it can do so too to other human beings. Perhaps an inventor of perfumes suddenly imagines new smells, smells in his mind's nose. Perhaps cooks imagine new tastes. How inadequate words are to describe such sensations! They have been used for visual and tactile man and they are inept to describe what the perfumer and the chef need to tell us. Can it be, too, that there is vestibular thought, in which one imagines or remembers the horrible sensation of being on a boat, rocked inevitably and regularly by the sea? All such sensations contribute to our sensory picture and memories of our world; and they all make use of different parts of the cerebral cortex.

If the meaning of sensation depends on the connexions between different regions of the cortex of the cerebral hemispheres, what happens when these regions become disconnected? This occurs when tumours grow between two areas; it happens more commonly when there is a stroke, a sudden blocking of the blood supply to a region of the brain. In cases such as these, it may be that something is known and recognized when presented in one half of the visual field and unknown when it is presented to the other. If the connexions between the secondary visual areas and the speech area are destroyed, the patient will know what an object is and what a visually experienced sensation means but he will be unable to say the name of the object or to explain the situation. It is clear that he still knows what the thing is, as he uses it properly. For instance he will pick up a razor and shave with it; but he no longer has the word 'razor' available to relate to the object. When the right cerebral hemisphere has become disconnected from the left, the left can still carry out certain activities if they do not need thought, conceptualization, ideas and words. When this occurs, one can give such a patient a gardening fork, indicating that he should use it in the garden. He will then show that he knows how to do so but he will be unable to explain what he is doing or to answer a question on how to use the fork.

One part of the brain can know an object while another part does not recognize it. The left hemisphere is likely to know the object, in the sense that it can name it and put it into many different categories; the right hemisphere is likely to know it, in the sense that it knows what to do with it; but it cannot name or categorize it.

Words such as 'know' and 'understand' and 'perception' are either popular or philosophic terms; they are too vague to have the clearcut meaning needed in science. Even the word 'I' is useless. If the right cerebral hemisphere knows something and the left does not, then where does 'I' come in?

Chapter 18

Speech and Other Symbols

For he can spraggle upon waggle
at the word of command.

Social animals living in groups, unsocial animals meeting for
sexual intercourse, parents and offspring, all need to communicate with each other. In nature there are hundreds of ways
of communicating; using the voice is only one of the ways.

Man is a typical social animal; he communicates by appeal-
ing to the eyes and the ears of his fellows. He makes use of
signs and gestures; he uses his face and the rest of his body to
communicate his emotional state; and he uses his voice to
make exclamatory and other emotional sounds, to laugh, to
cry, and above all, to speak. The expression of emotion and the
language of gesture are innate; speech is learned. His speech is
wonderfully developed compared with that of all other
animals, but it is not something essentially new in evolution,
something that only he has got. But what he has evolved that
no other animals have is writing.

The time in which we live is marvellous; for we are now
reaping the harvest of a hundred years and more of the investigation of the whole universe by scientific methods. Four
of man's wishes have been achieved. He is able to have sexual
intercourse as often as he likes without producing children; he
can fly, even better, faster and farther than the birds; he can
visit other planets, or soon will be able to; and he can understand the language of the birds and some other animals and
speak with them. Konrad Lorenz first learned to communicate
effectively with birds; and in the United States, they have
advanced considerably in learning to speak with porpoises and

whales. Von Frisch has decoded the dancing language of bees and now any of us can learn where to find nectar and honey. Lorenz and his colleagues now lead birds far more effectively than St Francis ever did by preaching at them.

If two human beings have no language in common, they can tell each other of their needs by means of the language of gesture. We also use this language to add emphasis to our vocal speech. The degree to which we do this depends on the culture in which we were brought up. One can tell, even when standing behind someone talking, whether he is a Southern European or an inhibited man from Northern Europe. In the Southerner not only are the hands used for self-expression, the whole trunk is mobilized as he swells and shrinks at the different points in the discussion.

We express our feelings in our speech whether we want to or not. There is the force and the tension heard in the voice. There are the accompanying expressions on our faces, our smiles, usually natural, sometimes put on, sometimes almost but not quite smothered, there are expressions of disgust, of disdain and all the others described in novels. Then there are the forceful communications of rage, fear and hatred, there is the involuntary pallor, blushing, the beads of sweat, the retracted upper lids with the eyes seeming to start out of the head.

In this Chapter, we will first consider some of the symbols man has developed. Speech is his most important symbol, whether it is used for communication with others or for inner speech and thought. Inner speech is one of man's most valuable evolutionary acquisitions. For nearly all thought depends on inner speech; and most of the other symbols man uses depend on the symbols of speech.

Using Symbols

The higher levels of the cerebral hemispheres make a model of the world, based on some inborn modes of perception and on a great deal of learning. This mental world parallels the real world, with some distortions; it is a symbolic representation of reality. Man has the ability to make use of symbols to a degree vastly greater than any other animal. Indeed, it may be said that the ability to construct and use symbols is the main feature of general intelligence.

Symbols provide us with a kind of shorthand; and, like shorthand, they are economical of time and space. They are effective because the symbol is taken as equivalent to certain things or events of the physical world. From a first set of symbols, further symbols can be evolved. Finally, all the symbols are translated back into the things and events of the real world.

There are a great many different kinds of symbols and of ways of making use of them. One of the simplest relationships is for the symbol to be a part of the whole that it represents. Instead of the total event or the whole act of behaviour, a small part is shown, and the animal who understands the symbol assumes the whole for the part.

A symbol in which the part is taken as a token for the whole is the piece of cloth or teddy-bear that baby humans, chimpanzees or other monkeys will accept as a substitute for their parents. They take this with them when they go to sleep and will cling to it when awake, obtaining physical comfort and psychological reassurance from physical contact with this symbol. Other examples of tokens in which the part is accepted for the whole are photographs of people we love, or the hairs of Mahomet's beard, treasured in a thousand mosques.

From the point of view of communication between human beings, an important system of symbols in which the part is taken for the whole is the natural language of gesture. This is one of the ways in which most vertebrates communicate with each other. In this case, the part is usually an incomplete part of a total act of behaviour, and it signifies intention. Human gestures are usually a précis of the total act. When we point with outstretched arm and index finger, this is a part of following one's upper limb in the direction indicated. When we threaten someone, it is a part of the total movement of aggression and fighting. Much of this gesture-language is innate. Deaf-mutes who are not taught to speak, make use of an inborn natural sign-language, mainly based on gesture. This language is international and largely independent of the language of the speaker. And so deaf-mutes of different countries have little difficulty in understanding each other. This innate sign-language has been elaborated by the Red Indians of North America and by some of the original tribes of Northern Queensland. They used these sign-languages for communication among tribes which were ignorant of each other's verbal languages. Some of the evidence for the innate origin of the languages based on gesture comes from the fact that many of the signs used by the Australian aborigines, the American Indians, and deaf-mutes of all lands are the same.

This language of gesture is closely related to the intention-movement signs of many animals. When a bird makes movements preparatory to taking-off, the other birds understand that they should take wing, and do so. When a male monkey merely bares one or two of its upper teeth, the other monkeys take this initial sign of threatening behaviour for the total threat, and behave accordingly.

Whatever else human speech has eventually become, it started as a sign of a vocal nature. And thus in its origins it resembled all the noises other animals use to signal to each other.

Some words of all languages remain as the smallest parts of gestures. This is clear in the case of onomatopoeic words, such as screech, rumble, clatter, borborygmi. Instead of having to drop the saucepans and crockery on the floor, we make the smallest part of this sound in our speech; and the words 'clatter' or 'crash', a part of the sound of falling crockery, symbolize the total event. Onomatopoeic words are gestures made audible. Only a few words are onomatopoeic. Other words are another kind of symbol, having no intrinsic relation to the thing they stand for; their relation is agreed upon by convention.

If I say 'When you hear the bell, come for some food to the kitchen', all the grammar can be left out. For it really amounts to saying 'bell – food – in kitchen'. If we ring a bell whenever we give a dog some food, the animal will soon learn to associate the sound of the bell with the food. All that is needed is that the two should often be presented at the same time. If we present the food only in the kitchen, the animal also learns that when it hears the bell, food will be provided in the kitchen. We can also teach the animal to respond to the word 'food'. And so in the end we have taught the dog the entire meaning of the sentence 'When you hear the bell, come to the kitchen for food'.

Once a dog has learned to associate the symbolic sound 'rats' with the presence of this animal that he likes to hunt, then if one says this magic word to him, he understands all that the word 'rats' means to him. And it is, I think, not fanciful to believe that he also sees, smells and hears a rat in his mind's eye, nose and ear. For him too a heard sound has by convention become an auditory symbol for a whole complex, a conception, based on past experience. It is not only nouns that the dog can learn by the process of psychological association. It can learn the meaning of such verbs as hunting, walking, eating; it can learn the meaning of such adjectives as good or bad. All the more intelligent animals such as dolphins, rats, cats and dogs can master some of the basic symbols of human speech. Similarly if we take the trouble, we can learn those of the speech of other animals. We can learn the alarm calls and the threatening cries of birds, the noises made by elephants, and their interpretation.

As language is more developed in man than it is in dogs, we can learn to understand the instructions about food in the kitchen far quicker than the dog can. That is to say, we have had to have a period of learning too; but our learning was of all the symbols alone – words. Once we have learned them, we do not need to go through repetitions of the act. The dog has to learn the act, and then the important words, such as 'bell' or 'food'. We see in this example how the words in this sentence are symbols, standing for certain known things; and we see that the ability to learn and to use these symbols is not particularly human, for higher animals can learn the symbols we use in our speech.

Children who are very defective mentally may be unable to learn this essential symbolic aspect of speech; they repeat the words they hear but these sounds have no meaning for them. They cannot grasp that each sound has a symbolic relationship to some thing, quality or activity in the world.

One of man's nearest relatives, the chimpanzee, whose brain is in many respects similar to his own, shows little aptitude for developing speech, although he is very clever. But birds, who are no relations of ours, have developed it. This does not seem to be realized. We use such phrases as 'parrot learning' to mean a senseless repetition without any understanding of the meaning of the repeated sounds. But this is not necessarily so. A parrot can be taught to associate a certain word, such as 'nut', with receiving that delectable object. Whenever nut is said to it, it may repeat the word and it eventually learns to expect something good to eat; and it may well expect to receive a nut. If this is so, it has learned, just as a child learns, to know that the sound 'nut' is to be associated with the object of that name, and that when it says 'nut', it hopes to be given one. This is speech, just the kind of speech we use.

The elementary symbols of speech are the nouns and verbs. After that, there come less simple words, the symbols of these symbols. These are classes of words representing other words. Such are the general and abstract nouns and verbs.

No explanation of these words can be better than that given by Diderot two hundred years ago. He asks 'How about abstract ideas?' And he gives the answer: 'The abstract sciences arose out of the signs of language. The fact that a number of actions have some one thing in common has given rise to words like "vice" and "virtue". "Ugliness" and "beauty" came into being because several objects were found to have a common property. . . . Every abstraction is only a symbol from which all particular notions have been removed.'

Some of these symbols have been called portmanteau words. Words such as 'the law' stand for a host of facts: executions, judges dressed up in wigs made of horses' tails, barristers in shorter wigs, endless arguments, court-houses. 'Music' stands for certain regular sounds, presented in an order, the instruments which make these lovely sounds, the human voice. No matter how abstract and generalizing they may be, nouns, verbs, adjectives and adverbs are symbols of facts or actions within our universe. Prepositions and conjunctions are symbols of relationships; the relationships symbolized by prepositions are mostly of time or space; those of conjunction are logical symbols. For instance, the preposition 'in' in the phrase 'in the kitchen' is a symbol of a particular spatial relationship applying to any two objects. Conjunctions such as 'although' or 'nevertheless' express a general logical relationship. Some words are not symbols but are a part of the machinery of language; such are many of the conjunctions and articles such as 'an' and 'the'. These mere mechanisms are omitted in some languages.

Man's speech is not only a means of communication like that of all other social animals; it is really something quite new. Even if the new features are developed from elements already present in the speech of species less developed than man, and are thus a quantitative development, they are so great an advance that the quantity has become quality. Man's speech allows him to sort and to classify, to make categories, generalities and abstractions. Finally symbols of other symbols allow us to create the universal symbols of algebra, geometry and arithmetic. Such systems of symbols have their own existences and their own rules. We follow these rules and carry out operations on the symbols of symbols without having to visualize any objects represented during the process of working out. This allows us to arrive at solutions to problems which can then be translated back into the world of reality. This is a great saving in time and mental effort. Formal logic is another and similar system of symbols, underlying and providing us with symbols for reasoning. Musical notation is another system, similar to writing; indeed the clef signs were originally letters. The page of the score consists of various symbols representing the sounds the players should make. It is almost unbelievable that such beautiful music as that of Beethoven's quartets could come out of just a few dots, all looking much the same, printed on paper.

Writing enables man to make use of what has been learned. Thus man has at his disposal not only what he has learned during his own brief life, but also the whole of culture, all that his species has acquired during its progress in and out of various epochs of civilization and savagery. It is thus that each generation, though no more intelligent, can start by standing on the shoulders of the previous generation.

We take writing for granted, except when we are laboriously learning it at school. And yet, as the Lady Sei Shonagon wrote in *The Pillow-book* in Japan at the beginning of the eleventh century (translated by Arthur Waley):

Writing is an ordinary enough thing; yet how precious it is! When someone is in a far corner of the world and one is terribly anxious about him, suddenly there comes a letter, and one feels as though the person were actually in the room. It is really very amazing. And, strangely enough, to put down one's thoughts in a letter, even if one knows that it will probably never reach its destination, is an immense comfort. If writing did not exist, what terrible depressions we should suffer from!

Another symbol developed by almost all mankind is money. This is a token standing for other objects or events. It is a symbol representing status and prestige, it represents all one can obtain by means of it – the necessities of life, security, luxuries.

There are many second-order symbols of money. These are cheques, notes promising to pay actual money, tickets showing that money has been paid and that a service is still owed.

The chimpanzee, although he has not developed money on his own, is capable of understanding this symbol. Some important investigations were done in the 1930s in Professor

Yerkes's Yale laboratories of Primate Biology in Florida by Dr John B. Wolfe and Dr John T. Cowles. They showed that chimpanzees could learn to work for token rewards. These anthropoid apes learned to work for poker chips which they could collect and then hand in for food. Moreover, they learned the symbolic meaning of chips of different sizes and colours. They also learned that one sort of chip was useless as currency as no food was ever exchanged for it. It should be made clear that in these experiments the food was out of sight until it was exchanged for the poker chips. The chimpanzees acquired such confidence in their currency that they would work on problems for chips as readily as for the food directly. It is not in the nature of these animals to become capitalists; for although they soon learned that they might have to collect twenty or thirty chips to buy a certain food, they would not hoard chips. They liked to exchange them for food as soon as they were exchangeable. The chimpanzee's enthusiasm for work is related to the number of tokens he has. If he still has some, he is unwilling to work for more.

These intelligent animals, then, are able to grasp that the act of pushing a lever is a symbol, that if they engage in this activity, they will eventually be rewarded. They understand that the chips, on the face of it meaningless objects, are symbols, promising that something rewarding will come their way. Moreover, they can learn that chips of different sizes and colours have different symbolic meanings: they can learn that a white one means one grape, a blue one two grapes, whereas a brass one has no exchange value. In fact, the chimpanzees understood this coinage so well that one wonders if they would be able to cope with the monetary system of these islands.

The ability to perceive space and to relate it to one's own body depends on a region between the temporal, parietal and occipital lobes of the right hemisphere. The ability to think spatially, to visualize a building in the three planes of space and related to its surroundings, depends on the cortex of this region. Many curious abnormalities in handling symbols associated with this kind of perception occur when this region of the brain is damaged or disconnected with other parts. Patients with lesions here may not understand the significance of the position of the hands of the clock (and note that we refer to the clock in terms of parts of the body – face, hands). If one asks them to put the hands to indicate a quarter past three for instance, either they cannot do it at all or else they do it wrong. They make mistakes in drawing maps and explaining where things are on maps. Also, in this region of the right hemisphere resides the ability to form the symbols of modelling and sculpture, the three-dimensional representation of a three-dimensional object, but in this case abstracted and generalized, and often represented on a different scale from the original. The actual object has at first to be apprehended in three dimensions, then abstracted into a generalization, and then represented again in space as a particular example of the generalization.

The ability to make use of the symbols of mathematics depends on association areas of the cortex of both hemispheres. An essential region is in the left hemisphere at the junction of the temporal and parietal lobes, in front of the occipital lobe's secondary visual area. A possible explanation of the association of mathematical symbols with this region may be that these symbols began with counting; and counting was abstracted from touching or moving the digits of the hands and perhaps the feet, this being the first and essential digital system. It is doubtless related to counting things seen; and so it is near the visual area, as well as the tactile and kinaesthetic areas.

After developing the use of his own digits for counting, man evolved the abacus, which is still used effectively in the East. With this instrument, addition, subtraction, multiplication and division are done visually, by the manipulation of bobbles in rows. Our numeral system also depends on moving figures from column to column.

If a child is bad at mathematics but is good at most other school work, this is most unlikely to be due to any defect in its brain. The reasons are undoubtedly all those factors implicated by psychotherapists and psychologists; and most important and, most common of all, bad teaching.

Within the realm of mathematics, the most visual are geometry and the use of graphs. Here we see that spatial elements come into mathematical ability. This form of symbolization is related to the ability to envisage space and to locate things and ourselves in space, which depends on the right hemisphere. The region in the left hemisphere on which mathematical ability depends is between the regions for organizing speech and visual perceptions. This indicates that both verbal and visual symbolizations enter into mathematical thinking. Mathematical symbolization also needs the contribution from the auditory parasensory area, enabling us to use inner speech, when we make concepts in our minds.

We talk about mathematical ability as though it is one entity; but it is not. It is made up of the functions of many parts of the cortex; and in different people, different regions will be used.

The ability to use symbols to represent aspects and parts of reality is one of the most advanced functions of the brain. Hughlings Jackson recognized as a general principle that when the brain atrophies, the functions most recently acquired disappear first, those longest developed during evolution remaining till the last. In accordance with this principle, we find that when the whole brain degenerates, the patient first loses the ability to grasp and to make use of symbolic thinking. The way this is usually shown up is by getting the patient to explain proverbs. For instance, when he is asked for the meaning of the proverb 'A rolling stone gathers no moss', he will explain in detail to you that a stone that keeps on moving is not able to grow moss as it is moving. When the proverb 'A burnt child dreads the fire' is read to him, he will explain that of course the child is frightened of the fire because he has been burnt. Or 'A drowning man will catch at a straw' will obtain only the response that he does this in an effort to stop himself drowning. The symbolic meaning of the proverbs, which is their whole point, escapes him, and usually he cannot grasp it even when it is explained to him.

The ability to form and use symbols depends on the working of many parts of the cerebral cortex of both hemispheres. Professor Geschwind of Boston considers that man's outstanding ability to use verbal symbols depends on the connexions in his brain between all the parasensory association areas. Man is able to see a circle, to feel the circumference of a circle with his hands or feet, to draw a circle in the air with his hand or foot; on account of the connexions between the visual, tactile and kinaesthetic areas, he can abstract a common circularity from these three senses. For this common feature, one verbal symbol is made, the word 'circle'. Had there been no connexions between the secondary sensory areas, he would not have been able to recognize the one common feature. Seen circle, felt circle and circle drawn in space would have been as different to him as the smell of a violet is to the feel of a cube. Indeed, it would be more different; for on account of these interconnexions we are able to make meaningful comparisons, and from the different sensory inputs to deduce similarities and differences. I do not mean here the more obvious assimilation we make all the time when we create perceptions from all the sensory inputs, so that we know from the smell and the sight that this is a daffodil. I mean such facts as the ability to recognize a rhythm, for instance, in three different sensory modalities. We are able to recognize a rhythm of long–short–long heard as dash–dot–dash from a morse buzzer, we recognize it when it is tapped on our hands, and we recognize it again flashed in the visual field by lights.

The use of symbols is a great economy in the activity of the brain, and it saves time during thinking and remembering. Instead of nerve impulses having to make the complete circuit round the original paths, they need only make a smaller circuit. By this I mean that when we remember having a picnic last summer, we don't go through the whole experience again, taking as long as it took when it happened. The first symbol is the word 'picnic'; this separates that sort of event from every other sort of event. Then we have the symbols 'last summer'; these are two sorts of symbols, the symbols of words and the symbols of divisions of time. Again, as soon as we have thought 'last summer', we have restricted the neural activity to certain selected experiences and we do not have to recollect other experiences.

Speech and the Brain

For he is good to think on, if a man would express himself neatly.

Turning noise into the phonemes of speech needs the working together of many parts of the brain. Those babies born without cerebral hemispheres can make various sorts of noises, but they cannot learn to shape them into speech. The ability to endow these sounds with the correct symbolic meaning needs the highest levels of the cerebral hemispheres. But communication by means of the sounds of emotion, the cries of alarm and fear, the snarling of anger, can still be performed by animals in which the cerebral hemispheres have been removed. Electrical stimulation of the hypothalamus can produce them.

The turning of basic sound into speech forms a good example of how the nervous system organizes many functions. An act in its basic form can be performed by the lower levels of the central nervous system. Each higher level of the brain then makes the act more complicated, more subtle, better adapted. At all times the original and crude response can be produced, and the highest levels left out. We humans too can howl with pain, we can groan, we can shout and roar; we can bare our teeth when we threaten, just like monkeys.

The history of the neurology of speech began about 160 years ago. It has recently been unravelled by Dr Macdonald Critchley and this account is taken from his paper on the subject.

In 1836, a general practitioner living in a small town between Nîmes and Montpellier named Marc Dax read a paper to the Congrès Méridional de Montpellier. He reported that he had noticed that lesions disturbing the faculty of language were always in the left cerebral hemisphere. He noticed this first in 1800, after he had seen a cavalry officer 'with impaired memory for words after a sabre wound on the left side of the head. His second patient was the naturalist Brussonet, who had lost his memory for words. This proved to be due to a large ulcer on the surface of the left hemisphere.

Dax had now seen three such cases, a coincidence which impressed him. He subsequently collected more than forty similar cases without any exceptions coming to light, and he was able to add others from his library. From all this data he concluded that when the memory for words is impaired from brain disorder, one must look to the left hemisphere.'

This penetrating observation aroused no interest until it was rediscovered by the anatomist and founder of physical anthropology, Broca. In 1861, he published two papers proving by means of twenty-two post-mortem examinations of brains that the ability to use language depends on the left cerebral hemisphere. Before he published this evidence, Dax's son Dr Gustave Dax, had been collecting further evidence in support of his father's original ideas.

Since he had been a student, the younger Dax had been intensely interested in 'alalia' or speech loss, and applied to submit a thesis upon this subject, but he was not allowed to do so. Patiently he collected case-material and evidence from the literature. He wrote a Mémoire which he presented to his local confrères in 1858 and again in 1860, entitled: 'Observations tendant à prouver la coincidence du dérangement de la parole avec une lésion de l'hémisphère gauche du cerveau'. Later he sent it to the Académie de Médecine, where it was received in 1863. Dax *fils* was bitterly hurt by the fact that subsequent writers continued to pay no heed to his work, and failed to give the credit due to his father. ... Lélut, commenting upon the younger Dax's report to the Académie, had said that 'that mysterious organ, the brain, would be even more mysterious if its two halves were found to subserve different functions'.

But Bouillaud, a neurologist, who had already made important contributions to the anatomy of the brain, accepted the new idea, as he did not regard all the ideas of the phrenologists as nonsense.

Critchley has added to this history: 'Today the contributions of the two doctors Dax are no longer forgotten in the world of medicine. But even now the quiet little town of Sommières knows little of its two distinguished oppidans. No plaque adorns the wall of their dwelling in the Place du Bourguet, and though a number of eponymous streets are there, visitors will look in vain for a "rue des deux docteurs Dax".'

However, that is not the end of the story; for, owing to Critchley's investigations, the town has now put up a plaque to honour these two original thinkers who contributed to our knowledge of the brain.

While the early history of this contribution to neurology was being made in France, the founder of British neurology, Hughlings Jackson, was showing the national genius for compromise. He viewed the problem from two different standpoints, he explained in 1864, which he called his 'radical' element as opposed to his 'conservative'. His radical side urged him to the conclusion that the faculty of language resides on the left side of the brain. But a conservative respect for principles which he had long held stood in the way. The one side pointed to facts which he himself had observed independently and which had been confirmed by Broca. The other side of him protested that the observations were not yet numerous enough. 'Granting the duality of the brain, it is difficult to understand how disease of *one* hemisphere – be it right or left – can produce speechlessness. If one hemisphere be the duplication of the other (as the right eye is of the left) there ought to be disease on both sides in complete speechlessness.' He concluded his article: 'I wish to keep most clearly in view that a great deal may be said on both sides. My object is to be a mere witness, especially as there are very great advantages in being neutral.'

These words were the last to be said in favour of the two

cerebral hemispheres being equal and equivalent. Till that time, it had been assumed that cerebral functions, such as thinking, remembering and speaking, needed the working of both cerebral hemispheres and probably of the entire brain.

The next step forward was made when it became clear that there is a large area on the left side of the brain, mainly in the temporal lobe, that is the essential part for the understanding of speech. This region surrounds the secondary auditory area on the left, and it includes a large part of the neighbouring parietal and occipital lobes. Nearer the occipital lobes, the more visual aspects of language are organized, that is, the written and printed word, written music, and other written signs. Patients with this part of the brain damaged may be able to read but they do not understand what they are reading; they read the words but do not understand the sense of printed symbols. They can speak and they may be able to write. They may recognize the letters and they know that they should make sense; but this does not happen. The patients can understand the meaning of everything except that of written or printed symbols. This condition is due to a disconnexion between the main speech area and the visual parasensory area. The connexions between the parasensory tactile and kinaesthetic region of the parietal lobe and the speech area remain intact, and so the patients will know the letters if they are drawn on their bodies so that they feel them. The connexions between the parasensory auditory area and the speech area are also intact, and so the patients will understand the letters when they are spoken and they hear them. A patient with this condition can copy writing without knowing what it is that he is writing; he does this just as he might copy a drawing. This task involves only the visual parasensory areas and the regions for the skilled use of the hand. A patient with this lesion cannot turn print into cursive writing, into his own handwriting; to do this involves knowing the meaning of the letters and of the written words and sentences, and this needs the working of the speech area. For what we call speech includes all thinking that makes use of inner speech.

This indeed is so much of our thinking that many people have considered that all thought is verbal and that there can be no such thing as thought without words. If talking to oneself is a sign of madness, we are all mad. When a stroke ruins the speech area of the left hemisphere, internal speech is severely disrupted, thought is almost impossible and intelligence is greatly impaired.

Sometimes a small lesion in the brain can destroy the connexions within the grey matter of the left temporal lobe. This can result in the patient being able to hear words but being unable to understand them; they sound like a meaningless gabble to him. But other symbolic sounds retain their meaning. The patient can understand the postman's ring and go and get the letters; he can understand the meaning of a code of knocks on the door. Provided words are not used to explain, he can still learn a code of knocks, say, two rapid knocks, open the door; three slow knocks, go to the window and see who is there.

The cerebral organization of articulation of the words is performed in the motor region of the frontal lobe, by a region of the cortex that is just above the temporal lobe and immediately adjacent to it. In fact, the whole region for the organization of speech is in one large area. The front and upper part of this area organizes the executive parts of speaking, the actual making of the sounds, including phonation; the middle part organizes all the thinking and the understanding of the symbols of speech; the posterior part organizes the visual aspects of speech, the visual symbols, signs, letters, written words and musical notation.

When a stroke involves the speech region of people who on account of deafness from infancy use lip-reading and finger-spelling, they can no longer communicate in these ways. Dr Macdonald Critchley who studied one of these patients found that in his finger-spelling, the patient made the same sorts of mistakes as are made by normal people who have this area damaged by a stroke.

Some children have an innate difficulty in recognizing letters and in acquiring memories of visual symbols. This makes it almost impossible or very difficult for them to learn to read. This disability runs in families. Although only one child may have this disorder in such a pronounced form that he cannot read, other members of the family may stutter or may be slow in learning to talk. The children with specific reading disability have difficulty in recognizing the letters and in learning them; they often write mirror-writing, or rather, they write some letters the normal way round and others in mirror-writing. These children cannot learn to spell, and learning foreign languages is very difficult for them. As these facts are inadequately known, these children suffer much unhappiness, and they may become so discouraged at school that they give up trying to learn, and appear stupid. In fact, they are intelligent and some of them are gifted at mathematics, the ability for which resides in other parts of the brain. They can do all school work that does not rely on reading. Every now and then the question flits through one's mind – what happens to the thousands of such children coping with the 8,000 characters of Chinese script in the schools of Communist China?

If an accident destroys the speech area on the left side of the brain in a young child, the child immediately loses its ability to speak. But if the accident occurs early enough, the child learns to speak again. The critical age is about four. After that age, the damage to speech is permanent. Up to the age of four, the speech area can be organized in either hemisphere. After that age it is organized in the great majority of human beings on the left. Once this has happened, the right hemisphere seems to be of no use for the many functions culminating in speaking and thinking with verbal concepts. Aphasia, the loss of the functions making up speech, is a common result of a stroke affecting the left hemisphere. Eventually these patients recover some parts of the total abilities of speech. It is thought that they recover as some of the surrounding area of the left hemisphere recovers from the first shock. There is, however, a little evidence that in a few patients the right temporo-parietal region may contribute to speech. Some patients in whom a stroke or a tumour affects the right hemisphere make mistakes in naming things.

The ability of the brain of the young animal to provide other pathways and other regions of grey matter for functions that are needed when the original area has been destroyed is well-developed; it becomes less as the brain gets older. If the motor region of the cortex of a dog or monkey is experimentally removed, the animal eventually recovers much of its former motor skill. One wonders what part of the hemispheres have taken over the functions. By removing further regions of the grey matter, one can demonstrate that it is the surrounding area of cortex that is doing this. If the region of grey matter removed at the first operation is large, the subsequent recovery is only slight. Compensation for this damage to the brain depends on the age and the development at that time of the brain and on the amount of brain tissue that is damaged or removed.

Although there are a great many nerve fibres laid down within the brain and spinal cord, their function is not immutable. Once a block occurs between two regions of grey matter, communication between the two areas is not stopped; there are other ways round. The result of this is that when there is damage to small regions of the brain, particularly occurring early in life, there may eventually be no impairment of function. Other connexions can be made; we just have to send the trains a longer way round instead of sending them by the blocked direct lines.

One of the features of the anatomy of the central nervous system is what engineers call over-wiring and those who study the theory of communication call redundancy. There is not one route between A and B; there are many possible routes. It is on account of the efficiency of over-wiring that it is difficult to draw conclusions from lesions of parts of the brain about the function of these parts. In the central nervous system very small lesions cause no obvious disturbances, and the defects due to larger lesions are soon covered up and the patient is no longer aware of them.

This raises the question whether a need to perform a certain function can bring about physical changes in the developing nervous system or even in an already developed nervous system. It looks as if this is so though, with our present knowledge, we do not know how this happens. One finds that when children have suffered much damage to their brain at birth or within the first year of birth, speech and all abilities related to speech develop badly. This is so not only when the damage is on the left side of the brain, perhaps fairly near the future speech area, but also when it is on the right hemisphere, in parts having nothing to do with speech. One of the explanations for this poor development of speech in these children is that other functions develop before speech. Such functions are skills in co-ordinating the limbs, in co-ordinating the hands with the eyes, the ability to learn one's way about, the ability to learn about the space within which one lives. If the parts of the cerebral hemispheres where these abilities take place are destroyed, then some of these skills develop in regions that are not yet occupied and developed; and so some of these functions become organized in the left side of the brain, where speech is normally organized. If this is so, then speech, which develops late, finds its normal region fully occupied, and so it does not develop well.

A region of the brain may not be committed and occupied for two reasons; it may be that all possible connexions are there but not yet used, or it may be that the nerve fibres are there, the lines laid down, but they have not yet acquired their myelinated sheaths and so they are not conducting nerve impulses in the normal way. Up to the age of ten or so, vast areas of the cortex are not yet myelinated; and up to the age of twenty, large areas of the frontal lobes are not yet myelinated. These regions may well be like the proverbial white sheet, waiting to be written upon.

The example of the transfer of the speech area from one side of the brain to the other brings up the question how many other mental faculties could develop in other parts of the cerebral hemispheres. How much of the cerebral cortex do we actually use? Are there parts totally unused? Are there parts which, though used, could still be used to a far greater extent? We live in a town with thousands and thousands of rows of houses. We are not certain if they are occupied or not. And if they are occupied, we do not know if they are fully or only partially occupied. If they could all be filled – and we do not know how many there are – there might well be no end to what we could learn and assimilate, no end to what we might achieve.

This discussion shows us another feature of the cerebral cortex: what the brain can do depends on what we have put into it. If we have put nothing in the larder, we will find little there when we open the door. The cerebral cortex is stocked with what we have learned. If we picture it as a railway system with lines, trains, junctions and stations, it is waiting for us to put things into the carriages.

We assume that the child learns to speak in some such way as the following, though this is certainly a simplified version of what really happens. The child at some time both sees a dog and hears it barking. He then learns 'That sort of noise and that sort of sight are both dog.' Anatomical structure provides the child with connexions between the visual and the auditory parasensory areas, and these meet in the left temporal lobe. Here the first symbol is made: the sound 'dog' symbolizes the particular seen object making that kind of noise. The child may also learn to associate the smell of dogginess and the sensation of patting the dog. To make these mental connexions, there must be anatomical connexions established between visual, auditory, olfactory and tactile parasensory areas, and the motor association areas. There might be connexions to the gustatory parasensory area; but in the case of 'dog' these remain unused; the child of our culture does not think of a particular taste when he hears or pronounces the symbol 'dog'. If once a dog bit the child, then the memories of 'dog' will be steeped in emotion of a painful kind. Connexions in this case are made to the lower parts of the temporal lobes and possibly to more basic parts of the brain in the hypothalamus. Whenever that child again hears barking, the sound he has learned to associate with dog, he will re-experience a part of the painful emotion felt at the time he was bitten. This is necessary knowledge; though it may be unfortunate that the first meeting with a dog was not typical of the whole class of dogs and their behaviour. The earlier these associations are formed, the longer lasting they seem to be. And the more emotional associations there are, the more firmly they will be established.

When the child learns to read, it must learn to associate the visual symbol with the heard symbol of the actual object in the world. Then it has to relate the seen, heard, felt, and remembered object with a certain pattern of articulatory movements needed to say the word. The ability to write depends on establishing connexions between the temporal lobe region of speech and the frontal and parietal regions where movements of fingers are organized.

Learning musical notation is somewhat different. In this case the child has to have an auditory image to associate with the written note; and this auditory image includes the note sung or played on any instrument. Confirmation that this ability resides in a different region of the cortex is shown by the fact that damage to the cortex that takes away a person's ability to read letters, words and numerals may leave intact his ability to read music.

One realizes that learning to speak and later learning to read and write are no simple matters and that they both demand a well-developed brain with a great many pathways working properly. It is in no way surprising that mentally defective children may not be able to achieve these skills.

No single part of the brain does what we call 'thinking'. For really there is no such thing. The word is used for remembering or trying to recall, for imagining, for solving problems in the mind or in reality, and for many other mental activities. It is thinking that a chess-player does when he works out the possible results of moving his king. It is thinking that a dress-designer does when he imagines a new dress or when a salesman designs a plan of campaign to get the money out of peoples' pockets. Most of our thinking uses words, concepts and logic.

But there is thought without words. Much of our dreaming is without words. If a painter has a stroke which takes away his ability to use speech, he may still have his mental images of things visual, forms, colours and visual relationships and memories, and he may still be able to create paintings; his originality may be unimpaired. Similarly, sculptors can still model and carve. The parts of the cerebral hemispheres that are essential for abstract thought are in the left temporal lobe; the parts essential for painting are mainly on the left, but they are in the occipital, the parietal and the frontal lobes.

Thoughts can be auditory. A composer thinks in auditory images when he imagines a melody or a piece of music. I presume a composer does not have to say to himself, 'Now I will play that again in the minor': he just hears his theme played in the minor key in his mind's ear. Thinking may be partly auditory and partly ideational or conceptual, as when a conductor plans how he will organize the playing of a symphony. It will be partly auditory and partly kinaesthetic, partly tactile and partly motor, as it is for a bassoon player, remembering how to play a piece or composing for his instrument. For the ballet dancer, it will be mixed visual, auditory, kinaesthetic and very much motor; for the footballer, it will be mainly motor and kinaesthetic, and it will include a great element of the sense of space. All these aspects of thinking are mixed, and they come to the person's mind, mixed and higgledy-piggledy, one rapidly leading to another, and never sorted out, as they have been presented here.

Thinking about smells does not necessarily need words. If we try and remember the name of a smell, then we do use words; but we can bring an olfactory image into our minds of the smell of lavender, of the earth freshly rained upon or of toadstools, without using words. Though the question then comes up: would we be able to think of the smell of a toadstool without first thinking the word 'toadstool'. The answer, as usual, is not simple. The smell of toadstools might come spontaneously into our minds without us having to think the word; and in that case, we would think or imagine the smell without using the speech area of the brain. Or we might get a visual picture in our mind of the toadstool, and from there the smell of it; here again, we would not need the word. But the way I arrived at the smell of toadstools just now was via the word. I thought in fact of the word and of the visual images of various toadstools at the same time; I cannot really say which came first. That is typical of how we think. We make a short-hand conglomeration of words and visual images, secondarily auditory images, and thirdly and a long way after, kinaes-thetic, tactile and olfactory images. Needless to say, the exact mixture varies from person to person. Someone who can read and write is more attached to words than someone who is illiterate.

When the stimulating electrode is applied to the speech region of the hemisphere of a conscious patient, he finds that he is unable to speak. He might have been intending to say something, but he cannot do so. Or if he is talking when the brain is stimulated, he has to stop. Afterwards, the patient says that he stopped speaking as he could not find the words; he could not remember the words he wanted to say. As soon as the electrode stops stimulating, the patient knows the name of the object which a second before he could not remember.

At first sight, it seems strange that actual speech does not occur when the speech area of the hemisphere is stimulated. For if phenomena as complex as whole scenes from the patient's past can be produced in this way, why, one wonders, is speech not produced, or at least a torrent of words. One might have hoped for what Hughlings Jackson often referred to as 'that monosyllable so beloved of English swearers'. Thinking about the matter further, however, one might say that it is not really unexpected, that electrical stimulation of the speech region does not give rise to speech. For the calling up of memories from the past is the reproduction of something already laid down in the brain, something already there. But stimulating the brain never causes intellectual activities, such as logical or any other kind of thought, planning, forecasting or learning. All these activities, including speaking, are new creations every time they occur. Each time we speak, we have to think out what we are saying. This kind of high-level activity always needs the combined activity of a great many different regions of the brain.

Once the speech region has organized speech so that we know what we intend saying, then the motor patterns of the necessary phonemes and sentences with their cadences and rhythms are organized by lower levels of the brain. The motor strip, situated in front of the central fissure (see Figure 22) shapes the sounds of speech. This region when stimulated electrically causes movements of the tongue, lips and larynx. Stimulation here (or anywhere) never produces words.

It may have struck some readers that we have used the word 'association' in two different ways; with an anatomical meaning and with a psychological meaning. Nerve fibres connecting two parts of the cerebral cortex are called 'association' fibres; and we speak also of the 'association' of ideas. The reason for this is that the first investigators of the anatomy of the cerebral hemispheres introduced the word 'association fibres' for this very reason: they thought that these fibres joined or associated two areas of the cortex, and that this junction formed the basis of the psychological association of ideas and words. Now although this may be so, it was undesirable to use the same word for the two meanings; for it prejudged the whole issue of the neural basis of psychological functioning. Even though the association of ideas certainly needs association nerve fibres, the statement that two areas of cortex are joined by association fibres does not tell us anything about the mechanism of association in the psychological sense. And it may lead us to think that there is no problem here, that psychological association is explained by saying that there are association fibres between two areas of cortex. It must then be said that we really do not know what we mean when we use the psychological word 'associate' or when we say that the child learns to associate: we do not know what this means at a neural level, or what are the neural mechanisms involved.

How We Speak

For his tongue is exceedingly pure so that it has in purity what
it wants in music.

Among most mammals, the parts of the body used for talking
and singing are the lungs, the trachea or windpipe, the larynx
with the vocal cords, the mouth, tongue, teeth and lips, the
nose and the nasal sinuses. This vocal apparatus is like a
musical instrument, a wind instrument such as the bagpipes.
The lungs are the bag of air, ready to be squeezed; the windpipe is the conduit-pipe; the vocal cords are the reed; and the
rest of the apparatus is a complicated and variable resonance
box.

The differences in the sounds made by various mammals
largely depend on differences in the resonance boxes used. The
South American howler monkey has a resonance chamber developed from its hyoid bones, the two little bones beneath the
lower jaw on which part of the tongue is rooted. In this small
monkey, this chamber is larger than the brain; it is connected
to the windpipe and the animal's throat. If one takes this vocal
apparatus out of the dead monkey and blows up the windpipe,
one can make the howling noise the monkey makes.

We make the sounds of singing and speaking by breathing
in and then blowing the air out through a narrow opening
between the vocal cords. The sound is made just as it is when
a child makes a noise with a toy balloon. He blows it up and
lets the air escape rapidly through the narrow neck of the
balloon. The noise results from the vibrations imparted to the
air in the narrow neck. The neck of the balloon is the larynx
in most mammals, and in it there are the two vocal cords, which
work like the double reed of the oboe or bassoon. The slit-like
space between the two cords, like that between the two reeds, is
narrowed or widened, and the air is forced between this gap of
varying width. The edges of the vocal cords, like the reeds, are
made to vibrate by the column of air issuing out between them.

When one of the two vocal cords is paralysed, the person can still talk; the voice is then like an instrument with a single reed, like a clarinet or saxophone. In ordinary speaking, this defect cannot be heard, but it impairs the ability to shout and to cough effectively.

Speaking is subsidiary to breathing; the body's needs for air come first, and speaking has to be fitted in with these necessities. We sing and talk while we breathe out; and so we have to breathe in enough air both to oxygenate the blood and to last to the end of the sentence. The messenger in *Alice Through the Looking-Glass* 'was far too much out of breath to say a word, and could only wave his hands about, and make the most fearful faces at the poor King'. The reason was that, after running, he needed all the breathing he could do to get rid of the carbon dioxide out of his lungs and get more oxygen in; and the body considers this to be much more important than speaking to a King. A singer and a wind-instrument player have to train to keep constant both the volume and the force of air coming up the windpipe so as to keep the note constant throughout its length. In their cases the other requirements of the body have to take second place to this emission of a pure note. When they take in breath, they must do so rapidly, so as to go on with the music, and quietly too. When they record or broadcast and are near the microphone, we may hear them taking their breath in, which is inaudible at a concert.

Patients who have had their larynxes removed on account of cancer can learn oesophageal speech. They are taught to make a constriction in the oesophagus or in the lower part of the throat and the air is vibrated through this. These patients swallow air, and expel it out of their oesophagi, passing it up in the usual way into the back of the mouth and nose. They are often helped in their first attempts by drinking beer; this provides them with carbon dioxide to belch out the words. The first patient I ever met who was doing this spoke with a strong Glasgow accent; and he spoke so well that I never knew his speech mechanism was not the normal one.

The larynx produces the basic material, sound. This is then

shaped into the sounds of speech by the throat, nose, lips, teeth, tongue, palate and sinuses. The pitch or fundamental frequency of the human voice depends on the size of the resonance chambers, on the thickness of the vocal cords, on the tension on them, and on the length of the vocal cord vibrating. The note depends on the number of vibrations made by the vocal cords per second. The fundamental frequency of human voices is between 100 and 400 cycles a second; the voice of males is between 130 and 145 cycles a second and of females between 230 and 255 cycles a second; the female voice is thus seen to be about middle C. It is surprising to find that human speaking voices cover the range of twelve tones. Usually no person can make sounds of a greater range than two octaves, though some singers, such as Yma Sumac, can cover considerably more than this. The lowest note of the basses of cathedral choirs is about 66 cycles a second, and the highest notes of soprano singers are 1,056 cycles a second, about four octaves higher. Most trained sopranos can reach the third F sharp above middle C; Erna Sack in her heyday reached the C above that. However, if one includes the overtones, the male voice makes use of frequencies up to 7,500 and the female voice up to about 10,000.

The reason why male voices are deeper than female is that the vocal cords and the resonance chambers are larger. The increase in size occurs in both sexes at puberty. In boys, the lower limit of the voice drops by about an octave, and that of girls by a sixth; the girl's upper limit may rise a little. This is such a large change in the boy's voice that it takes him some time to learn to control it. If puberty never comes, the voice remains that of a boy, but the volume of sound that can be made is greater. If castration occurs after puberty, when the voice has already broken, the voice remains that of an adult male.

The loudness of the sounds we make depends mainly on the pressure of the air forced up between the vocal cords. For good sound production, long vocal cords are needed. Singers can produce some notes in two different ways, one they call the chest note and the other the head note. In fact, these notes have nothing to do with their heads or chests. The chest notes are produced by putting a fair length of the vocal cords together and the head notes by putting just the top edges of the cords together. Ordinary mortals cannot do this; singers have to train to do it. Further, good singers cover up the change in the sound when they ascend the scale and have to change from one sort of voice to the other. Monkeys and lemurs have longer vocal cords than man and they are better sound producers. But the edges of their cords are sharp, and this gives them shrill voices. It seems to be that rounded edges to the cords give a voice that is mellow and pleasing to our ears.

Singing voices considered beautiful by people of Western culture have a large proportion of frequencies at 500 cycles a second. Curiously enough, male voices considered beautiful have overtones between 2,400 and 3,200 cycles a second; this is a very high overtone and well beyond the frequencies to which our hearing is most sensitive.

As every parent knows, the baby is born with the ability to make sounds. As it starts moving its limbs it starts making similar movements with its laryngeal muscles and its mouth, producing the sounds of babbling. It starts imitating the sounds of speech without understanding them. It can do this only if it has adequate hearing. Children born totally deaf hardly ever learn to speak perfectly. Their speech is slow and often nasal; they make glottal stops, like Cockneys and Glaswegians. Their speech is inefficient, much breath being wasted. The intensity of the sounds they produce varies greatly, and they are liable to make loud noises with breathing, gasping or sighing.

Until a few years ago children with severe but incomplete deafness were often regarded as mentally defective, because they did not learn to speak properly and could not understand much of what was said to them. Such children make strange noises, for when one learns to speak, one tries to imitate what one hears; and if one hears speech wrongly, one naturally reproduces it wrongly. To speak properly one has to hear properly. Moreover one must listen to the speech of others and also to one's own speech. One hears one's own speech by two routes: via the air in the ear; and via the bone which surrounds the middle and the inner ear. One hears other peoples' speech only by the first route. The child with a great disturbance of hearing does not hear correctly by either route. If he hears the speech of others incorrectly, he will model his own speech on what he hears, and he will inevitably learn to speak incorrectly; moreover, hearing his own speech sounding like their speech, the poor child cannot grasp how his speech is wrong. He cannot understand why no one understands him and he is liable to become discouraged and give up talking. It is important to investigate hearing as soon as possible in those children who do not learn to talk or who appear to hear badly; for much can be done to help them. A child who starts its training at the age of three will always speak better than a child who starts at six.

What the partially deaf child hears when we talk to him varies with the kind of deafness he has. This affects the speech the child can make. In order to hear consonants, one must hear up to at least 2,000 cycles a second and to hear them properly one should hear up to 6,000 cycles a second. Those who have studied partially deaf children consider that if the child cannot hear frequencies above 1,600 cycles a second, the accuracy of hearing speech is reduced by 40 per cent. When deafness is incomplete, it is usually the higher frequencies that are not heard, though occasionally it may be the lower or the middle frequencies.

The young child usually learns to make the correct sounds through the adults around reinforcing the right sounds and discouraging the wrong ones. Thus the child under the influence of the usual system of rewards and punishments practises correct sounds and avoids all other possible sounds. The child does not learn to speak only by listening to the sounds made by adults. It also looks at lip movements, just as stone-deaf people are taught to do. Children learn to speak before they use consciousness in learning skilled movements. They do not learn as a ballet-dancer learns to dance; they imitate naturally, and do not know what they are doing with their muscles, lips and larynxes. Indeed, how the child knows what to do with this apparatus so as to correct its first attempt at making a sound is very difficult to understand. The child as it learns to speak has not only to learn to pronounce individual syllables and words; it has to learn the rhythm and cadence of the language, the shape of the sentence; it has to learn to co-ordinate its breathing with these requirements of language; and above all it has to learn the language, the meaning of the words, phrases and idioms.

I think that one of the reasons why foreign languages cannot be learnt perfectly after the age of eight or so is that differences in the sounds are not heard; it may not be a matter of not knowing how to make the sound. Certainly most Japanese do not hear the difference between 'r' and 'l'; Harrow and Hallo sound the same to them.

The movements needed for speaking require a long educa-tion, rather longer than that needed for writing. As making the sounds of speech depends on muscles, speaking is managed in the same way as all other movements. States of psychological tension and emotion affect the voice; and we are very quick to catch this communication of the other person's emotional state. Thus nervousness can ruin good singing. The ability to remain relaxed in front of an audience is therefore one of the necessary accomplishments of singers and actors; for if they become tense, all the muscles used in singing and speaking will become tense. This will spoil the beauty of the voice and will be communicated to the audience.

Saints and other psychotics who hear voices or hear people talking about them, are actually saying the words they hear but enunciating them without forcing any air through the vocal cords. Microphones placed over the larynxes of such patients detect the words enunciated though they detect no sound. These otherwise inaudible sounds have been recorded on tape, amplified, and then played back to the patient. The patients then recognize them as the voices they hear.

In Lyons, some of these psychotic patients have been operated upon, the facial, lingual and laryngeal kinaesthetic sensory regions of the cortex being removed bilaterally. After the operation, the hallucinations have ceased and the patients no longer hear the voice of the deity or his saints.

Chapter 19

Learning

For he is docile and can learn certain things.

Learning, Retaining and Reproducing

Learning is the process by which experience changes behaviour. We use the word 'learning', only when the change in behaviour is long-lasting or permanent.

In everyday speech, we speak of learning and remembering when these activities are performed with the aid of consciousness, and we use the terms only when we are considering psychological activities. In neurology, the words are not usually limited in this way. For it is also learning when a worm learns as it slides along a specially constructed Y-tube to avoid the limb of the Y that gives it an electric shock; and no one knows if a worm thinks or not or if it is conscious in the same way as we are. It is also learning if the reflex withdrawal of the hind-limb gradually becomes less and less when the same stimulus is frequently applied. It is learning when any neural activity, innate or acquired, becomes changed by experience. And so we use the term 'learning' to mean any lasting change in behaviour that is not the result of fatigue or disease. This way of using the word anchors it in the physiology and anatomy of the nervous system, where it belongs.

That all behaviour springs from the activity of the nervous system and from the body within which it dwells was taken for granted by nineteenth-century anatomists, physiologists and most psychologists. It was accepted by most intellectuals in Russia for sixty years before the 1917 revolution. But in Western Europe and North America, the general intellectual climate has been anti-intellectual and obscurantist. And psychology and neurology have been under the influence of the fashions of the time.

When one and the same word is used by different groups of workers, misunderstandings and errors will occur if the activities meant by this word are not the same. The word 'learning' usually implies some permanent or long-lasting change brought about by experience. But this kind of definition is too wide; for it would include the behaviour of man-made machines, such as tape-recorders, automatic lifts and the matrices of gramophone records. Learning belongs to biology and to living organisms; in the definition there should be the idea of the ability to profit by experience. This relates the term to the essential conditions of life, to the adaptation of the learning organism to its environment. When an animal has learned something it is better able to keep alive.

Learning is a biological mechanism and it is most developed in the higher animals. But animals with little learning ability also do very well. It is probable that the behaviour of most insects, including that of ants and termites, is almost entirely determined by inherited instincts; yet they have been in the world millions of years longer than mammals and they are far more populous.

Before considering some of the neural aspects of learning, we must remember that much behaviour does not depend on learning; it is inborn. As we ascend the scale of vertebrates, the proportion of what has to be learned to what is innate becomes greater. Conversely, among the animals lowest in the scale, learning is unimportant. Just how important it is among vertebrates we have only begun to find out during the last twenty years.

Further, we now realize that behaviour is not innate *or* learned; it is innate *and* learned. And, what is innate is not necessarily there when the animal is born. Its seeds are present within the central nervous system, and it will come to fruition at some time when the development of the central nervous system and the rest of the body has reached the appropriate state. It needs also the right circumstances in the environment to bring it out; otherwise it will remain a potential but unused form of behaviour.

Whatever the neural process of learning is, it is an active process. It seems that mere repetition can reinforce what has been learned but something active has to take place on the first occasions when something is being learned. We have to make efforts to learn, we have to concentrate. This is so whether we are learning a poem by heart, learning to ride a bicycle or learning Greek.

Hypotheses to Account for the Neural Basis of Learning

We do not know what happens in the nervous system when learning occurs. Neurologists, biochemists and psychologists have put forward various hypotheses, none of which can be adequately tested at present. These hypotheses fall into two groups: those envisaging changes occurring between neurons, changes in their connexions; and those envisaging structural changes occurring within the neurons themselves.

Most neurologists favour hypotheses that assume that learning means establishing connexions. We know very few facts about this, but we assume that when something is learned, new routes between neurons have become easily available; or it may be that routes already present are made more passable. Learning may be a matter of directing nerve impulses along one pathway rather than another, of developing one pathway and not others.

It is thought that frequent use allows impulses to pass more easily and so they follow a well-used path rather than other routes. Eccles concluded from some of his work on this problem: 'Activation of synapses increases their efficacy; . . . some regression of synaptic function occurs with disuse.' How this mechanism might work is that use makes the cell-body and the dendrites enlarge, and a larger neuron would provide a larger surface for connexions with other neurons. With disuse, it is suggested, the neuron might shrink and would then provide a smaller surface for connexions.

It seems to be a general principle of neural organization that if connexions are not used they cease to work. We know certain definite instances of this. For example, experiments have been done in which one eye of a kitten is kept closed by the lids being sewn together when it is born. When the stitches are removed three months later, the kitten is virtually blind in that eye. The brains of these kittens in which the eye had been kept closed have been examined. The neural structures connected to the covered eye were found to be abnormal: the neurons were small and their dendrites and the spines on them were smaller than in the normal kitten. Structures laid down before birth had deteriorated. If new-born rats are allowed to live in the light for four weeks and then put in the dark for the next four weeks, changes are found in the synapses between the optic nerve fibres and certain neurons of the midbrain where a relay on the visual pathway occurs. With electron microscopical methods of investigation, research workers are now finding changes in the synapses when the young animals have been kept in the dark for periods well under four weeks. Young animals reared in the dark for only a few days have smaller ganglion cells in the retina and there are fewer vesicles in the nerve-endings within the neurons of the retina. Thus we find that the experience of living affects not only the neurons of the visual pathway but also the receptor organ itself, the retina.

This experiment with the kittens sometimes happens naturally with children. A young child develops what is called a lazy eye. As far as we can tell, at first there is nothing wrong with the eye or its connexions; but for some unknown reason the child uses only one eye. Eventually this lazy eye becomes almost useless; by the time the child is grown up, all that he can see with this eye is whether it is light or dark. But if one covers up the eye the child prefers to use so that he is forced to use the lazy eye, this eye will develop normally and the child ends up with two normal eyes, like everyone else.

The next two questions, neither of which we can yet answer, are how are the routes opened up, and what is the nature of these routes – what sort of connexions are made between neurons which are lasting or permanent.

We have some evidence that use and disuse affect the connexions between neurons, and that the number of vesicles in the nerve-endings at synapses diminishes when no nerve impulses pass. There is some evidence obtained from rearing animals in the dark and taking them out into the light that dendrites grow when they are used. If the dendrites are larger, they provide more room for connexions. Some investigators find that the spines on the dendrites increase with use; this would enlarge the area for synaptic connexions still more. If all of this is confirmed, then we can see how use could provide vast numbers of inter-connexions and disuse would cut them down.

On the other hand, we must remember that the brain is an organ which is degenerating and becoming atrophied from about the age of forty onwards. As we are learning more and more the longer we live, our brains should be getting more complicated, with larger dendrites with more spines upon them. This is not so; the opposite is true. With advancing age, the brain does not develop further; it atrophies. Exactly when the atrophy becomes really advanced is difficult to establish. At the hospital where I work, we used to notice that when we asked this question of our friend Dr J. G. Greenfield, a world authority in neuropathology, the age at which this occurs would go up year by year, as he himself became older.

It has been suggested too that protein is passed out of nerve-endings, and that the protein of one neuron unites with the membrane of the other neurons with which it is connected. The neurons connected in this way would form a harmonious unit, impulses tending to pass this way rather than between other neurons. It has been suggested that this hypothetical passage of protein of one neuron to another could constitute a mechanism by which the experience of one cell could be passed on to affect another. For, as we shall see later in this chapter, masses of neurons remote from those first affected by the experience can acquire the same change, though in a weaker form.

Connexions that are made when an animal learns should be thought of too in terms of large bands of nerve fibres as well as in terms of synapses. One supposes that when something is learned by the cerebral hemispheres, connexions are made between two parts of the brain. When a blind person learns Braille, we presume that connexions are made between the secondary tactile area for the index finger and the speech area. When he feels a certain configuration of dots, they then automatically bring first the letter, and later the word, to his consciousness.

Much learning of this type also demands connexions between the cortex and structures deeper in the cerebral hemispheres, such as the thalamus and the large motor centres in the middle of the hemispheres between cortex and hypothalamus. Many of these connexions could not be made in babyhood or even during early childhood. For when mammals are born, many of the nerve fibres within the brain are rudimentary and cannot yet carry nerve impulses. The nerve fibres that will become myelinated may not have a myelin sheath at birth or even for years after birth. If learning depends on these fibres making connexions between two regions of the brain, it cannot occur till these fibres have completed their development and are ready to conduct impulses. One reason why certain things can be learned only at certain times is that the neural structures needed for this learning may not yet be adequately matured. For instance, if puppies two weeks old are put on a table, they crawl around and keep falling off and hurt themselves. At this age, they cannot profit from this experience and learn. The reason for this is that the parts of the brain needed for acquiring knowledge about edges and ledges is not yet developed, nor is the part of the brain that corrects tendencies to fall when the feet are not placed firmly on a surface. But at this age, when they are placed on their backs, they can turn round and right themselves, for these reflexes are active already at this time.

The first step in learning is the sensory input. There must be stimulation from the environment; something has to be experienced, to be seen, smelt or felt. For learning to take place, this stimulation needs to come at the right time. We now know from much experimental work on young animals deprived of their normal psychological environments and the usual stimuli that once the right time for acquiring a skill or a certain behaviour has passed, this skill or behaviour can never be properly learned.

The invention of the technique of sensory deprivation has made it clear to us how important the usual environmental stimulation is for normal development. In this technique, from the time of weaning or earlier, various aspects of the usual environment are removed and the young animal is brought up bereft of them. Such animals never become normal. The sensory deprivation occurring in infancy and during their early months ruins their ability to learn anything and they never adapt to many of the features of their environment. Puppies reared in isolation from puppyhood to maturity are always unable to respond intelligently even to dangerous features of their surroundings. What is very surprising is that they do not respond adequately to painful stimulation and they cannot localize painful stimuli accurately on their bodies. Such puppies would put their noses into flames and never learned not to do this. They seemed to be indifferent to being pricked with a needle and they often damaged themselves by bumping into things or falling off heights. When they did fall or even if someone accidentally trod on one of their paws or on their tails, they never yelped; they did not seem to feel the pain. And when they were obviously hurt, they did not learn to avoid the painful stimulus.

It is obvious that if the needed stimulation comes before the nervous system is sufficiently developed to receive it, it can have no effect. But also if the stimulation comes too late, learning cannot take place. The critical period for learning is particularly short in the case of imprinting in young birds and mammals. It may be as short as hours, according to some

315

investigators, or days, according to others. In birds, this period starts a few hours after hatching and it never lasts for more than ten days.

Normal social and emotional development probably also needs the correct stimulation at the right time. We can observe evidence of this in those fortunately rare cases of children who have been completely neglected from birth. Sometimes illegitimate children in the country are put away in haylofts or barns to conceal their existence from the neighbours. They are taught nothing, not even to be house-trained or to speak. These children then grow up mentally defective. Even if they are found and rescued by the age of four or five, it is too late; though they can be taught a lot, their speech is always inadequate and their brains never reach the standards of their siblings. To a lesser degree, the same thing sometimes happens in orphanages. Rows of beds of illegitimate children fill these institutions. The children never have the love normally given by parents and they get nothing more than rudimentary care of the body. They usually grow up unintelligent or even mentally defective, and they are equally defective in social and emotional development.

That we speak our own language perfectly and the languages we learn later imperfectly also depends on learning this skill at the right time. The nervous system develops in such a way that it is ready to learn to speak between a short time after birth and the age of four or five. Languages learned a few years later are not spoken perfectly. The ability to speak a language is a mixed motor and sensory skill, as in fact, all skills are. It is necessary to hear all the sounds, the subtle differences between similar but not identical sounds, the rhythm and lilt of the language, where the voice goes up or down, where the accent on a word falls. One has also to work tongue, throat and lips, to control breathing, so that the right amount of force in expelling the air is used, the amount of air taken in must be controlled so that it takes one along to the end of the sentence. And all this has to be managed at one and the same time. From some time after birth until the age of six or seven, normal children can learn all this perfectly; and without much difficulty they can learn two or even three languages at the same time, without muddling them up. But later, most of us cannot acquire this skill. We may learn to write and read the new language perfectly; but to acquire the right inflexion and the accent and the ability to speak so that no one can detect that the language is not our mother-tongue hardly ever occurs.

But those of us who still want to learn foreign languages after these early milestones have been passed need not worry; for though we may not learn to speak a new language like the natives, we know from thousands of examples that we can go on learning languages beyond the age of eighty. There are so many activities adding up to the simple word 'learning' that although some of the processes become less efficient with ageing of the brain, our actual experience of learning helps us in learning new material.

The critical period during which a language can be learned perfectly is a few years in humans; in most birds, it is a few weeks or months. Thorpe of Cambridge University has found, for instance, that the chaffinch has to learn most of its song, and that this learning has to occur during the early weeks of the bird's life and also during the first spring. If the bird is hand-reared and isolated from other birds from the time of hatching, it sings only very simple songs and it never learns the song of its species correctly. Its song will be elaborated if it hears another chaffinch singing, even though the other chaffinch has also been hand-reared and isolated and has never heard another bird sing. The singing of these birds is so dependent on learning that chaffinches from different parts of the country sing differently. Just like the human inhabitants of these islands, they have regional accents; though the birds do not base their pecking-order on them.

An essential part of learning is the observation of the results of behaviour; or rather, this is so for the higher forms of learning. The animal needs to know the answer to the question whether the new thing or new event is good or bad. It can then learn to avoid or cultivate it.

If necessary connexions are destroyed, learning cannot occur. When monkeys have had their temporal lobes removed in experimental operations, they can no longer learn what objects are. They can see them alright, but they cannot recognize their meaning. They keep picking up everything, smell it and examine it by mouth to see if it is edible and then put it down. A minute later they may pick up the same object without any signs of recognizing it, treating it as though it is something strange and new. They cannot retain anything they may have learned about the object. When certain tracts of nerve fibres are divided in the frontal lobes of dogs or rats, these animals are unable to learn essential social relationships. They treat their fellows as objects, walking on them and taking food even from animals larger and stronger than themselves. Although they get bitten repeatedly, they are unable to learn from this punishment and keep on doing it.

Learning is made far more effective if strong emotion accompanies it. Indeed it seems to be that the stronger the emotion, the more firmly fixed the knowledge will be. A child or a chimpanzee will have learned after receiving one prick from a needle on a syringe to fear the needle. When something is learned with strong emotion, it is likely to be retained for years. Unless it is repressed, it can be recalled easily, it remains familiar, and we have no doubt that it is ourselves to whom it happened.

Something happening only once may be fixed in the memory for ever. Professor Yerkes has recorded that once one of their chimpanzees escaped from its cage and wandered around the colony, making a nuisance of itself, refusing to go back. One of Yerkes's assistants got a revolver intending to fire a bullet near the animal's legs and frighten it back into its cage. The chimpanzee who had been born and bred in the colony had never seen a revolver before. Unfortunately when the man fired, he hit the animal by mistake in its leg. The terrified chimpanzee immediately rushed back to its cage and stayed there. From that moment the chimpanzee was terrified of the revolver. The staff of the colony could always make the chimpanzee do as they wanted merely by showing it the muzzle of the revolver. As Yerkes points out, the chimpanzee saw the revolver only once and very briefly. Yet the traumatic experience of being shot in the leg fixed the memory of the object for ever.

Rats in laboratories will also learn and retain for months an experience that has occurred only once, if it is painful and unpleasant. It has been shown that if a rat put in a hammock in a cage, the floor of which is electrified, gets a shock every time its foot touches the floor, this rat will learn after only one shock never to touch the floor of the cage again. In other experiments, it was shown that when rats learn something to the accompaniment of fear, this will be remembered even after both cerebral hemispheres have been removed. The cortex is needed for learning; but once the task has been learned in association with fear, the knowledge is passed on to deeper levels of the brain. This passing on of acquired knowledge from one set of neurons to another is a feature of neural organization.

Undoubtedly the same thing happens with the young human. An experience fixed with emotion is firmly fixed and it may remain for life. It can influence the child's behaviour always, forming the basis of certain aspects of its character. Such emotions are terror, disappointment, great interest, happiness at being rewarded or appreciated.

One of the main theories of Adler's school of psychology is the importance of early childhood memories in the formation of character. Adler considered that the person's first memory is a clue to that person's whole personality. Whatever the person remembers longest has been fixed with a great deal of emotion and remains a fundamental influence in his character. Looked at from the outside, such an experience may not seem very interesting or important. But seen with the eyes of the small child, it may have a deep and important meaning.

Emotions such as love, the arousal of interest and enthusiasm are effective in helping children and adults learn; though few professional teachers are capable apparently of making use of these adjuvants to remembering. The one method they make most use of is boredom; this deters remembering and learning. But rote memory is helped by frequent repetition even though this is inevitably accompanied by boredom.

Physical or psychological pain is effective in fixing things in the memory. For thousands of years teachers and parents have made ample use of physical pain; now that many people disapprove of whipping children, only psychological pain is used.

A great deal of learning is naturally rewarded by pleasure or pain. When a young animal learns a skill or the parts of a skill, it experiences pleasure: this reinforces what it has learned and makes it want to do it again. But if the animal makes a wrong response, it is not rewarded or it may even be hurt. The pleasure could be that accompanying satiety from eating or drinking enough, or it could be the feeling of contentment from being in a correctly adjusted environment, correct in terms of humidity, temperature, flow of air and other physical factors. The punishment could be the mounting hunger felt with the failure to find food or the mounting frustration and discomfort from failing to find a partner for sexual activity. Whether these rewards indicate that connexions are made with the pleasure and aversive centres of Olds, we do not yet know.

In the simplest forms of animals, the reward or punishment must follow the activity quickly for the animal to learn by experience. For such animals do not have memories long enough for them to connect what they have just done with success or failure, with pleasure or pain, if there is much delay between the act and its reward. Learning probably always involves what the psychologists call temporal contiguity.

Many simple forms of learning and the kind of learning that take place at lower levels of the central nervous system do not need emotional accompaniments. Imprinting, for instance, occurs automatically without such rewards. Learning occurs with habit, with a routine of behaviour frequently followed. This occurs with a minimum of emotion.

As learning causes changes in our brains and as we are

learning all the time, we see that every brain must be different from every other one, apart from the fact that each one starts off with a different inherited constitution. Every brain is different according to what its possessor has put into it. One person has learned a new language, another has learned the feel of the patina on the violin. These differences in the brain cannot yet be detected by the histological and biochemical methods of investigation now available.

There is a group of quite different hypotheses proposed to account for learning. These propose that nerve impulses cause some long-lasting or permanent chemical change in the nucleus of a neuron. It is thought that the arriving nerve impulses cause electrochemical changes in the post-synaptic neuron, and that these cause changes in the ribonucleic acid of the chromosomes. Once this molecule has been given a new shape, that shape remains. This changed ribonucleic acid alters the protein molecules of the entire neuron. If the neuron is changed in this way by the arrival of nerve impulses, the change is permanent. It is suggested that this is how experience can affect neurons permanently.

These views were worked out by Professor Hydén of Göteborg. He has perfected a marvellous technique of micro-dissection for dissecting out cells and parts of cells smaller than a grain of dust; and he has also worked out ways of weighing this material and estimating its various chemical constituents. He has shown that when certain neurons are often stimulated, more ribonucleic acid is made in their nuclei and more protein is formed within the cell-bodies. In a typical experiment he took rats and divided them into two groups. The rats of one group were kept in the dark, each rat being alone. The other rats remained together so that they lived and played together, and they were also taught to carry out some tasks requiring visual or auditory discrimination. Examination of their brains after death showed that those with minimal sensory stimulation had little ribonucleic acid and protein in the neurons of their brains whereas those which had used their brains had far more of these substances. In another series of experiments, he trained rats to climb and do tight-rope walking upon a wire to get food. These rats had an increased content of ribonucleic acid in the vestibular nuclei, those concerned with balance. In some other experiments, Hydén and his colleagues showed that disuse leads to a diminution in the quantity of ribonucleic acid within the nuclei of the neurons. From these experiments we may conclude that use of neurons means that they make more protein and with disuse, they make less; we may not conclude that this protein is different from the previous protein and that experience has had any effect on the protein of the cells, of the ribonucleic acid of the nuclei or on any constituents of the system.

If neurons that are much used build up more protein than unused neurons, then one might expect a total brain of neurons to contain more protein if it is used than one that is not used much. Experiments done at the University of California in Berkeley have shown that rats that learned a lot develop heavier brains than rats left in ignorance. One group of baby rats was left alone and another group was put in a stimulating environment. When the two groups of rats were killed after eighty days, it was found that those from the stimulating environment had brains 4·6 per cent heavier than those from the dull environment.

Not only environmental and psychological factors must be supplied for normal development, but also the right diet is essential; and the ingredients must come at the correct times. There are certain crucial periods in the development of the brain, some occurring before and some after birth, when certain ingredients in the diet and certain hormones present in the bloodstream are essential; if this stage is passed without them, the brain will never be normal.

It is interesting to see that experiments have proved that two quite different sorts of things are necessary for the developing brain: food taken in by mouth, which we call a chemical factor, and excitation and stimulation to the whole animal, which we call a psychological factor. In reality, both are physical factors.

Making Two Brains into One

Weber, who early in the nineteenth century was the first scientific investigator of sensation and perception, observed that children taught to write with one hand could then produce mirror-writing with the other hand, without any further practice. Psychologists later found that this transfer of training occurs for a great many kinds of learning. In all of them, the untrained side of the brain learns more quickly than it would have done had there been no training at all, though it performs less well than the trained side. In the last decade this kind of learning has been investigated in detail by two research workers in the United States, R. S. Myers and R. W. Sperry.

We assume that when something has been learned, a change takes place in the brain. In the case of learning to write, the changes, whatever they are, occur mainly in the left cerebral hemisphere. Without any further training or reinforcement, these unknown physical changes are transferred to the right hemisphere. When the changes are long-lasting, we speak of memory. Realizing that something physical is conducted from one hemisphere to the other, we can look for the anatomical pathways along which these changes could pass.

The main bridge between the hemispheres is the corpus callosum; this bridge or commissure is shown in Plate 11. In this photograph of a human brain, the middle parts of both hemispheres have been cut away to show the corpus callosum. At both ends it curves round and continues downwards for a short distance, out of sight. On the right side, a part of the frontal lobe has been pulled away so as to show the thickness of the grey matter covering the white matter.

The corpus callosum is by far the biggest of all the commissures joining the two halves of the brain. It is the most recent one, having evolved in company with the two cerebral hemispheres, which it links together. The first parts of the hemispheres to evolve were linked by a small structure called the anterior commissure, shown in Figure 26, and the hippocampal commissure, linking the two hippocampi.

Some functions of the corpus callosum can now be explained with the help of Figure 23. It will be seen in this figure that each half of the retina receives light from the part of the world

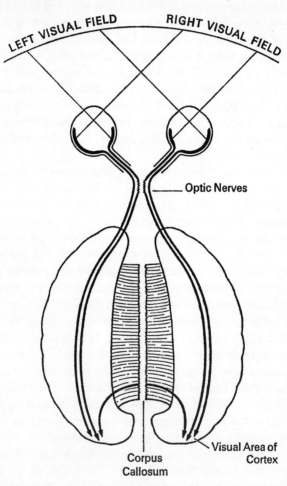

23. Diagram to illustrate experiments in which the optic chiasm and the corpus callosum are divided

opposite it. The right half of both retinae receives from the left visual field, and the left half of both retinae from the right visual field. Each occipital lobe of each hemisphere receives nerve impulses from the half of the retina on its own side; the right occipital lobe receives from the right half of the retina of both eyes and the left occipital lobe from the left half of both. Thus what is seen in the right field goes to the left cerebral hemisphere and what is seen on the left to the right hemisphere. Between these two areas of the hemispheres there are nerve fibres running through the corpus callosum, connecting one point with another of the two occipital lobes.

In order to find out the role of the corpus callosum in visual learning, Myers in 1955 cut through the corpus callosum and the optic chiasm in cats. When this is done, all the nerve fibres from the left eye go to the left hemisphere and all those from the right eye go to the right hemisphere; for the operation divides those fibres that normally cross. And so after the operation, the left eye and the left cerebral hemisphere form one visual system and the right eye with its hemisphere form another. These cats were then taught two different solutions of a problem. One solution was taught to the left hemisphere via its eye and the other solution was taught to the right hemisphere via its eye. For instance, one cerebral hemisphere was taught to make the animal press a lever for a food reward when it saw a white circle, and the other hemisphere to do so when it saw a white square. After the corpus callosum had been cut through, transfer of training did not occur. Each hemisphere then learned independently and neither knew what the other hemisphere had learned. Each system, consisting of one eye and its hemisphere, functioned well and behaved as was expected; it acted as if it had no cognizance of the existence of the other hemisphere.

Myers and his colleagues in further experiments found that it is possible to teach each hemisphere an absolutely opposite and contrary solution to one problem. At first, they cut through the corpus callosum in some monkeys. Then they trained one hemisphere to make the monkey depress the lever when it saw the outline of a square, and the other hemisphere to make the monkey depress the lever when it saw the outline of a circle. The first hemisphere was also taught that it must not allow the monkey to touch the lever when the circle appears, and the second hemisphere that the lever must not be touched when the square appears. Thus each hemisphere learns exactly contrary things, the one that the circle is bad and the square is good, and the other that the circle is good and the square is bad. The monkeys with corpus callosum divided had no difficulty in learning this task. The animals had no emotional problems, no difficulties, and showed no evidence of mental conflict. Intact monkeys would have had severe and intense symptoms of neurosis if they had tried to learn these contrary solutions to problems.

They found in further investigations that each hemisphere of an animal with the corpus callosum divided can be taught the contrary solutions to a problem at the same time. In each teaching session, first one hemisphere is taught something via its eye and then the other one is taught the opposite information via its eye; then for the next five minutes the first eye is trained again, and so on throughout the session. A cat or monkey with division of the commissures and the optic chiasm ends up by learning its two different solutions to a problem in the same time it takes the normal animal to learn one solution; and it achieves this without any mental or emotional conflict.

The solution to a food-obtaining problem can also be based on tactile clues instead of visual ones. In this case, the one hemisphere is taught to press a lever when the forepaw examines and feels a certain tactile sensation and the other hemisphere is taught to press it when exactly the opposite sort of tactile sensation is felt.

What each hemisphere learns via its own sensory input coming from the opposite side of the body is learned better and retained longer than what it learns by transfer across the corpus callosum. What has been learned, for instance, by the left hemisphere coming from the left halves of both retinae (things seen on the right) is well retained, whereas what has been learned in the right hemisphere (things seen on the left) from transfer from the left hemisphere is poorly retained and soon forgotten.

We presume that under normal conditions, what is learned by one hemisphere is automatically transferred to the other via the corpus callosum. It is first learned by one hemisphere, and then a weaker carbon copy, so to speak, is kept in the other hemisphere. We do not yet know how this transfer is done nor what mechanisms are entailed in the word 'automatically' used in the above statement.

To find out when what has been learned is transferred and also how much of it is transferred, similar training experiments have been done in various species of animals. When a cat learns something, it usually acquires the knowledge and training in both hemispheres at the same time. On the other hand, man usually acquires it first with one hemisphere, and then later transfers it to the other one.

The experimental situation of dividing the corpus callosum has been used in the treatment of certain epileptic patients. The idea has been to stop the severe fits from spreading from one hemisphere to the other and hence from one side of the body to the other. The effects of the operation were similar to those produced in cats and monkeys. After the operation, each cerebral hemisphere acted independently, as if it were ignorant of the existence of the other. There were no obvious intellectual defects and with superficial observation nothing abnormal might be noticed. Any activity usually performed exclusively by one hemisphere could still be performed. Each hand could work separately. The patient could move each finger; he could use a spoon and fork and he could hammer in a nail with either hand. But the left hemisphere did not know what the right hemisphere was doing or what it had just done. Any activity needing the two hemispheres to work together could not be carried out properly. The patient could do certain things using only his right hemisphere, but he could never explain what he was doing. The independent activities of the right hemisphere had lost their connexions with the speech

327

area, and so the patient could not explain them. He could not
write at all with his left hand. Right-handed people of course
cannot write well with the left hand; but these patients had not
even the slightest idea how to do writing with their left hands,
this hand had no knowledge of the shapes of letters and
words.

The anatomical situation is illustrated in Figure 24. This
represents a section through the two cerebral hemispheres,
made from side to side through the frontal and temporal lobes.
The corpus callosum has been divided. This section separates
the right hemisphere from the region of the left hemisphere
that organizes speech, reading, writing and all thinking relying

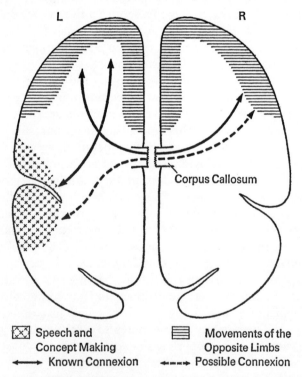

⊠ Speech and Concept Making	☰ Movements of the Opposite Limbs
⟵⟶ Known Connexion	⟵- - -⟶ Possible Connexion

24. Connexions between the speech area of the left cerebral hemisphere
and motor regions of both hemispheres

on speech. As each hemisphere is responsible for the movements of the limbs of the opposite side, the right hemisphere
can still direct the left limbs, and the left hemisphere can still
direct the right limbs. As speech, reading and writing are
organized only in the left hemisphere, cutting the bridge
between the two hemispheres means that the right hemisphere
cannot direct the left hand to do things connected with speech,
such as writing letters, numbers or words. This is the same for
any movements requiring verbal organization or backing. If
the patient has been accustomed to make use of a verbal
concept for the organization of a movement, he can no longer
do it. Say, for instance, he wants to tie a reef knot with the
left hand, and say that he usually does this by saying to

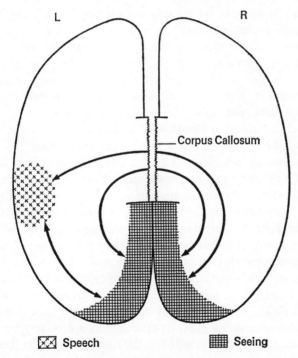

☒ Speech   ▦ Seeing

25. Connexions between the two visual areas and the region of the
left hemisphere for reading and writing

himself 'first, right over left, then left over right'; after division of the corpus callosum, he will be unable to do it. But if for years he has tied reef knots with his left hand without ever thinking about it, he will probably still be able to do so.

There are similar disorders with the faculty of vision. If we present something to such a patient in his left field of vision, he can see it but he cannot explain it or write about it. He cannot read anything presented in this field, though he can read it when it is shown him in the right field. This situation is explained by Figure 25. The left hemisphere sees what is in the right visual field and the right what is in the left. When the corpus callosum is divided, although the right hemisphere can still see what is in the left field, it cannot communicate it to the left hemisphere. As reading is organized in the left hemisphere, the patient sees the printed page shown him on the left; but it no longer makes any sense; the letters are meaningless lines of black on a white page. As soon as the page is shown him in the right field, he not only sees it, it makes sense and he can read it. For the connexions between the reading areas and the visual areas of the left hemisphere are intact.

If such a patient is blindfolded and something is put in his left hand, he knows what it is, but he can neither say what it is nor describe it in writing. That he knows what it is is shown by the fact that he knows what to do with it. If it is a comb, he combs his hair, if it is a toothbrush, he brushes his teeth. Yet he cannot explain what he is doing with the left hand. With the right hand, he does all these things, and he can give a suitable running commentary as he does so.

If a patient with the corpus callosum divided has to copy a drawing in which spatial factors are important, such as copying a cube, he can do it alright with his left hand but fails to do it with his right. The connexions between the region controlling the left hand and the visuo-spatial region are intact, for both these functions are directed from the right hemisphere; but the connexions between the region controlling the right hand and the visuo-spatial region are divided; and so although the patient can use the right hand he can no longer draw something in which the representation of space is needed.

All this work on the corpus callosum shows us that the environment we see is a product of the organization of the two hemispheres. For all nerve fibres from the left half of both retinae go to the left cerebral hemisphere and all those from the right half of both retinae go to the right hemisphere. In order for whole objects to be seen, the two hemisphere inputs have to be joined. This is done instantaneously by fibres crossing in the occipital end of the corpus callosum. Similar fibres in the middle regions of the corpus callosum are used for the integration of sensation acquired through paired limbs. When we feel something with both hands, we make the sensations into a whole; we don't have to think 'On the left hand it feels rough, on the right hand it feels rough too; and so it must be rough all over'. Before we realize what something is, this information from the two sides of the body has been integrated; and the main pathway for this is the corpus callosum.

When we examine patients with lesions cutting off a part of either hemisphere from the speech area, the patient cannot tell us about his defect. Indeed most of these patients are ignorant of having a defect. This is because 'I' – if we have to use such a philosophical concept – resides somewhere within the speech area on the left. In such a case, 'I' honestly does not know what the right cerebral hemisphere is doing. These patients are difficult to understand, for there is another problem for the neurologist. In most of these patients, the gap left by the sensory deficiency is filled by confabulation. When a sensory input is suddenly cut off, the result is not usually a state of blankness or nothingness; the patient does not say he feels or knows nothing. Spontaneous input or hallucinations fill the gap. The patient does not say, for example, that his left arm is lacking in all sensibility; he says that that limb is not his and that it should be thrown away. This has nothing to do with intelligence. The person with the corpus callosum cut through really has a split mind.

From Myers's investigations on cats and monkeys and from

the work on man, we can draw the following conclusions about the functions of the corpus callosum. It is needed for transferring what one hemisphere learns and making it a common possession of the brain. It is essential for keeping each hemisphere informed about what is happening in the other one. It is necessary for learning any skill that is bilateral, using both sides of the body. The co-ordination of movements, apart from the reflex part of movements laid down at lower neural levels, depends on the passage of impulses across the corpus callosum between the motor regions of the two hemispheres. It is needed when any motor skill depends on vision. It is also necessary for us to make our visual conceptions of the world, our concept of distance and space, in the world around us.

Chapter 20

Recording and Remembering

For he made a great figure in Egypt for his signal services.
For he killed the Ichneumon-rat very pernicious by land.

Memory

Memory is the storage of what has been acquired by learning.
At first a new event is registered; it is then stored or retained –
and finally it is recalled and produced again. Memory includes
what one might call a sense of pastness; what is remembered
is localized in the past. Memory is also accompanied by a
feeling of familiarity. It entails the feeling that what is remembered is a part of ourselves, that it once happened to us. This
feeling does not accompany the return of material one has
learned from someone else.

The neural functions that should be included under the term
'memory' depend on how one chooses to define the term.
Provided one avoids misleading uses, one might include as
many levels of neural functioning as possible. It may be
permissible to include all skills learned during one's life. But,
although the mechanisms involved are probably the same as
those used in memory of a more psychological kind, it is not
convenient to include skills and habits. We do not normally
include the kind of remembering when we sing back a bar of
music immediately after hearing it or repeat words which we
have just heard. Yet when perception is based on successive
sensations, it can justifiably be considered to depend on remembering. What we choose to include under the term of 'memory'
is a matter of convention. Neurologists tend to use the term

'memory' only for those kinds of remembering that are upset when there are disturbances of cerebral functioning.

Memory at Lower Neural Levels

The sorts of memory mentioned so far are functions of the cerebral hemispheres. But all the essential features of memory occur also at lower neural levels. In the following two examples, the experience has been fixed and retained by neurons at spinal level.

The first example comes from a patient with cancer. To stop the pain, which was most severe in her case, she had an operation on the spinal cord. This operation normally makes the whole of the body below the level of the operation on the spinal cord insensitive to pain. It does not interfere with the tactile forms of sensation, and so the patient can still feel the ground he walks on and knows where to put his feet. This particular patient had had a car accident six years earlier which had caused a severe and painful fracture of the right knee-cap. The knee-cap had been removed, the pain went, and the patient had forgotten all about it. But after the operation on her spinal cord, she found to her amazement that any painful stimulus applied to her right lower limb produced the identical pain she had had in the right knee six years before. The stimulus did not merely produce the pain in her knee; it caused all the sensations which she had had six years previously when her knee-cap had been fractured.

The second case shows the same thing. At one time I was studying the problems of the relief of pain sometimes experienced by patients after amputations of limbs. One of these patients was a young man, who had lost his leg during the Korean War. During the course of a day, I carried out various procedures to the stump of his lower limb, many of which were painful and all of which had the effect of sending into the spinal cord a barrage of nerve impulses from that limb. On the night after these tests, the patient was suddenly woken from his sleep with severe pain in his absent leg. He immediately knew what this pain was. For five years previously, before he had had his leg amputated, he had been playing ice hockey, had fallen, and had had the outside of his leg cut open by a skate. On the present night he re-experienced the identical sensations in his phantom leg that he had had at that time. It was not that he remembered having had this injury; he felt all the sensations again in his absent leg that he had previously felt.

In these two patients, the pattern of activity of certain neurons within the spinal cord has undergone some permanent change as a result of the pain in the lower limb. What this actual change is, we do not know; but the presence of some change was shown by stimulating the same neurons again on another occasion, several years later.

This is really the same phenomenon as memory, though we do not think of this sort of thing when we use the term. This same sort of memory has also been seen occurring within the neurons of the sensory nerve of the face. During the last war, a dentist and a doctor in the United States became interested in the pain in the face that pilots sometimes got during high-altitude flying. This was before planes were pressurized. They found that many of the pilots got pain in the teeth as well as pain located in the facial sinuses, where it might be expected to occur. In going into the dental histories of these pilots, they found out that the pain was felt in those teeth that had sometime before been subjected to some trauma, such as dental treatment. This trauma could have been extraction of the tooth or simply a filling. To reproduce these results once more and to investigate this phenomenon further, one of the two, the dentist, did some routine fillings. Ten to sixteen days later, the other one, the physician, applied a painful stimulus to the inside of the nose. The pain caused by this stimulus was felt not only at the place where the needle pricked the inside of the nose; it was felt also in the tooth that a few days before had been treated. In a further investigation, they divided the patients into two groups. In one group the dental fillings were carried out under general anaesthesia, so that the patient was unconscious at the time. In the other group the dental fillings were carried out with local anaesthesia, so that the nerve carrying impulses from the tooth to the central nervous system was blocked. They found that the phenomenon still occurred in the group of patients in whom the fillings had been done under general anaesthesia; stimulation of the nose still caused pain in the treated tooth. But it no longer occurred in the patients in whom the fillings had been done with a local anaesthetic. This showed that if the nerve impulses were prevented from reaching the brain, the recording and retention of this experience did not occur.

What has happened here is that the painful stimulation has caused some change in the lower level of the brain, in the part to which the nerve from the face goes. It is a permanent or a long-lasting change. This is memory occurring at a low neural level. There is the registration of an experience, its storage and then its recall. When the material is recalled, it returns with the stamp of the past upon it, and also the sense of familiarity. The experience has become a part of this region of the sensory system, and it alters subsequent behaviour. We presume that the neurons concerned have been altered in some way. When they are stimulated (but not with every sort of stimulation), they work together and in the same way in which they worked on the previous occasion.

The change in the next case must have taken place among the neurons of the thalamus within the cerebral hemisphere.

This is another example of memory occurring in lower levels of the nervous system. A builder's labourer had a painful in-growing toe-nail. He fell off the scaffolding and broke his back cutting the spinal cord in two. From then on, he was completely paralysed in the lower part of his body and he could feel no sensation. If he was pricked, pinched, moved or touched anywhere in the lower part of his body, he could not feel it. If the toe-nail were squeezed or banged, he felt nothing. And yet after this injury to the spinal cord, he still continued to be aware of the painful toe-nail. This means that certain neurons at a higher neural level than the spinal cord had been changed by the pain. They continued to register pain in the toe-nail, even though all impulses from the foot had been cut off.

Two facts need emphasis here. The first is that these phenomena occur only very rarely. The second is that they exist, whether they are rare or not; and their existence shows that this sort of memory occurs at these lower levels of the nervous system. It is important to realize this, for it appears that all the functions of the higher levels of the nervous system are elaborations of functions already present at lower levels.

The same sort of retention of change due to experience occurs at higher levels of the nervous system. At this level it involves the thalamus and the neurons of the cerebral cortex; but this is not the remembering of psychology. In some patients when there has been a severe pain going on continually for a long time, the neurons related to this sensation and this part of the body became altered in some way. This is shown up this way. In normal people, all parts of the cerebral cortex can be stimulated electrically at operation and the patient does not experience pain. When the sensory regions of the cortex are stimulated, the person feels tingling, a feeling of numbness or a sensation of the part being moved or about to be moved. But in patients with persistent pain, the electrical stimulation of large regions of the cortex does cause pain, and it causes the identical pain from which the patient suffers. One sees here that the cortex has become altered; areas that normally have nothing to do with pain now subserve the conscious perception of pain. The pain has changed these neurons, and they now make their owner suffer pain when they are excited.

Highest Level Memory

When we speak of having a good memory or of trying to remember something, we are thinking of the highest neural level of remembering. We know very little about this ability; we do not understand how neurons store experience or what physical events occur when we commit something to memory.

For this memory of a mental sort, consciousness is needed. It is necessary for registering the experience and for its recall, but it is not used for its retention.

The terms 'consciousness' and 'being conscious' are unsatisfactory. When we are conscious, so much of our mental and psychological activity is in fact unconscious. We make use of conscious effort only in small parts of our mental activities. An intriguing example of this can be seen in very short-term remembering. If we are partly listening to what someone is saying, and he then accuses us of not paying attention, we find that we can prove him wrong by repeating to him his entire last sentence or more. It has all been recorded for us, just as on tape; but until his accusation we were paying no attention to it. It was being recorded but not thought about, probably not even understood. Then when we play it back we take in its meaning. This is a remarkable mechanism and really a most useful one. We can make use of it to take in two conversations at once. We listen to one of them and understand it as we hear it; and we let our short-term memory take the other one down and then attend to it later.

A remembered scene is not the same as the original scene. It is pale and weak in all respects. The accompanying emotion is far less, much of what was first experienced has dropped out of the remembered scene, much else has become changed or distorted and a great deal has been forgotten. How vivid the remembered scene is depends on its importance for the person. If it was important, it will have originally had, or later acquired, much emotional accompaniment. And so the intensity of a remembered scene or event usually depends on the amount of emotion associated with it. It is the same with the intensity and the reality of hallucinations.

As the memory of an event is not exactly the same as the experience of the event, all the neural pathways and neurons activated during the original event cannot have been activated during the remembering of the scene. As the remembered event or scene has additions as well as omissions, it is clear that other neurons are working in producing what has been remembered. Some neurons may be the same; but the original pathway used when the entire event was experienced is not used when the event is recalled. What is recollected is a shortened and compressed version; it arrives in consciousness with memories of emotions rather than the emotions themselves in their original intensity. Remembering is similar to imagining a scene; in some respects, remembering is re-imagining. The memory is a reconstruction, based on the original experience.

As our memories give us a sort of symbolic representation of the previous event, it was surprising to learn that Penfield evoked such real pictures of the patients' past lives when he stimulated regions of their temporal lobes. For what Penfield obtained was, as he wrote 'not a memory, as we usually use the word, although it may have some relation to it. No man can recall by voluntary effort such a wealth of detail. . . . Many a patient has told me that the experience brought back by the electrode is much more real than remembering.' Whole scenes from the past were thrust into the patients' consciousness. The patients always recognized the scenes as having happened to them, although till the electrode had been applied to their brains they had no idea that they had retained these memories.

One might have guessed that memories aroused so unnaturally as by the electrical stimulation of a small part of the brain would appear distorted and jumbled up. But this was not so. The scene would appear like a film: in the proper order and at the proper pace. As long as the electrode was kept on the same point of the cortex, the remembered event continued to appear. When stimulation was stopped, the internal film stopped, and the patient no longer remembered the scene from his past; when stimulation was started again, the story went on from where it had been left off, or it began again at the beginning.

The actual reminiscences in most cases were trivial. It seemed most unlikely that they had any special significance for the patient. They were not usually the sort of material that is repressed. Penfield has recounted that one of his patients said to him: 'You forced me to live things again that I'd forgotten. What were you doing? Were you stimulating my subconscious mind?' As Penfield wrote, 'Her question seemed naïve. And then I stopped to consider. Wasn't that exactly what my electrode had done?'

The stimulating electrode breaks into the storehouse of memories and taps the store. The patient does not have to do the work of recalling. Suddenly, there is an episode out of his past before his eyes. And with that experience there is the emotion recorded at the time; not a memory of the emotion; the patient feels that same emotion in its original intensity. He experiences the same interpretations of the event that he had at the time. Penfield explains it: 'Thus evoked recollection is not the exact photographic or phonographic reproduction of past scenes and events. It is reproduction of what the patient saw and heard and felt and understood.' And what is obtained from raiding the patient's store in this way is far more detailed than anything the patient can summon to memory in the normal way.

Had Penfield not shown us this evidence of the existence of these remembered experiences, we would probably not have thought that this sort of record exists. One would have thought that only the symbolic representation of it is in the brain. For the normal process of recall does not reproduce these realistic scenes, unrolling before one's eyes.

Penfield and some other workers in this field have concluded from their observations when stimulating the temporal lobes that the record of all we have experienced remains in the central nervous system. Nothing is forgotten. Penfield writes:

Since the electrode may activate a random sample of this strip from the distant past, and since the most unimportant and completely forgotten periods of time may appear in this sampling, it seems reasonable to suppose that the record is complete and that it really does include all periods of each individual's waking conscious life. . . . The stream of consciousness flows inexorably onward, as described in the words of William James. But, unlike a river, it leaves behind it a permanent record that seems to be complete for the waking moments of a man's life, a record that runs, no doubt, like a thread along a pathway of ganglionic and synaptic facilitations in the brain. This pathway is located partly or wholly in the temporal lobes.

Most psychologists, however, regard forgetting as a normal process. They consider that it is normal to forget the large accumulation of trivialities that are at first registered and committed to short-term memory. How the content of memory is sorted out so that certain experiences are forgotten and others retained and how it is divided so that some will be retained for days and others for years, we do not know. One imagines that some sort of review goes on; but this is merely a verbal simile and brings us no nearer knowing what is happening in the nervous system.

One naïvely thinks that forgetting is due to the event not being retained. One supposes that it is soon discarded, perhaps leaving no trace, no change in the brain. But the little knowledge we have of this subject indicates that this is not commonly so. It is surprising to find that a great deal of what we have experienced is still there. In fact, forgetting is usually an inability to recall.

Apart from Penfield's striking physiological evidence from stimulating the brains of subjects undergoing operations, there has always been good psychological evidence that far more is retained than might seem possible. Merely carrying out free association on one's own shows that one has stored a lot of material one never realized. We need merely to rest and relax (while remaining vigilant and avoiding falling asleep, which is easier said than done) and all sorts of things come to mind that we did not know we knew or imagined we had forgotten. We suddenly see a face and we realize we saw that face yesterday just in front of the British Museum. It is just the same with our dreams. A strange episode appears at first to be the product of fantasy. But if we let ourselves associate to that episode, we recognize it as a distortion of an insignificant event which happened on the previous day. It was so unimportant that we would not have imagined that it could have been recorded, stored and remembered.

That a lot of material has been retained is shown to us by the behaviour of elderly people whose brains are becoming atrophied. Old people, with millions of neurons atrophic and dead, come to remember scenes and experiences from their distant pasts that they had forgotten they knew. They are able to recall and they relate episodes from their years of childhood and youth, which had never come to light during the intervening years. All this time these memories had been stored and apparently forgotten. Yet the fact that their recent memories are poor is shown by their relating these events two or three times during an evening, unconscious that they have already told us all this half an hour before.

There is a great deal of evidence from psychology that older memories tend to be retained better than recent ones, and that the longer something has been remembered, the more likely it will be retained in the future. Fixation of what has been retained improves with time, and conversely, the more recent memories are the more vulnerable. This holds throughout the time scale: something registered for a few seconds is more vulnerable than something registered for five minutes, and something retained for a day is more likely to disappear than something retained for a year. If we keep recalling something, it is less likely to be forgotten. Whatever memory is, it improves with repetition.

During psychotherapy, similar memories from the past roll up, though they had not been recalled before. Often they return with full emotion; and the adult will be raging at the way one of his parents was treating him at the age of four. This again makes one wonder how much of what we experience we ever forget.

The ability to recall is not the only criterion there is of the retention of something experienced. This can be deduced also from the ease of re-learning. If one knew a language at the age of five, had never spoken it since that time, and had apparently forgotten it completely, one will learn this language far more quickly at the age of twenty than someone who had never known it at all. Something, then, must have remained.

The ability to recognize also shows us that something has been retained. When we fail to remember something and somebody else reminds us of it, we then recognize that what he has remembered for us is correct. This shows us that we had registered and stored it; the failure was only in recall. Recognition is sometimes used as a test for memory. Objects are shown to the patient and then removed. A few minutes later some of these objects are shown him again, this time together with new objects he did not see before. If some memory traces remain, the patient will be able to divide the material into two groups, the part that is familiar and the part that is new.

Recognition depends on retention. It is a more complicated mechanism than at first sight appears. For what is remembered is never identical with the experience that gave rise to the memory. Recognition starts one step away, so to speak, from the perception of the re-presented material. Recognition is a more sensitive indication of retention than recall. We may be unable to remember something and even to do so when it is described to us; but should it be presented to us again, we immediately recognize it.

An example of failure to recognize a retained experience as a memory was recorded by Claparède, the founder of the Geneva school of psychologists. He had a patient who had the typical disturbances of memory due to years of alcoholism. To test her memory, he concealed a pin in his hand and stuck it into her fingers while shaking hands. Some minutes later, as he was leaving her, he proffered his hand to shake hands with her again. She pulled her hand away, but she apparently had no idea why she did so. When he asked her why, she said 'But hasn't one the right to withdraw one's hand?' And when she was questioned further, she said that he might have a pin hidden in his hand. When Claparède asked 'What makes you think I want to prick you?' she replied that it was an idea that came into her head. Then when she was asked to explain this surprising idea, she said 'Sometimes people do have pins hidden in their hands'. But she never remembered that she had been pricked a few minutes before, and she did not recognize these ideas as being based on memory.

Recognition has many degrees: one can recognize something completely, or one may merely recognize it as being rather vaguely known. When something is recognized, it evokes a feeling or emotion of familiarity. In fact, familiarity is a necessary part of recognition. Whether this emotion of familiarity is the same as the strong sense of familiarity, discussed in Chapter 16, is not known. Certainly the sense of familiarity occurring before an epileptic fit or that occurring during stimulation of the temporal lobe at operation feels different to the patient from merely recognizing a familiar object or event. But under these abnormal conditions, the emotion is pure and isolated; and so one might well expect it to feel different.

Closely related to the sense of familiarity is the part of recognition sometimes call 'my-ness', the feeling that it has happened to me, that it is a part of me. This makes the recognized object feel different from something one has merely heard about or read about in a book.

In certain disturbances of the brain, such as may occur with prolonged alcoholism or after severe head injuries, material may be registered and retained, yet when it is reproduced the sense of familiarity is lacking, and the subject does not recognize it.

The failure to recognize one's own thoughts as coming from something one has read leads to literary plagiarism. The sense of familiarity and the localization in the past does not accompany the thought as it arrives in consciousness. That is why, if one wants to write one's own thoughts, it is essential not to read what other people have written on the subject; one cannot trust one's memory. The mechanisms of recognition may be dormant; and what has been taken in from reading or hearing may appear to be one's own marvellous contribution.

A blow to the head temporarily stops the higher levels of brain function; this is well-known and is the condition of concussion. During this time the patient does not always lie pallid on the ground. As many footballers know, he may go on with what he was doing at the time. This state was first described in 1501 by the first great Mogul Emperor, Babur. He wrote in his memoirs:

As I turned round on my seat to see how far I had left them behind, my saddle-girth being slack, the saddle turned round, and I came to the ground right on my head. Although I immediately sprang up and mounted, yet I did not recover the full possession of my faculties till the evening and the world, and all that occurred at the time, passed before my eyes and apprehension like a dream, or a fantasy, and disappeared.

During this time, mental functioning is apparently normal; it is only the continual registration and storage of experience that are not working. Mental testing during this time may reveal that the person is not working at his most efficient intellectual level, or it may not show anything abnormal. The case of one patient has been recorded in which the patient's mental functioning was so good that he learned to type; yet this period was included in the patient's period of absence of memory. Although he always remembered how to type, he never remembered learning the skill. Cases such as this show us that memory for recent events can be normal while complete memory during that period is deranged.

The reproduction of retained material without knowledge that it belongs to oneself may cause some strange abnormalities of memory in patients after head injuries.

One patient who was seen in the Hospital for Head Injuries at Oxford during the war had a vision of a horse in a cloud as he recovered consciousness. He had a clear view of the horse. He said it was a brown cob, galloping with its head up, coming from right to left. This vision soon passed, and he then became conscious that he was in bed and that two nurses were making his bed. He asked them what had happened. They told him he had had an accident. He then asked whether it was anything to do with a horse, and they replied that they did not know, but that he had already told them that it was due to a

345

horse. He himself had no recollection of having spoken to them before and no knowledge that he had had an accident and no memory of the horse. Later it was confirmed by the police that a runaway horse was the cause of his accident and that it must have passed by the patient from right to left. Even when the story of the accident was pieced together and told to the patient, he could not remember anything about it; nor could he remember the horse as he saw it in the vision.

Sometimes a vision of what had actually happened occurs suddenly, and the patient does not know why he is seeing this vision. Something, perhaps an episode in a film or the sight of a car, brings the whole event back to his mind, even though he did not know that he had retained any recollection of the event. Professor Ritchie Russell, who has studied thousands of cases of head injury over the past forty years, has reported the case of a patient who was injured while standing on a tramway island. He recovered consciousness twelve hours after the head injury. On several occasions in the ensuing weeks he would suddenly have a vision of the huge tyre of a motor lorry bearing down on him, while he threw up his arms unable to escape. In fact this was exactly what had occurred. But the patient could never remember these details of the accident. The vision that spontaneously came into his mind might just as well have happened to someone else.

In cases such as these, material has been retained. It is unaccompanied by the usual sense of familiarity or by the feeling of my-ness, and the patient cannot recall it by voluntary effort.

A patient who has had a severe head injury may come to the doctor two weeks later and say that for the past two weeks he does not know what has happened, that he has no memory of anything that happened since a minute before his accident. During most of this time he may have been normally reading, writing letters, playing cards, as patients do. Although he has been behaving normally, in the true sense of the word he has been unconscious; he recovered consciousness only when he started to have continuous memory. During the period between his head injury and the day when he came to, he remembers either nothing or a few scattered isolated events.

From cases of head injury, we have learned that the first part of memory, the fixation of the experience, takes time. The time varies from a split second to about a minute. During this period what was happening to the patient can never be recollected. If the head injury is very severe, this period of permanent absence of memories is longer. The more severe the damage to the brain, the longer this period can be. There may be obliteration of all memories for months or even years: what was normally registered and stored has disappeared. The most recent memories go with less severe head injuries, the older memories go with the more severe damage to the brain. Although we usually consider memory as short-term and long-term, these divisions are really matters of degree, the one merging into the other. The longer a memory has been established, the more firmly it is fixed. As time fixes memories, those things that have been retained for a short time may disappear for ever. The result of this for young children is that a severe head injury can sometimes obliterate the child's memories of its entire life before the injury. The child's mental state is then reduced to that of babyhood. Everything he ever learned, he has to learn all over again.

We understand very little of the neural processes underlying the retroactive effects of trauma to the brain; we understand still less about the recovery of some of the forgotten material. For sometimes, months after the head injury when the patient's cerebral processes are again normal, the period of absence of recollections before the head injury shrinks, so that in the end the patient can recall a large period of the time that he had previously forgotten, and he ends up with a short period of absence of memories just before the injury.

Experimental studies of this obliteration of what has already been registered have been undertaken in cases of head injury and in electroshock treatment of psychiatric disorders; for in this case too the patient does not remember what occurred for a brief moment before the shock to the brain. Here also it proves impossible to bring back memories for the split second or few seconds immediately before the trauma to the brain, although we can be sure that this material was taken in.

When we recall something from the past, we may have to make some mental effort. We search for what we hope we have retained. Exactly what parts of the brain are used for this activity and what we are doing in terms of the physiology of neurons and synapses, we do not yet know.

Whatever the physiology of this recalling ability is, a conscious effort to look for the past experience is not always the best way of finding it. The retained experience may come to mind spontaneously. After we have suspended control, suddenly what we were trying to remember is there before our eyes. This may also happen when we are asleep; on waking up, we find we have remembered it. Whether the process of searching goes on when we are asleep, we do not know. Certainly memories may return during dreams, under hypnosis, and during various states of dimmed consciousness. More automatic and less controlled thinking can be more effective for recall than conscious control. And so one should have confidence in unconscious processes of thought to fulfil one's needs. They mostly do so, though they sometimes arrive too late. Only after one has written a paper or given a lecture does one suddenly know how one should have done it.

Memories can be brought to mind by the psychological process of free association. When we do this, we relax and let one memory bring up another. Sometimes an event reminds us of a similar event that occurred before or a sensation brings to mind another occasion when the same sensation was experienced. The sense of smell as is well-known to us all is particularly evocative of memories.

Memory is an important ingredient of creative thinking. Strange as it may seem, creation comes from pouring a great mass of ill-assorted things into the mind, leaving them to ferment, and then getting something new out of it. The mechanism of getting something out is an ability that depends on character as well as on intelligence. It is done with effort, with searching concentration, with merely sitting and waiting, or with sleeping, lying around or doing other things. A lot has to be put in and all of it has to be stored. For memory consists of experiencing, retaining the shadow of the experience and recalling; they are also the essentials of creation.

As the biological purpose of memory would seem to be the organization of present behaviour in the light of previous experience, it is obvious that some sort of classification is necessary. It seems likely that the contents of the mind are classified and cross-indexed in many different ways. When we try to remember something, we can seek it via many different routes. If, for instance, I try to remember the name of a particularly beautiful East African starling, I first remember that the name was that of a German, then that it probably ended in 'dt'. I also know that it is in J. G. Williams's book on *Birds of East and Central Africa*, and that in this book, the colour plate of the starling and the description of the bird are on different pages. And I also remember that this starling has an orange eye. Thus I find that in my mind Hildebrandt's starling is classified under the heading of foreign names of birds, sub-heading German, birds in Williams's book, sub-heading starlings, and most important of all, I have in my filing system a visual picture of the bird, so that I can match a proffered picture of it against my visual memory of it, and then recognize the bird.

It is probable that the more cross-indexing there is, the better. Material is probably classified in accordance to its effect, pleasant or unpleasant, as usual or unusual, as what happens on holidays, as games to be played at silly parties, as nursery rhymes, as jokes to amuse ten-year-old children, and so on.

But this is all armchair psychology, and tells us nothing about how the brain organizes these psychological mechanisms. Penfield has reported the case of an epileptic patient who shows us other aspects of this mechanism of classification. The patient was a young man who would get fits when he saw someone grab something from someone else. On one occasion he saw

349

someone snatching a rifle away from a cadet on parade, on another a man snatching his hat away from the cloakroom attendant; on both occasions he had a fit. Seeing someone grab or snatch something 'would immediately produce a vivid recollection of an occasion when he was thirteen years old. At this time he was playing with a dog, grabbing a stick from its mouth and throwing it. The patient would associate the two events, become confused, and have a seizure.' As Penfield was operating on the left temporal lobe, he stimulated one point, and the patient suddenly cried out: 'There he is!' When Penfield questioned him, he said: 'It was like a spell, he was doing that thing: grabbing something from somebody.' As any sort of grabbing of something from somebody precipitated his fits, this brain must have classified experience to include a category of grabbing something from somebody.

The Anatomy of Highest Level Memory

Until the last war, the subject of memory would have been dealt with entirely by psychologists; neurologists would have had nothing to say. That this is no longer so is due to the findings of Penfield, to the enormous numbers of head injuries there were in the war and the fact that they were looked after in the British and Canadian medical services by neurologists and neurosurgeons, and to a change in intellectual climate among neurologists, psychologists and psychiatrists. There has also been a swing away from psychopathology towards a physical and material outlook. Before the war, cases of head injury were put in the surgical wards of the hospital. There, no one took any interest in their psychological state, as surgeons are not trained or interested in psychology. It was mainly due to Sir Hugh Cairns that in the British army and air force, these patients were put in special hospitals and were treated in special units by neurosurgeons and neurologists.

We have already related Penfield's findings when he stimulated certain parts of the temporal lobes in patients. Penfield has made many other important contributions to this subject by studying the effects of cutting out parts of the temporal lobes in the treatment of brain tumours and of epilepsy. When certain parts of the temporal lobes are cut out, the record of a life is cut out with them. It is as if one's memory is in a filing cabinet and someone has taken it away. In principle, just like a tape-recorder, what is stored in a person's memory could be consulted by anyone. We have two ways of doing this. We have the psychological way of asking its owner to tell us what is there; and we have the physiological way of electrically stimulating certain parts of the brain. This aspect of one's memory should perhaps be emphasized, as we regard our memories as so personal, so much a part of ourselves, almost as ourselves. Yet in fact once the registered experience is stored, it is there to be tapped, almost regardless of us.

When all the front parts of both temporal lobes are cut out, the faculty of memory is destroyed. But each neuron or each circuit of neurons within this region of the brain is not the repository of something experienced; it is not a kind of pigeon-hole in which a memory is stored. Penfield has emphasized that when he stimulates a little spot of the cortex and this stimulation produces a flashback, cutting out that little spot does not remove the flashback. After it has been cut out, the patient can still remember the whole episode by using his memory in the ordinary way; the remembered event has not gone. It is only when a very large area of the temporal lobes of both hemispheres is destroyed that the entire memory is ruined.

In Chapter 21, certain aspects of a case will be related in which this operation was done. The disastrous results were that the patient could not recognize anybody. He treated his own mother, to whom he had been very attached before the operation, in the same manner as he treated the nurses in hospital, calling her 'Madam', and he no longer showed any emotional attachment for her. Here we see that his sensory input is normal, and that he makes a perception from what he receives. He can recognize the moving object as a woman. But the significance of that particular woman depends on previous experience of her; that is to say, it depends on memory. With no remembrance of her, there is no accompanying emotion, such as one is used to having in relation to one's mother. He perceives a woman and behaves to her as he would to any unknown woman. He 'not only could not remember anything that had happened recently, he could not remember anything of his past'. When the doctors tried to get him to talk about the town he lived in, his own house, his family, he could not answer the questions and did not seem to understand them, 'as if their object was entirely unknown to him'. The patient lived without a past and without a future.

Scoville, a neurosurgeon in the United States, has cut out most of the hippocampus, the amygdala and the medial part of the temporal lobes in some patients with severe mental disorders and also in one mentally normal patient who had uncontrollable epilepsy. Immediately after the operation, these patients could not find their way to the bathroom, they could never again find the way about the hospital, they had completely forgotten everyone in the hospital and could not recognize any of them. The epileptic patient remembered nothing about being in hospital before his operation and no events for a year or two before that. But his memory for his earlier life was intact. Scoville and Milner reported on this young man's case as follows:

Ten months ago the family moved from their old house to a new one a few blocks away on the same street; the patient still has not learned the new address, though remembering the old one perfectly, nor can he be trusted to find his way home alone. Moreover, he does not know where objects in continual use are kept; for example, his mother still has to tell him where to find the lawn mower, even though he may have been using it only the day before. She also states that he will do the same jigsaw puzzles day after day without showing any practice effect and that he will read the same magazines over and over again, without finding their contents familiar. This patient has even eaten lunches

in front of us without being able to name, a mere half-hour later, a single item of food he had eaten; in fact, he could not remember having eaten luncheon at all. Yet to a casual observer this man seems like a relatively normal individual, since his understanding and reasoning are undiminished.

Patients who have had the anterior parts of the hippocampal regions cut out or damaged on both sides of the brain cannot remember what happened for a few years before this operation. But they remember the more distant past with ease. They cannot learn anything new as they cannot retain it. Provided they are paying attention to what they are doing, they can retain it for a few minutes; but as soon as anything else comes along, what they have just been doing and recording all disappears. Every new event washes away all trace of the events that have just occurred. What they are doing is at first recorded; but it is not permanently recorded. Obviously the hippocampal regions are necessary to make a recorded event into a lasting memory. It looks as if the shortest term remembering of the sort used for immediate learning takes place in the hippocampus and in the related parts of the hypothalamus. Here the mechanism concerned with holding capacity takes place. But this part of the brain seems to have nothing to do with long-term storage, for what is remembered for years. In order to learn, one does not need the hippocampus; but in order to retain what one has just learnt, one does. It appears that long-term storage needs the lateral parts of the temporal lobes, all the part that lies lateral to the hippocampus.

If electrodes are placed inside the front parts of the hippocampus on both sides and then stimulated, the patient cannot commit things to memory. This electrical stimulation interrupts the ability to record and to register experience. Not only is this so, but stimulation here also disrupts what has recently been committed to memory; what has most recently been stored is most vulnerable. Stimulation here for five seconds destroys what the patient has remembered of the previous day; stimulation for ten seconds destroys what he has retained of the previous few days. This part of the hippocampus, we may

conclude, is the part where the continuous recording of events goes on, and where what is registered is fixed. We see once again from this work that the fixing of memories is related to time; what has been stored for only a short time is vulnerable, and the longer a memory has been retained, the more firmly fixed it is.

Something similar to this electrical stimulation occurs when epileptic fits continue for hours, a fortunately rare occurrence called status epilepticus. During these attacks, it is not surprising that the patient cannot store memories, for he is unconscious. But also the longer the duration of the attacks, the longer the period will be of obliteration of memories before the attacks. This may extend for years back, the patient never regaining his memory of what happened during this time. These repeated fits may damage the brain, and the damage then falls most heavily on the hippocampal region of the temporal lobes.

The entire function of remembering, however, is not carried out within the temporal lobes. The memories of things seen are stored around the visual areas of the occipital lobes, the memories of things smelt around the olfactory area, and so on for other sensations. These different areas of the cortex are connected to each other, so that the memory of something seen brings up automatically the smell of the thing, the feel of it, what to do with it, and all other associations. What we have learned in the last ten to twenty years is that total memory, the committing to memory of events and the storage of everything we remember, is localized. It has always been assumed that so general an intellectual function would somehow involve most of the cortex of both cerebral hemispheres. We now know that certain parts of the temporal lobes and their connexions are the essential parts for the ability to store day-to-day experience and that they are the storehouse of all our experience.

The cerebral hemispheres do not work alone, independently of the rest of the brain. The regions to do with memory have connexions with the thalamus, the hypothalamus, with the septal area, and with the mid-brain.

It seems that we must envisage something like this. When something happens to us, this affects the neurons of all sensory parts of the brain. Something has been seen and heard. Messages are also sent to the association areas of the cortex, to the speech area, to areas concerned with emotion and kinds of emotion such as familiarity, belonging to oneself. And messages are sent to the parts of the temporal lobes particularly concerned with memory. The experiments reported in Chapter 19 are important for many reasons; one reason is that they show us the anatomy and physiology of the transfer of learning. What is learned by one region of the brain is transferred in time to another region; and this happens without any further input from the world, without any more opportunity of learning. The changes affecting neurons and synapses constituting learning can be transferred from one part of the brain to another. We also saw examples of this in the earlier part of this chapter, where neurons of the central nervous system had become changed by some experience of pain and they remained changed after the painful experience had been removed.

Most or perhaps all functions performed by the cerebral hemispheres are elaborations of functions present at lower neural levels. The cerebral hemispheres add consciousness and mind to the basic behaviour; but nothing fundamental is changed. They add the psychological to the neural.

Chapter 21

Character, Personality and the Brain

For he is a mixture of gravity and waggery.

In all branches of biology we learn about the normal from examining the abnormal. Whether this is a good way of learning or not, it is bound to be so. If, for example, a patient comes with his wrist dislocated and the bones have been displaced backwards, one will compare the position of the wrist with the patient's other one and will note the displacement. From the examination of the two wrists, one will have learned about the position of the normal as well as the abnormal. If the displaced one had never come along, one would probably never have observed the normal relationships of the bones of the wrist.

That is a very simple example. Deducing the normal from the abnormal is less satisfactory in the case of the brain. We might consider an imaginary case of a patient with a tumour invading the left hemisphere who has disabilities of speech. Here again, we are bound to draw certain conclusions. But what deductions of general validity for anatomy, physiology and psychology we may legitimately make remains a matter of controversy. We would all consider it reasonable to draw the conclusions that in the normal, the affected part of the brain has something to do with speech. Now suppose that careful testing of this patient's speech disorder shows that he understands everything we say and that he can read and write, count and sing familiar songs; and that he makes mistakes in naming things, that he forgets a lot of words and cannot find the right one. What may we conclude? As the patient understands everything and yet cannot carry out the expressive part of speech, one conclusion might be that there is an anatomical basis for the division of speech into two parts – understanding and expressing. How far-reaching this division should be, one cannot say. Further cases will appear in which there is the opposite picture – no defects in expressing speech but defects in understanding. This would support the idea that the division of speech into two parts is meaningful and has an anatomical basis. But there would in fact be controversy on the facts to be interpreted. Some neurologists would claim that in patients whose main speech defect is expressive or motor, there are always slight defects in understanding and reception; and in those whose main defect is in understanding, there are always some difficulties in finding the right word, in constructing long sentences. Others will deny these facts; they will say that when the lesion is sufficiently small, only expressive or only receptive or only some other aspect of speech is damaged. One of the reasons for such a controversy is that those who favour a localizing view can conceive of the anatomy of lesions which might cause certain defects within the ability of using speech. Whereas those who stress that the disorder of speech always involves all aspects of speech, whatever and wherever the lesion, are unwilling to explain these observations on the basis of anatomy. They would say that this is not an anatomical problem and that one must not project into anatomy answers to questions that are not in this territory. Some psychologists and neurologists claim that speech always disintegrates in more or less the same way, and that the position of a lesion in the brain makes little difference. Others think that the manner in which speech disintegrates in any particular person is related to the way in which that person first learned to speak. They point out that, no matter how large the tumour affecting the speech area is or exactly where it is in the speech area, those aspects of speech that have become most automatic, such as giving one's name and address, or saying the days of the week, tend to remain intact.

From this example, concerning which one might erroneously believe that there are no grounds for getting angry, we see that there is little generally accepted knowledge about the function of small regions of the brain. When it comes to more complicated matters, so important to us all, such as the possible relationships between character, personality and the brain, there are fewer facts upon which all people with a right to an opinion are agreed.

It is nevertheless worth examining what we do know about the subject, even though we know we will end only with the vague general concepts.

It is only during the last thirty years that research workers in the many branches of neurology have come to investigate the physiology and anatomy of personality. Before then, the subject of character and personality had been left to psychologists and psychiatrists. It may have been reckoned that ultimately this subject would have to be related to the physiology and anatomy of the brain. But it appeared as if everyone had agreed that the time when this correlation would be made would always lie in the future. Freud, who was a neurologist before he invented psychoanalysis, always thought of psychoanalysis as being based on the physiology and anatomy of the nervous system. Yet, as it turned out, psychoanalysis and Jung's contributions increased the distance between a scientific study of the neural aspects of personality and psychology and psychiatry. Those influenced by Freud, Groddeck and Jung, and their successors, seem to have known nothing of the scientific method. Such psychotherapists established schools, behaving more like priests than scientists.

In the early years of this century, the facts that were known to neurology about personality concerned the effects of various hormones: the excitement and anxiety caused by excessive thyroid hormone, the lack of energy and intellectual dulling from too little of this hormone, the feeling of excitement and anxiety following an injection of adrenalin.

That the frontal lobes are somehow related to personality could have been deduced during the past eighty years or so. But this did not happen. Most neurological text-books merely stated that the frontal lobes have to do with man's intellectual attainments. There was no evidence for this belief. It seems to have arisen merely because the frontal lobes are large and well-developed in man and man is an intellectual animal.

Scattered throughout the pages of medical literature are the names of certain famous patients. We have already mentioned two of these, Dr Beaumont's Alexis St Martin, and Wolf and Wolff's Tom. More incredible is the case of Phineas Gage, studied in Boston in 1848 by Dr J. M. Barlow, and published in 1868.

Phineas Gage was a capable and efficient foreman who in 1847 suffered an amazing accident. During some rock-blasting operations, an iron bar four feet long was blown through the front part of his head. The iron bar entered the left side of his face below his eye and remained stuck in his skull with its end protruding through the top of the front of the skull. Gage was taken in an ox-cart a distance of three quarters of a mile, and then about one hour after the injury got out of the cart by himself and walked from the cart to the surgery. This large bar remained in his face and skull till his death twenty years later. From the position of the bar it may be deduced that the greater part of the left frontal lobe, the front part of the corpus callosum and most of the medial and front part of the right frontal lobe were destroyed.

Before this accident, Gage's employers described him as most efficient and capable. After it, 'his mind was radically changed'. He became

irreverent, indulging at times in the grossest profanity (which was not previously his custom), manifesting but little deference for his fellows, impatient of restraint or advice when in conflict with his desires, at times pertinaciously obstinate yet capricious and vacillating, devising many plans for future operation which are no sooner arranged than they are abandoned in turn for others appearing more feasible. . . . His friends and acquaintances said he was no longer Gage.

When he eventually died, a post-mortem examination was carried out, and it was confirmed that both his frontal lobes had been greatly damaged. The skull and the iron bar are now in the Museum of the Harvard Medical School.

Until that time, it was generally held that the entire cerebral hemispheres work as a totality to produce thinking and all intellectual activities. But here was a case in which a large amount of the hemispheres had been destroyed and yet purely intellectual activities had not suffered. Also till that time, it had not been appreciated that the brain has anything to do with personality and character. It was true that this was indeed claimed by the phrenologists, but they had been relegated to the realms of quackery. Here was a case in which the personality and character had been disastrously altered by a lesion of the frontal lobes.

To those who studied his case one does not know what must have been the more extraordinary: the fact that Gage was still normal intellectually, that his memory was normal, and that he could perform his job; or the fact that he had suffered an extraordinary change in his character and personality.

Although the case of Phineas Gage became famous in medical literature, all the implications were not really grasped. Doctors were amazed that such a large amount of the brain could be damaged and that the patient could walk and talk immediately after the injury and that he could go on living for years. They were also amazed that so much of the frontal lobes could be damaged without causing a great defect in speech, in calculation and thinking ability. That character and personality could be changed so disastrously came as a striking fact to all who knew about the case; but still no one seems to have drawn conclusions about the frontal lobes being related to character and personality.

About sixty years had to pass before neurologists and neurosurgeons, psychiatrists and psychologists fully grasped that these subjects included the relation of character and personality to the brain. If one wants one date, one might take the year 1939 as an important one. For in that year Klüver and Bucy published their first long paper on the effects of removing certain parts of the temporal lobes in macaque monkeys. The essential parts that they removed were the phylogenetically oldest parts; these are the parts that evolved in relation to the

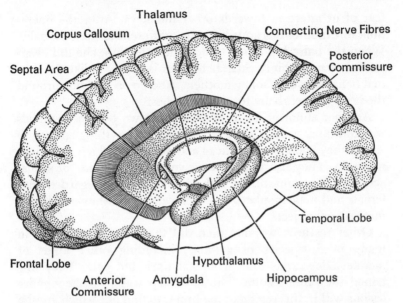

26. The amygdala and the hippocampus in the depths of the opposite temporal lobe. The three commissures, anterior, posterior and corpus callosum are shown

hypothalamus and septal area. They are shown in Figure 26. In this figure a good slice of the cerebral hemisphere has been cut off so that the amygdala and hippocampus are revealed, although they are really buried deep inside the temporal lobe. The large band of nerve fibres connecting these regions of the temporal lobe to the septal area and the hypothalamus can be seen, encircling the thalamus.

When the amygdala and hippocampus were removed from both cerebral hemispheres of the macaque monkeys, some amazing changes in the animals' personalities occurred. Normally these monkeys hate men and bravely attack them or else they hide away from them. But these animals showed no emotion of any sort when they were handled by humans. They were neither aggressive nor fearful; they had become docile and indifferent. Even if they were hit or bitten by other monkeys, they did not seem to mind. They showed no

361

fear of or affection towards other monkeys. After the operation, one mother macaque became indifferent to her own baby. When the baby continued to demand attention, she did eventually react and bit it. Such behaviour is totally unlike the normal behaviour of monkey mothers, who go on carrying around the body of their baby for days if it dies.

Another abnormality of behaviour shown by these animals was continual eating. They would pick up anything and try to eat it; they even chewed sticks and ate meat, which macaques never do. They also had the same voracious appetite for sexual activities. They masturbated the whole time and regarded both female and male monkeys and even cats and cushions as legitimate sexual objects.

Other research workers then did the same experiments in many other species of animals, including other kinds of monkey, dogs, rats and agoutis, lynxes and cats. They obtained the same results. The next step was to make smaller lesions within this region of the brain, to find out which are the crucial regions the removal of which causes the various parts of the total picture. It now appears that the increased sexuality is obtained only when a particular part of the cortex of this oldest region of the temporal lobe is damaged. If the amygdala and hippocampus are cut out while leaving this region of cortex intact, the rest of the picture obtained by Klüver and Bucy is obtained but not excessive sexuality. The voracious appetite for food results from damage to a neighbouring region of cortex. It is probable that the lack of aggression is due to removal of the amygdala.

In Chapter 18, the effects of dividing the commissures connecting the two cerebral hemispheres were described. These operations have now been combined with removal of the amygdala on one side of the brain. At first the optic chiasm, the corpus callosum, the anterior commissure and the hippocampal commissure are divided in a ferocious macaque monkey. This produces a monkey in which things seen with the right eye go only to the right side of the brain and things seen with the left eye go only to the left side. The

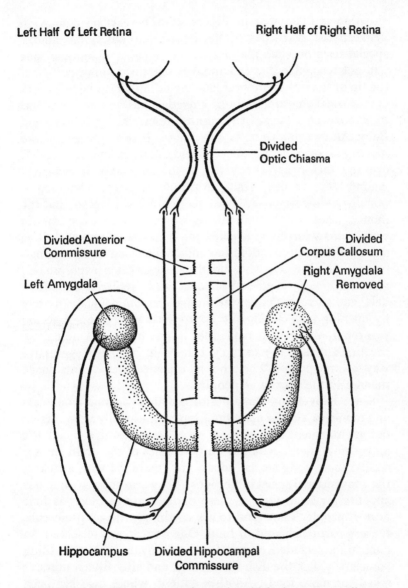

Left Half of Left Retina

Right Half of Right Retina

Divided
Optic Chiasma

**Divided Anterior
Commissure**

**Divided
Corpus Callosum**

**Right Amygdala
Removed**

Left Amygdala

Hippocampus

**Divided Hippocampal
Commissure**

27. Diagram to illustrate experiment in which the corpus callosum, other commissures and the optic chiasm are cut through; in addition the right amygdala has been cut out.

situation is illustrated in Figure 27. There is no connexion between the two sides of the brain; but unless one makes special tests on such abilities as the transfer of training, one will not recognize that this monkey's brain is abnormal. Now the tip of the right temporal lobe including the amygdala is cut out. Normally cutting out one amygdala has no effect; one has to remove both to get the results described by Klüver and Bucy. An amazing thing is now found. If the right eye of the monkey is covered with an eye-shield, it sees people with its left eye and this eye is connected to the amygdala in a normal manner. The monkey reacts to people in its usual way, emotionally and aggressively. Now the left eye is covered, and the monkey sees people with its right eye; but this eye has no connexions with the amygdala, for it has been removed. The animal is now quite indifferent and docile when he sees human beings. As Downer, who did these remarkable experiments, wrote: 'One can in effect "remove" and "replace" the amygdala, and thereby change the animal's emotional state, merely by opening and closing the appropriate eye.' We are seeing two totally different personalities in one monkey. One half of the brain makes the monkey behave in its usual aggressive way towards people. The other half makes it behave in a docile manner to the very same people.

Since Klüver and Bucy performed their operations on cats and monkeys, similar operations have occasionally been carried out in humans. The patients who have effectively had the amygdaloid nuclei removed on both sides of the brain show a similar increase in sexual behaviour, combined with a lack of the conventional social inhibitions. They also show a voracious appetite for food. One of these patients ate as much as four normal people. They tend to eat anything, with no preference for any particular kind of food. One patient was observed 'to look for a secluded corner far from anyone, eat everything voraciously, lick the dish incessantly, and after fifteen minutes asked for more food'. Another patient, whose case has been well documented by Terzian and Dalle Ore, had this operation performed on account of extremely severe epilepsy originating in these parts of the brain and uncontrollable outbreaks of aggression and rage, making him dangerous to everyone including himself. He also had terrifying hallucinations and automatic behaviour during which he often tried to strangle people or to commit suicide; at times he would fly at people, including the doctors. After two operations one on each temporal lobe, the patient's personality was completely changed. He showed no aggression and no emotion of any sort. Terzian and Dalle Ore reported:

The patient no longer manifested the slightest rage reactions towards the nurses and doctors upon whom before the second operation he used to rush as soon as they came into sight. The patient on the contrary now assumed an extremely childish and meek behaviour with everyone and was absolutely resistant to any attempt to arouse aggressiveness and violent reactions in him. He was completely indifferent towards everyone, including his parents.

He not only expressed no emotion, it was clear that he felt none. He was unable to display emotion to such an extent that even his voice became monotonous, losing all the variations in intensity, pitch and tone that normally demonstrate the emotions we are feeling, whether we want to show them or not. His face usually wore 'a conventional and unmotivated smile. An emotional expression was noticed in the patient's face only once when he saw his image in a mirror, betraying a childish satisfaction because he had found human features in a lifeless object.'

When neurologists and psychiatrists learned of the importance of the front parts of the temporal lobes for controlling and organizing drives, such as sex, hunger and aggression, they began to examine some psychotics and aggressive psychopaths to see if they had abnormalities in their temporal lobes. In fact, brain tissue damage is a rare cause of such abnormalities of personality.

At the same time as we were learning about the effects of removing the anterior parts of the temporal lobes upon personality, similar observations were being made on the effects of removing the anterior parts of the frontal lobes. Jacobsen did this operation on chimpanzees at Yale. After the operation, the animals became lethargic and apathetic; they no longer took any interest in life. And, what turned out to be more important, Jacobsen noticed that these animals no longer became worked up or upset about things. If, before the operation, a chimpanzee had been upset by failure to do a psychological test, after the operation, it no longer cared.

After this operation, some of these animals were not lethargic but were very active in a restless and agitated manner. All of them were easily distracted; their responses to everything were insufficiently prolonged. They kept leaving one activity and going on to others, and then would go back to the first one; they ate bits of one thing and would then leave it, start eating something else, would drop that and go back to the first thing.

Damage of the same sort as that caused by this operation to both frontal lobes may occur in man. It often results from people trying to shoot themselves without knowing how to do it. They usually put the barrel of the revolver against the right temple and fire. If this does not kill them, and it may well not do so, it usually causes what is called a through-and-through gunshot wound; the bullet goes through one side of the head and comes out of the other. It commonly damages one or both optic nerves, making the person blind in one or both eyes. What may happen in such patients is that after this damage to the frontal lobes of the brain, the depression is gone. This is not only because they have made their gesture; it is that their personalities are now different. They are more like Jacobsen's chimpanzees; they are indifferent to everything.

During the frequent wars which characterize our century, damage to the frontal lobes of the same sort occurs. The sort of apathy of a self-sufficient kind that may occur from this damage to the brain is made clear if I quote from the notes I made on a typical severely injured patient I saw in Italy in 1944. The patient was a lieutenant in the New Zealand army. He was picked up soon after being injured, and it was noted that his brain was oozing out of the wound in the front of his head. When he was operated upon twenty-four hours later, the roofs of both his orbits were found to be shattered and the front of the brain on both sides was reduced to pulp. Twenty-one days after the injury, his state was as follows:

His condition is best described as one of apathy. He lies in bed doing nothing and responds to nothing, except that sometimes he follows with his eyes anything that is happening. He leaves his lit cigarette on the bed; he holds up the paper in front of him as if he is reading it, when it is put in his hand. Recently I observed him lying on his back with the paper held up in front of him; on his chest was the feeding cup where someone had put it, and the spout was between his lips; but he was making no attempt to drink from it, nor did he put it down; he just lay there with the feeding cup full of tea touching his lips, his paper in his hand; and he did nothing. The greater part of the day he spends sleeping or lying on his bed with a paper held in front of him, pretending to read it, but never turning over the pages; however when I handed it to him upside down, he did turn it the right way up.

But this is not the whole picture, for he does sometimes get up and put on some of his clothes, go to the table to eat or look out of the window. Such activities are done with an intense preoccupation with what he is doing at the moment and an equal indifference to any circumstances relating to other people. What he does, he carries out perfectly, as he puts on his shoes and laces them, eats his food with the other officers with correct manners; he spreads jam on his bread and cuts it and makes a sandwich of it, all neatly. While I was talking to him and trying to take a medical history from him, he got up, put on the top of his pyjamas and went and looked out of the window, all while I was asking him questions and attempting to examine him; he went through these activities just as if I were not there. As I talked to him and examined him, he repeatedly stretched out to get a cigarette and light it, although I kept moving them away from him. I had the impression that each time he began again, he did not realize that he was not to do it. Once, as he walked about the ward, he defaecated while walking, showing no interest in this act whatsoever.

His speech is entirely normal and he seems to understand everything or at least everything simple. But he is unwilling to speak. It seems to need much effort for him to speak, and he does not make this effort.

This picture of apathy and total indifference to social relations does not last, though the amount of recovery varies from case to case. Actually, that young man's father wrote to me from New Zealand eight years later and told me that his son had eventually made a good recovery and satisfactory adjustment. However, after such lesions the patients are usually left with some degree of apathy or restlessness, tactlessness and lack of self-control, difficulty in maintaining attention and thus difficulty in learning and in planning, easy fatigueability and a lack of interest in anything.

In 1935, Moniz, a neurologist working in Portugal, came to the conclusion that if the operation of dividing the frontal lobes from the rest of the brain reduces the excitement and the frustration of the chimpanzees, it would probably do the same in patients. He therefore invented the operation of prefrontal leucotomy for the treatment of certain psychiatric patients.

The first results obtained from this operation resembled those obtained in the chimpanzee. But gradually the form of the operation has been changed so that many of the undesired results no longer occur. When much of the frontal lobe has been divided from the rest of the brain, the patients have a great reduction in activity and tend to be apathetic. All responses to the environment are diminished and there is less spontaneous activity arising from internal motivation and energy. In the most severely affected patients, the lack of initiative is such that the patient at first may stay in the bed or the chair he finds himself in until he is got out of it. When food is put into his mouth, he may do nothing about it; he merely leaves it there, having neither the energy nor the interest to chew and swallow it. When the patients are less severely affected, they are just placid; whatever they do, they do more slowly and less interestedly than before. They lack emotion, or rather, they lack any persistence in emotion. They may have insight into this lack of emotion and explain that since the operation they have no feelings. As one previously hypomanic and intelligent patient expressed it: 'I am dull, a bore, and I know it.' These patients cannot concentrate on anything for long and they have insufficient initiative to start doing anything. It may be that they do not have enough energy to arouse their own interest and to have the emotions associated with interest; it may be that having no emotions, they have no energy. When the effects of this operation are less extreme, the patient can carry on a routine, with the things he knows well how to do. But he does not undertake any new projects, he makes no plans, he lives without enthusiasm.

These patients are uninhibited; this leads at best to amusing situations, at worst to unpleasant ones. There is a lack of community feeling, the patient having little feeling for others and he lacks some of the usual social inhibitions. He may start undressing and going to bed in front of other people if he feels tired. His table manners will probably have become crude, and he may be greedy; but this is not the insatiable greediness of patients who have had the anterior parts of the temporal lobes removed. These patients are easy-going and uninhibited rather than malicious, for to be consequently nasty requires more concentration and persistence than they can muster. They are insensitive to criticism, both to self-criticism and to the criticism of others. They vary from being complacent to being fatuously self-satisfied. They are in general less concerned about their lives and the figures they cut in the world, and are more indifferent to what people think of them.

In a study made of neurotic patients, before and after the earlier kinds of leucotomy, carried out by Dr Petrie, she reported that one of the patients said she did not mind things going wrong any more. Dr Petrie found in this group of patients that their consciences had become less exacting, their standards had become lower, and whatever their performances, they tended to be satisfied with them and with themselves. The patients' ranges of interest shrinks, and they no longer enjoy anything very much. Where the changes are extreme, the patients are interested only in the situation of the moment, and that, only in so far as it impinges on them. Their reactions are more related to the immediate stimuli of the environment; the past and future are no longer important; nothing much matters any more.

The ability to let the past and the future go hang and to be occupied only with the present accounts for many of the effects of these operations. It frees the patient from remorse and guilt and stops him being apprehensive about the future. This alone removes psychogenic tension.

More careful examination of these patients than was practised at first shows that they do have defects in a pure intellectual sphere, in so far as there is such a thing. They tend to prefer the concrete to the abstract. This defect is the most typical one that occurs whenever there is any general atrophy of the brain. Careful testing of patients who have had leucotomies on only one side has shown that the operation on the left frontal lobe slightly impairs intellectual tasks requiring speech. This might be expected, for the region of the brain where the incision is made is not very far from the part of the brain where speech is organized. All patients who returned to the same job after the operation were less good at their work; and these patients included a judge with powers to condemn people to death and life imprisonment. The more intellectual their work was, the more affected were their capabilities. Dr Petrie concluded from her studies that 'the personality alters in ways that are particularly relevant to man's relationship to society'. Freeman and Watts put the matter well by saying that one would not call on a patient who has had a leucotomy 'for advice on any important matter. His reactions to situations are direct, hasty, and dependent upon his emotional state at the moment. . . . There is something childlike in the directness and ingenuousness of these people.'

These results may appear to be wholly undesirable. And further, one might think that the resulting changes in personality are a sort of assault on the very being of a person. This view may be justified. However, two points must be remembered. The sort of patients for whom these operations have been recommended are people whose lives are miserable and harrowing; and life with a changed personality without such misery may well be an improvement. It is difficult to make people who are unfamiliar with mental disease understand how terrible these diseases can be. One must not believe that most of these patients are quite contentedly inhabiting a fantasy world. The suffering of a patient with agitated depression is intense. The second point is that this form of treatment has been much modified and improved. One learns from one's failures as well as from one's successes. Since the early days of leucotomy, neurosurgeons have made many changes in the operation in order to avoid so much damage to the patient's personality. It was eventually found that an operation called orbital undercutting relieves anxiety and may cure depression. This operation consists of cutting through all nerve fibres connecting the grey matter of the base of the frontal lobes with the rest of the brain.

Nowadays brain surgery is little used for the treatment of psychosis or severe neurosis. This is not to avoid a procedure that did produce some disastrous results; it is on account of the great advance that has been made in the treatment of these conditions by drugs. This has enabled many patients to carry on with their lives without having to go into hospital and it has also enabled many patients to return home and to carry on with some sort of normal living.

From observations on neurotic or psychotic patients it is hazardous to draw conclusions concerning how these various parts of the brain contribute to our personalities. Yet if we do not try to make use of material such as this we may be discarding the only large body of data we have.

It certainly appears that the frontal lobes and their deeper connexions are important in giving us our general energy and our interest in living. Perhaps related to this motivating energy or perhaps something different is the ability to respond to the environment in a long-term way. The frontal lobes allow us to deliberate and to consider the consequences of possible courses of action. This foresight enables us to plan intelligently and adjust ourselves to future probabilities. The ability

to stop and think is a characteristic of man. Pleasure as a delayed and not an immediate reward illumines many aspects of
man's way of living, such as planning and following a career,
saving money for the future, building for unborn generations.

The frontal lobes are not the region of the brain concerned
with intellectual attainments. The social feelings and relationships that we learn appear to be laid down in the frontal lobes
with their connexions to the other parts of the brain. Patients
with these connexions divided are more like children, they live
for the moment, unconcerned with the future and are loath to
do anything unpleasant now for the sake of pleasure in the
future. The control necessary for living in a community depends on the frontal lobes. They have been affected by the
experience of living and by years of upbringing and by our
knowledge of how to relate ourselves to other human beings.

Not the whole of the frontal lobes are devoted to these
general activities. The parts in front of the primary motor
region are also concerned with movements, with turning, with
speaking and swallowing, with all the skills we have learned.
The parts nearest the mid-line are also related to the hypothalamus. These are the parts of the brain used for the control
of the bowels and the bladder and they are also concerned with
sexual activity. When this part of the brain is removed, none
of these activities is controlled; they are no longer fitted into
the rest of the patient's living, they tend to lead an independent
existence, the bowel and bladder emptying when they are full,
and sexual urges demanding immediate gratification.

When the changes and deteriorations of old age affect the
brain, the results vary according to what parts are chiefly
affected. It is common for the memory to go, as we all know.
When the memory becomes severely impaired, learning is no
longer possible. Commonly when intellectual capacities are
much diminished, the senile person confabulates. Perhaps the
ability to recollect if an event is a part of one's own past or is
something one has heard about becomes disturbed; and this
may contribute to apparent confabulation.

Similar changes are seen in the realms of personality, of

emotion, of social relationships. The senile person is less able to control his emotion, or rather, the manifestations of emotion; yet most of such people will say that the emotions they are showing are not deep. They may cry if they see anything sentimental or are reminded of an emotional occasion. Patients relate that they cry when they hear 'God Save the Queen' played in a crowd.

When the oldest parts of the temporal lobes degenerate, the effects are similar to those produced by removal of these parts at operation. One such patient would stuff everything into her mouth, which included her flowers and handkerchiefs, and would chew and try to swallow them.

When the front parts of the frontal lobes become atrophic, the subjects resemble the patients who had the early forms of leucotomy. At first, the patient loses finer sensibilities and may become indifferent to the feelings of others. As the lobes become more atrophic, behaviour becomes more ruled by the needs of the moment and less cognizant of social requirements. One patient I saw threw a chamber pot out of the window of a top floor of the house; she explained that as she had finished with it, she threw it away. These old people become indifferent to personal appearance; the preening instinct ceases to be important. At the same time, they become indifferent about good manners and the impression they make on others. Then certain basic features of their personalities come out. The obsessional personality becomes more marked; rituals and compulsions dominate their lives, the patient worries about the few things he has to do, and cannot think of anything else. The choleric person loses his temper even more readily. The jovial person becomes fatuous. The ability to make use of symbols deteriorates. The patient still understands the concrete and no longer understands abstractions.

When intelligence decreases, the similar patient can no longer read a book, but can still read the newspaper. For he cannot remember enough of the book to keep the general scheme in mind or to remember the plot of a novel; but he may still have enough memory to remember the theme of an article or an essay.

Eventually this ability goes and all he can take in is the information of the headlines. He has difficulty in composing letters, in thinking what to write, though he still retains the mechanical part of writing. When the right parieto-occipital region of the cortex atrophies, the old person has great difficulty in finding his way about. This may not be noticed as long as he remains at home; but it becomes clear if he is taken away. When these patients come to hospital, they cannot find their way to the bathroom, and on returning to the ward, they do not remember which is their bed. This difficulty in getting their bearings is always worse at night, in the dark. In the daytime, there are numbers of sensory clues, everything is clearly seen. At night, they may have to feel their way about, the light being inadequate to show up the total environment.

Eventually their exhibition of facile emotions goes off, and they become indifferent to everything. This indifference of senility may perhaps be a further stage in the contentment of later middle age that comes when desires have become less urgent and demanding. Between the indifference of age and the urgency of youth, there may be a period of serenity – or is that saying too much?

What we are seeing when the cortex becomes atrophic is the decay of the functions organized by this part of the cerebral hemispheres. According to the principle deduced by Hughlings Jackson, the most recently acquired functions disintegrate first, leaving the oldest established to the end. He also pointed out that when the higher level of function goes, the lower level one is released and manifested in an exaggerated form. The higher functions are often related to lower functions by exerting an inhibition on them, and this inhibition is removed when the higher functions go off.

One cannot sum up in a few well-chosen words the relation between the cerebral hemispheres and the hypothalamus and the thalamus – mainly because we do not really know what it is. It is not simply, as the early psychoanalysts conjectured, that there are lower parts which are a pool of instinctual urges, controlled by the educated and trained cerebral hemispheres above. The relationship between the two levels of the brain is a reciprocal one. Each part can bring the other part into activity and then the two parts of the brain work together.

It is on account of the reciprocal and intimate relation between the cerebral hemispheres and the hypothalamus and thalamus that psychotherapy is possible. The whole of our nervous systems and secondarily of our bodies can be influenced by all we experience, all we hear. Frequently repeated persuasion and explanation, the awakening of emotion, the reliving of experience and re-awakening of memories, all of this can have effects on our personalities and behaviour because the cerebral hemispheres influence the rest of the brain. The hypothalamus controls the autonomic nervous system and the endocrine system of the body, and in turn they affect many parts of the brain. Patients find it very difficult to understand how 'just talk' can help them or even cure their ills. But everything we have ever experienced and which made us what we are has entered our brains through some sensory channel, through the skin, the nose, the eyes or the ears. For us humans, a good deal of it has entered via the ears, in the form of speech. And so there is no reason why further talking should not continue to affect us and influence our personalities.

The pioneering work of Hess is only thirty years old, and the investigations of the parts of the cerebral hemispheres related to the hypothalamus have been undertaken only in the last ten years. Operations on the frontal and temporal lobes designed to affect human personality and behaviour have been done only since the last war. Our knowledge of the nervous system has grown so rapidly in the last fifty years that we can be sure that many of the present problems in animal psychology and in our understanding of the function of living cells will soon be solved. Lest we should have illusions about what science can do we should be clear about one thing. Science brings knowledge and this knowledge brings the ability to make new things and to change the world. But science does not bring happiness, except perhaps to those whose lives are dedicated to its service.

Glossary

Å = Ångstrom unit. 1 Å = 1/10,000 μ = 1/10,000,000 mm.

acetylcholine: the chemical substance used for neural transmission by cholinergic neurons, by parasympathetic nerve fibres, and by nerve fibres supplying muscles.

adrenal glands: a pair of endocrine glands resting on the kidneys. They consist of two parts, the adrenal cortex and the adrenal medulla.

adrenalin: one of the two hormones secreted by the adrenal medulla.

adrenocorticotrophic hormone: a hormone secreted by the pituitary gland that stimulates the adrenal cortex to release its hormones.

afferent nerves: nerves taking impulses to the central nervous system.

amino acids: chemical substances containing an amino group (NH_2), a carboxyl group (COOH), a hydrogen atom, and another group, attached to a central carbon atom.

amplifier: a device for increasing the amount of current, voltage or power.

amygdala or amygdaloid nuclei: large groups of neurons in the front part of the temporal lobe.

androgen: any compound which acts as a male sex hormone and causes the production of spermatozoa and the multiplication of the cells of the male sexual organs.

anion: a negative ion.

anthropoids: a sub-order of the primates; animals characterized by having nails on all ten digits. Living forms of anthropoids are the chimpanzee, gibbon, gorilla, man and orang outang.

anti-diuretic hormone: another name for vasopressin, a hormone produced in the hypothalamus and passed down the stalk of the pituitary gland and thence into the bloodstream. It inhibits the production of urine.

aphasia: a difficulty in organizing speech, there being no paralysis of the muscles needed for making the sounds of speech.

arthropod: a member of the largest division of the animal kingdom, which includes insects, spiders and crustaceans; animals
characterized by having an exoskeleton and externally jointed
limbs.

axon: the central part of the nerve fibre. It is an elongated process
of a neuron, usually single, sometimes double or triple, which
conducts nerve impulses over long distances in the central and
peripheral nervous systems.

brain-stem: the oldest and most basal part of the brain. It includes
the medulla oblongata, pons, mid-brain and hypothalamus.

cation: a positive ion.

cerebellum: part of the brain superficially resembling the cerebrum, hence its name of little cerebrum. It is usually considered
to be part of the brain, but W. S. Gilbert (1882) established
another convention, thus;

> When in that House M.P.'s divide,
> If they've a brain and cerebellum, too,
> They've got to leave that brain outside,
> And vote just as their leaders tell'em to.

cerebral cortex: grey matter of the cerebral hemispheres, forming
the outermost part of the cerebral hemispheres.

cerebral hemispheres: the largest and most recently evolved part
of the brain.

cerebrum: the two cerebral hemispheres.

cholinergic: nerve fibres emitting acetylcholine as transmitter
substance.

cholinesterase: enzyme that breaks down acetylcholine into inert
choline and acetic acid.

commissure: a transversely running band of nerve fibres connecting homologous parts of the central nervous system across the
mid-line.

confabulate: to recount made-up experiences glibly, mostly about
oneself; it is done to fill in gaps in the memory or to try and put
sense into a state of confusion.

cortex: Latin for the bark of a tree; used in anatomy to mean the
outer layers of any structure.

377

cutaneous: adjective pertaining to the skin.

cytoplasm: the living components of plant or animal cells, apart from the nucleus. Together with the nucleus, it forms the protoplasm.

dendrite: a branching process of a neuron, specialized for receiving nerve impulses from other neurons.

dopamine: a monoaminergic transmitter substance.

echo-location: echo-ranging: a method for finding objects and measuring distances utilizing the time taken for sound waves to travel.

efferent nerves: nerves taking impulses away from the central nervous system.

electroencephalogram: a record of the electrical activity of the brain recorded by electrodes placed on the skull.

electrolyte: a chemical substance which can form ions.

endocrine gland: a gland which passes its secretion into the bloodstream directly and not through a duct or pipe.

enzyme: a substance within a living organism which catalyses metabolic activities.

epilepsy: a disease characterized by the spontaneous or induced discharge of groups of neurons of the fore-brain.

ethology: the scientific study of animal behaviour.

excitation: the process of arousing a cell or a group of cells or an organism into activity.

extensor muscles: the muscles that straighten out the back and the limbs.

feedback: a term borrowed from radio technicians to mean the diversion of a small part of the output to control the input. It occurs both in natural and in man-made systems.

firing: the neuron is said to fire when it sends off a nerve impulse.

flexor muscles: the muscles that bend the trunk and limbs.

follicle-stimulating hormone: a hormone secreted by the pituitary gland which causes enlargement of the follicles of the ovary.

fore-brain: the part of the brain in front of the mid-brain.

fovea: a part of the retina on which light rays are automatically focused when detailed vision is needed.

gastric juices: the liquid and mucous substances secreted by the glands of the stomach.

378

gonadotrophic hormones: hormones secreted by the pituitary gland which act on the gonads.

gonadotrophin I: one of the two gonadotrophic hormones secreted by the pituitary gland; also called follicle-stimulating hormone.

gonadotrophin II: one of the two gonadotrophic hormones secreted by the pituitary gland; also called luteinizing hormone and interstitial cell stimulating hormone.

grey matter: the parts of the central nervous system made up mainly of neurons.

growth hormone: a hormone secreted by the pituitary gland which causes the tissues of the body to grow.

gyrus: smooth folds of the cerebral hemispheres and cerebellum.

hair-follicle: a little sac in the skin from which a hair grows. It is supplied by several nerve fibres.

hallucinations: perception of a non-existent object.

hormone: chemical substance secreted by endocrine glands or neurons.

horseshoe crab: an ancient and primitive arthropod.

hypothalamus: the central and basal parts of the brain.

inertia: a fundamental property of matter, making it resist change in its motion.

inhibition: the opposite of excitation.

ion: an electrified particle of an electrolyte carrying either a positive or a negative charge.

kinaesthesis or kinaesthesia: the sense of the movements and/or position of parts of the body.

lactogenic hormone: a hormone secreted by the pituitary gland; also called prolactin.

luteinizing hormone: a hormone secreted by the pituitary gland which stimulates the corpora lutea of the ovary.

mammals: vertebrates with mammary glands and hair.

medulla: the marrow or inner part of any structure.

medulla oblongata: the lowest part of the brain situated immediately above the spinal cord.

membrane: a boundary layer forming the walls of cells or tissues.

membrane, basilar: a layer within the inner ear which is thrown into folds when sound waves are transmitted to the inner ear.

membrane, tectorial: a layer within the inner ear covering the receptor cells.

metabolism: the life process of cells and organisms, divided into the building of tissues, anabolism, and the breaking down of tissues, catabolism.

μ: micron. 1 micron = 1/1000 mm.

mid-brain: the part of the brain above the pons and below the hypothalamus and thalamus.

mm: millimetre.

migraine: a particular sort of headache, characteristically restricted to one side of the head: hence the name, which is a contraction of hemicrania.

molecule: smallest particle of an element or a chemical compound, that retains all the properties of a larger mass of the same material.

monoamines: the chemical substances used for monoaminergic transmission in the central and the peripheral sympathetic nervous systems.

motor end-plate: the special end-organ where the nerve fibre terminates in the muscle.

msec: millisecond: 1 millisecond = 1/1000 second.

muscle: a tissue of animals' bodies consisting of protein fibres which contract when they are stimulated. Organs such as the heart and the bladder are made almost entirely of muscle. Limbs consist essentially of muscles attached to bones which are hinged at joints.

muscle spindle: receptors of the muscles.

myelin sheath: lipid sheath surrounding axons of myelinated nerve fibres.

myelinated nerve fibres: nerve fibres surrounded by myelin sheaths formed by Schwann cells.

myo-neural junction: another word for neuro-muscular junction.

nerve-cell: neuron.

nerve fibre: the long process of a neuron consisting of the axon surrounded by supporting cells.

nerve impulse: the brief activity passing along nerve fibres that constitutes the message. It is usually detected in experimental investigations by the electrical phenomena; but there are other aspects of it, such as visual phenomena, thermal phenomena, chemical events.

neuroglia: cells needed for the nutrition and support of neurons in the central nervous system.

neuron: nerve cell: the essential conducting unit of the nervous system. It consists of cell-body, dendrites and one or more axons.

neuro-muscular junction: the modified synapse where nerve impulses are transmitted to the muscle.

oestradiol: a hormone secreted by the follicles of the ovary, which causes female secondary sexual characteristics.

oestrogen: any compound which acts as a female sex hormone.

olive: a structure in the medulla oblongata consisting of neurons and making an eminence on the surface, which recalled an olive to earlier anatomists.

ommatidium: the unit of the compound eye of arthropods.

optic chiasm: the point of crossing of the optic nerves behind the two orbits.

optical isomers: chemical substances having the same composition and the same molecular weight but different properties with regard to the transmission of light.

oval window: small membrane-covered opening between middle and inner ear.

ovary: egg-producing organ in the female animal or plant.

oxytocin: a hormone produced by the hypothalamus and passed down the stalk of the pituitary gland and thence into the bloodstream. It aids the ejection of milk.

perception: the interpretation of sensation.

polarity: a field or circuit in which ions and electrons are flowing between positive and negative poles.

pons: the part of the brain situated immediately above the medulla oblongata.

potential, electric: the work done on or by a unit positive charge as it moves from infinity to some point in an electric field or as it moves from one point to another in an electric field.

primates: order of mammals characterized by having nails on some of the digits. Living forms of primates are the tree-shrews, lemurs, tarsiers, monkeys and anthropoids.

progesterone: a female sex hormone secreted by the corpus luteum of the ovary.

prolactin: a hormone secreted by the pituitary gland which stimulates milk-secretion.

protein: complex nitrogen-containing organic substances, which are essential components of living tissues.

protoplasm: the living material of the cells of plants and animals.

Purkinje cells: a large neuron of the cerebellum.

receptor: a neuron or a non-nervous cell specialized to respond to stimuli from the external or internal environment. If the receptor is not itself a neuron, it converts forms of energy into nerve impulses.

reciprocal innervation: organization making a muscle relax when the muscle with an opposing action contracts.

reflex: rapid, simple, innate reaction to stimulation. The reaction entails contraction of muscles, a muscle or a part of a muscle or the secretion of a gland.

reflex, scratch: reflexly organized scratching movements of vertebrates in which the hindlimb is brought forward to scratch the forelimb, trunk or head and neck.

round window: small membrane-covered opening between middle and inner ear.

Schwann cells: cells surrounding and nourishing nerve fibres of the peripheral nervous system.

semicircular canals: a part of the inner ear containing receptors used for signalling changes in position and movements of the head.

serotonin: a monoaminergic transmitter substance.

servo-mechanism: an automatic mechanism in which the output is partly controlled by feeding back a part of the output to the controlling elements.

somatotrophic hormone: a growth hormone secreted by the pituitary gland.

swim-bladder: a thin-walled sac lying in the body cavity in front of the vertebral column in fish, filled with gas and used in helping the fish live at different depths within the ocean.

synapse: the region where two neurons meet and where impulses are passed from one to the other.

testis: sperm-producing organ in male animal.

testosterone: the male sex hormone secreted by the testis.

thalamus: a large ovoid mass of nuclei in the centre of the cerebral hemisphere, consisting chiefly of relays between the cerebral cortex and lower level structures of the central nervous system.

thyrotrophic hormone: a hormone secreted by the pituitary gland, acting on the thyroid gland.

tissue: a group of cells with the same structure and with the same or similar function. The body of a plant or animal is considered to be made up of many kinds of tissues.

vasopressin: another name for anti-diuretic hormone, which is produced by neurons of the hypothalamus, passed down the stalk of the pituitary gland and thence into the bloodstream.

vertebrate: an animal having a backbone.

vertigo: sensation of rotation in which either the surroundings seem to rotate around the subject or the subject seems to rotate.

white matter: the parts of the central nervous system made up mainly of nerve fibres.

Index